INSTRUMENTAL
ARRANGING

INSTRUMENTAL ARRANGING

GARY WHITE
Iowa State University

Boston   Burr Ridge, IL   Dubuque, IA   Madison, WI   New York
San Francisco   St. Louis   Bangkok   Bogotá   Caracas   Kuala Lumpur
Lisbon   London   Madrid   Mexico City   Milan   Montreal   New Delhi
Santiago   Seoul   Singapore   Sydney   Taipei   Toronto

INSTRUMENTAL ARRANGING

14 15 16 17 18 19 QVS 20 19 18 17 16

ISBN-13: 978-0-07-301823-2
ISBN-10: 0-07-301823-6

Editor: Shirley Grall
Production Editor: Sue Culbertson
Cover Design: Hamilton Blake Associates
Printer/Binder: Quad/Graphics

Contents

Contents

Contents

Preface

Arranging music is both an artistic and a technical process. Creative thought and imagination are required to produce an interesting musical result, but there are a number of skills and techniques to be mastered as well. This book and the accompanying workbook provide an introduction to both aspects of the arranger's art. As an arranger, you must learn how to:

1. Produce neat and readable scores and parts. The technique of music calligraphy is beyond the scope of this book, but a brief introduction is presented in chapter 1. Basic information about preparation of scores and parts is included in chapter 2. Computer notation programs are now available that produce excellent performing materials and will be discussed briefly in chapter 1.

2. Write performance materials for each instrument, using proper notation and transposition. The technique of transposition is covered in chapter 1 and the details of transposition for each instrument in chapters 4–8.

3. Write within the practical ranges of instrumentalists of various ages and abilities. This information is contained in chapters 4–8, and a summary of instrumental ranges is contained in appendix A. The technical limitations of younger musicians is the subject of chapter 9.

4. Write with a thorough awareness of the unique tonal characteristics of each instrument/voice in each of its registers. Chapters 4–8 deal with this topic, and assignments are provided in the workbook that will help you develop this skill, but this is only a beginning. You should make careful listening to the sounds of the various instruments a part of your daily experience.

5. Recall or imagine the effect of various instrumental combinations. Chapter 10 provides general information on balance and blend, but you should be alert for interesting colors in the music you encounter and study scores to find out how the effects are produced.

6. Orchestrate the various texture types. A brief introduction to the basic texture types is contained in chapter 3, and specific techniques for scoring the various textures are found in chapters 11–14.

7. Compose effective introductions, transitions and codas and accompaniment textures. These topics are the subject of chapters 15 and 16.

8. Plan the form of an arrangement. Chapter 17 presents an introduction to this topic.

9. See a product of your creative imagination through to completion in an arrangement. Chapter 18 provides you an opportunity to do so.

Many of the musical examples in this book and the accompanying workbook are recorded on compact disks available from the publisher. This set of CDs is specially mastered to allow you instantaneous access to the examples. Constant listening is critical for developing skill as an arranger, and these compact disks will make your task much easier.

I would like to recognize the valuable contributions of the following persons and groups who have helped to shape Instrumental Arranging: Chuck Elledge, staff writer for Neil A. Kjos Music Company, who offered many valuable suggestions in chapter 9; Roger Bissell, trombonist and arranger at Disneyland, who was my consultant and coauthor for chapter 19, and who offered valuable suggestions on the other chapters as well; Prof. Roger Cichy, director of Iowa State University Marching Band, who coauthored chapter 20; members of the music faculty of Iowa State University, who read various chapters in their earliest form and offered valuable criticism; Janice Coleman, my student assistant throughout the project, who worked tirelessly and carefully; Sara Compton, my long time assistant, who produced most of the musical examples; Stephani Scherbart, who assembled the glossary; Prof. Anthony Lis and the students at South Dakota State University, who class-tested the earliest version of the book; Prof. Milan Kaderavek, and the students at Drake University, who class-tested later versions; and my own students at Iowa State University, who were also involved in class-testing. Prof. Michael T. Cox of Southwestern Baptist Theological Seminary, Prof. David F. Foley of Ball State University, Prof. John C. Nelson of Georgia State University, and Prof. Greg A. Steinke of University of Arizona reviewed the manuscript and offered valuable suggestions. My appreciation for these dedicated colleagues cannot be adequately expressed. Their support and encouragement were as valuable to me as their more concrete contributions. Finally, I would like to add a word of appreciation to my wife, Joan. She has stuck with me through many years of irregular schedules and preoccupation, as I have worked on five textbooks and hundreds of compositions and arrangements. Her patience and support are boundless.

A Fundamentals

As stated in the preface, the technique of the arranger consists of a number of skills and knowledge of many details of the inner workings of instruments and ensembles. In this part, we will deal with certain fundamental topics, including the notation of music, transposition, setting up scores and parts, and musical texture. Notation, transposition, and score layout are mechanical operations that you must master to communicate with other musicians, while musical texture is a part of musical analysis which is of particular importance in arranging. Since these topics are often not included in basic theory instruction, I have provided an introduction here. The chapter on texture is of particular importance, since it introduces terminology that we will use in many of the later chapters.

This book assumes that you have already completed a thorough study of the elements of music, including scales, intervals, chords, rhythm, the functional harmonic system, harmonic analysis using roman numerals, voice leading in two-part through four-part textures, and the classical forms.

It is crucial that you have a thorough grounding in the various styles of Western music. No amount of clever orchestration can mask stylistic inconsistencies in your writing. As an arranger, you must enter into the style of the music you are arranging in an unobtrusive way and this requires considerable sensitivity to the subtleties of style. For example, in music of the "common practice" period, characterized by functional harmony based on the major and minor scales, there was a preference for contrary motion between parts and an insistence on resolution of dissonances. In 20th-century jazz ensemble writing, on the other hand, there is a preference for parallelism and the acceptance of dissonances without their traditional resolutions.

The details of musical style go far beyond the scope of this book. If you need further background, I would recommend the study of a comprehensive music theory text such as Benward and White, *Music in Theory and Practice*, volumes I–II. Dubuque, Iowa: (Wm. C. Brown Publishers), or other, more specialized, treatments of style.

1 Music Notation and Transposition

Rules for Notation

As an arranger you are responsible for producing clear, readable, and error-free scores and parts. Errors in copying, notes which are placed ambiguously, and crowded or otherwise poorly spaced manuscript all contribute to unmusical results in performance. Performers will work very hard to overcome poor copying, but it is better if they are able to devote themselves to playing with good musical interpretation. The guidelines in the following sections should be carefully observed if you are copying your music by hand.

Output from computer notation programs is in the process of replacing hand-copied music in many areas. Several programs for the common personal computers are listed in the bibliography at the end of this chapter. If you are producing your materials by computer, the program may automatically observe correct notational procedures, but you can't always depend on the accuracy of such programs, and notation often reflects your musical intent in ways that the programs can't foresee. For this reason, you should study the following guidelines, even if you plan to use a computer program to produce your music.

Noteheads

Noteheads should be elliptical and just large enough to fill one space (figure 1.1).

Figure 1.1

The whole note is also an ellipse, but at the opposite angle (figure 1.2).

Figure 1.2

While noteheads that are little more than single pencil strokes are extremely difficult to read, the other extreme—noteheads that are circular and formed by a spiraling pencil stroke, are no better. Avoid the tendency to make notes on lines larger than those on spaces. The standards of printed music are the norm for music manuscript.

Rests

Rests should be drawn in the center of the staff (figure 1.3).

Figure 1.3

The whole rest can be used to indicate a full measure of rest in any meter containing four or fewer quarter note values (figure 1.4). The whole rest is not appropriate to fill measures in meters such as 4/2, where the whole rest is likely to occur within a measure of notation.

Figure 1.4

whole rests:

Stems

When the staff contains only one melody, the stems on notes that are below the third line should go up from the right side of the notehead, while the stems on notes on the third line and above go down from the left side of the notehead (figure 1.5).

Figure 1.5

up from the right

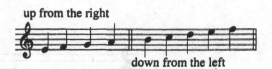

down from the left

Fundamentals

The stems of single notes within the staff should be one octave in length (figure 1.6).

Figure 1.6

one octave

When stemmed notes are in two or more ledger lines, the stems should be drawn to the center line of the staff (figure 1.7).

Figure 1.7

center line

Flags

Flags are always drawn on the right side of the stem (figure 1.8).

Figure 1.8

right side

If more than one flag appears on a note, the flags are approximately one space apart (figure 1.9).

Figure 1.9

one space

Beams

Beams should be a half space in thickness and spaced slightly less than one space apart (figure 1.10).

Figure 1.10

half space

When connected by beams, stemmed notes should be modified in length so that the beams cross no more than one line of the staff (figure 1.11).

Figure 1.11

beam does not cross more than one staff line

Beam groups of notes according to the beats in the measure (figure 1.12).

Figure 1.12

right   wrong   wrong   right   wrong   wrong

Two Parts per Staff

When two melodies occupy the same staff, the stems for the upper part should be drawn up and the stems for the lower part drawn down regardless of placement on the staff (figure 1.13).

Figure 1.13

Hns. I–II

If the upper and lower parts cross, the stems continue to be drawn in the same manner (figure 1.14). This makes it possible to distinguish between the parts.

Figure 1.14

Any rests in the upper part are drawn in the upper part of the staff, if there is room; otherwise, they are drawn in the space above the staff (figure 1.15).

Figure 1.15

If the lower part contains rests, they are drawn in the lower part of the staff, if there is room; otherwise, they are drawn in the space below the staff (figure 1.16).

Figure 1.16

If both parts have the same rests, it is not necessary to duplicate the rests. They are drawn in the usual location in the center of the staff (figure 1.17).

Figure 1.17

Vertical Alignment	Vertical alignment must be strictly observed. All notes which are to sound at one time must be placed directly over each other (figure 1.18).

Figure 1.18

If notes that are a second apart are to be placed on the same stem, the higher of the two is always to the right regardless of the direction of the stem (figure 1.19).

Figure 1.19

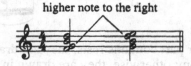

When two parts with separate stems are written a second apart on one staff, the lower of the two notes is always to the right (figure 1.20). Note that this is the reverse of the situation described above in figure 1.19.

Figure 1.20

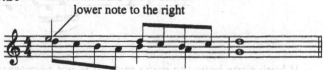

Dotted Notes	When dotted notes are on a space, the dot is drawn directly to the right of the note head, and when the note is on a line, the dot is drawn on the space above (figure 1.21).

Figure 1.21

When two dotted notes are a second apart it is sometimes necessary to adjust the position of the dots (figure 1.22).

Figure 1.22

Accidentals

Accidentals are placed directly to the left of the note they affect (figure 1.23).

Figure 1.23

right   wrong

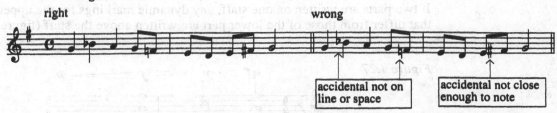

accidental not on line or space

accidental not close enough to note

When notes are a second apart, it is sometimes necessary to adjust the position of accidentals (figure 1.22).

When several accidentals are needed on a chord or pair of notes occurring simultaneously, they are arranged to be as compact as possible without allowing them to touch each other. If two accidentals are a seventh or more apart, they may be vertically aligned (figure 1.24).

Figure 1.24

When the interval between adjacent accidentals is smaller than a seventh, the accidentals are interwoven, with the higher accidental next to the note head and alternating with the lower and higher accidentals as shown in figure 1.25.

Figure 1.25

For more detailed treatment of this thorny notational problem, see *The Art of Music Engraving and Processing* by Ted Ross (pp. 130–135).

Dynamic Markings

Dynamic markings in instrumental music should be written directly below the first note to which they apply (figure 1.26).

Figure 1.26

If two parts are written on one staff, any dynamic markings for the upper part that differ from those of the lower part are written above the staff (figure 1.27).

Figure 1.27

Dynamic markings in vocal music are written above the staff to avoid conflict with the text (figure 1.28).

Figure 1.28

When   I _____ am with   you,

Dynamic markings for instruments using the grand staff (piano staff) are written between the two staves, if the dynamics apply to both staves (figure 1.29).

Figure 1.29

If separate dynamics are needed for each staff, they are written above the upper staff and below the lower staff (figure 1.30).

Figure 1.30

As a general rule, avoid placing dynamic markings on the staff (figure 1.31).

Figure 1.31

Articulation Markings

Articulation markings (staccatos, accents, tenutos, etc.) are generally placed on the opposite side from the stem and centered directly above the note head (figure 1.32).

Figure 1.32

Smaller symbols (staccatos and tenutos) may be placed in spaces on the staff, while larger symbols must be drawn outside the staff (figure 1.33).

Figure 1.33

Slurs and ties are usually placed on the opposite side from the stem and directly above the noteheads (figure 1.34).

Figure 1.34

In cases where stems go in both directions within a passage, there is a preference for placing slurs above the staff (figure 1.35), but you must use your own judgment in cases where the slurs might get in the way of other symbols.

Figure 1.35

When two parts are written on the same staff, it is necessary to place all articulations on the same side as the stems (figure 1.36).

Figure 1.36

Proportional Spacing

Observe proportional spacing within each measure. Generally speaking, give a half note almost twice as much space as a quarter note, a quarter note nearly twice as much as an eighth note, etc. (The engraver's rules for spacing are more precise, but beyond the scope of this book.) The rhythmic accuracy of performers improves when they read music that observes this principle (figure 1.37).

Figure 1.37

Clefs and Key Signatures

Clefs and key signatures should appear on each line of music in both score and parts (figure 1.38a). The exceptions to this rule are marching band and jazz ensemble parts, which do not repeat the clef and key signature (figure 1.38b).

Figure 1.38

a.

b.

Meter Signatures (Time Signatures)

Meter signatures appear after the clef and key signatures at the beginning of the piece and are *not* repeated on each system (figure 1.39).

Figure 1.39

Serenade

I

Bassoon I

Antonín Dvořák, op. 44
(1841-1904)

Moderato, quasi marcia

meter signature NOT repeated

When there is a change of meter, the new meter signature is drawn to the right of the bar line (figure 1.40).

Figure 1.40

Moussorgsky-Ravel: Pictures at an Exhibition, Promenade I, m. 1–2.

Trumpet in C

meter signature to
right of bar line

If a change of meter signature is to be made at the beginning of a system, it is written twice; once at the end of the previous system and a second time at the beginning of the new system (figure 1.41).

Figure 1.41

Grainger: Lincolnshire Posy, III (Rufford Park Poachers), m. 1–10.

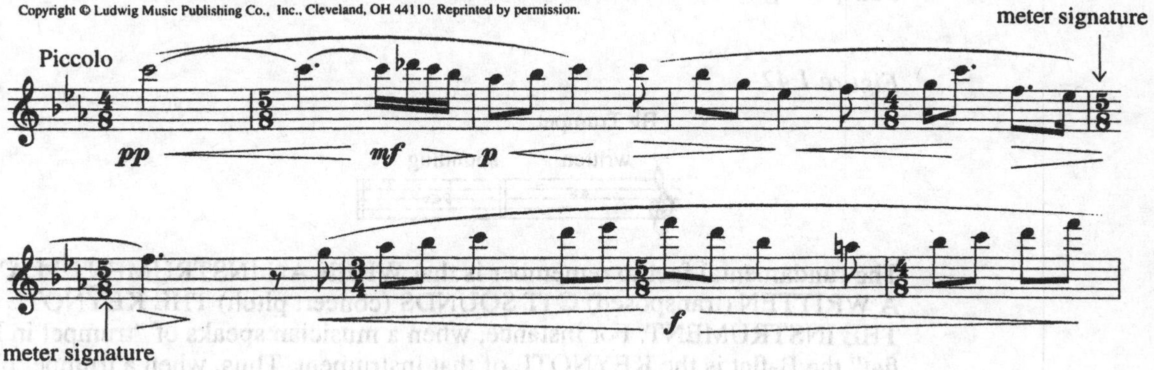

Equipment for Copying Music

Use a heavyweight paper that will stand up on a music stand and a medium soft pencil or ink in music copying. Errors should be carefully erased with a good quality eraser. Avoid crossing out errors since this results in confusion on the player's part. A seethrough plastic ruler, a plastic triangle, or other ruler is required for drawing straight lines (particularly bar lines).

If you are using a computer notation program, make sure that the printed copies are clear and dark. If you are using a dotmatrix printer, it will be necessary to replace the ribbon often to ensure quality reproduction, and laser printers require periodic cleaning and replacement of cartridges to continue to produce high-quality output.

Transposition

Since many instruments are transposing instruments (that is, they do not sound the pitch that is written for them) and scores are normally written with transposed parts, it is essential that you develop considerable skill in transposition.

Musicians refer to notes in two ways. Either they are "concert pitch," which means the instrument they are written for produces the same pitches we hear when we play the written notes on the piano keyboard, or they are "transposed," meaning that an adjustment has been made to compensate for the fact that an instrument doesn't produce the same pitches as the notes that are written. Another term which means the same as "concert pitch" is "sounding pitch." One says that an instrument *sounds* a B-flat when it plays a *written* C. "Sounds" in this context means "concert pitch," and "written" refers to the fact that the part is written for a transposing instrument. Figure 1.42 is an example of the way transposing instruments are shown in this book.

Figure 1.42

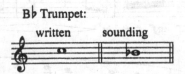

The fundamental fact to remember is that WHEN AN INSTRUMENT PLAYS A WRITTEN (transposed) C IT SOUNDS (concert pitch) THE KEYNOTE OF THE INSTRUMENT. For instance, when a musician speaks of "trumpet in B-flat" the B-flat is the KEYNOTE of that instrument. Thus, when a trumpet player plays a C in the part, a B-flat will be produced.

Many computer notation programs make automatic transposition available. While these programs save much time for the arranger, I have yet to encounter a program that will transpose without occasional errors. For this reason, I would urge you to check any automatic transposition carefully before giving it to a performer or conductor. This is another example of the principle, stated at the beginning of the chapter, that computer programs can't substitute for your personal knowledge about music.

Interval Transposition	One common technique for transposition is by interval. In this method, an interval of transposition is established, and all pitches are moved up or down by that interval, as shown in figure 1.43.

Figure 1.43

Interval transposition

Bb Major
to
C Major

Clef Transposition	Some musicians prefer to transpose by clef. In this method, a clef is chosen that would put the part on the correct transposed pitch, and the key signature is changed. For example, when given a concert-pitch part written in the bass clef, a baritone saxophone player can play the part by imagining it in the treble clef and subtracting three flats (or adding three sharps), and the correct pitches will be produced. (The player would also have to convert accidentals within the part.) Figure 1.44 shows how the previous example can be transposed from B-flat major to C major by substituting the alto clef and changing the key signature. Notice that it is sometimes necessary, in making a clef transposition, to change the octave of the clef (in this case by shifting it up an octave).

Figure 1.44

Clef transposition

Substitute alto clef and new key signature

Figure 1.45 shows the clefs necessary for several of the common instrumental transpositions.

Figure 1.45

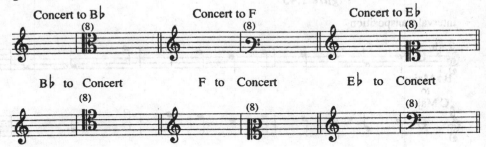

Tonal and Nontonal Transposition

If the music is tonal and written with a key signature (which includes the key of C major), then the transposition includes transposing the key signature (figure 1.46).

Figure 1.46

Tonal transposition

Eb Major
to
D Major

transpose key signature
as well as pitches

If the music is written without key signatures and is chromatic, the transposed parts will also appear without key signature. In this case, while particular care must be taken to insure that the line is transposed accurately, enharmonic notations may be freely written. For example, the A-flat on the second beat of figure 1.47 could just as easily have been written as G-sharp.

Figure 1.47

Nontonal transposition

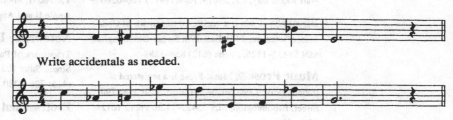

Write accidentals as needed.

Workbook: Assignments A–M, pp. 1–12.

Suggestions for Further Study

Several textbooks that teach the art of music notation and copying are available, including:

Harder, Paul O. *Music Manuscript Techniques: A Programmed Approach*, Parts I–II. Newton, Mass.: Allyn and Bacon, Inc., 1984.

Heussenstamm, George. *The Norton Manual of Music Notation*. New York: W. W. Norton & Company, Inc., 1987.

General references that provide solutions to many specific problems you are likely to encounter include:

Read, Gardner. *Music Notation*. 2nd ed. Boston: Crescendo Publishers, 1969.

Ross, Ted. *The Art of Music Engraving and Processing*. Miami Beach, Fla.: Hansen Books, 1970.

Stone, Kurt. *Music Notation in the Twentieth Century*. New York: W. W. Norton & Company, Inc., 1980.

A number of computer programs have been written to produce high-quality music graphics. Because this area is undergoing rapid development, you should consult a computer dealer to find the latest software. The following programs represent the software available for the Macintosh® and IBM® computers at the time of writing that were considered sophisticated enough to be useful to an arranger:

Macintosh® software. (Macintosh is a registered trademark of Apple Computer, Inc.)

Encore®, Encore is a registered trademark of Passport Design, 625 Miramontes Street, Suite 103, Half Moon Bay, CA 94019. Phone (415) 726–0280

Finale®, Coda is a registered trademark of Coda Music Software, 1401 East 79th Street, Bloomington, MN 55425–1126. Phone (612) 854–1288

Music Prose®, Music Prose is a registered trademark of Coda Music Software, 1401 East 79th Street, Bloomington, MN 55425–1126. Phone (612) 854–1288

Music Publisher®, Music Publisher is a registered trademark of Graphic Notes, 200 Seventh Avenue, Suite 125, Santa Cruz, CA 95062. Phone (408) 476–0147

Music Writer®, Music Writer is a registered trademark of Pygraphics, P.O. Box 639, Grapevine, TX 76051. Phone (800) 222–7536 (also available for Apple II and Apple IIGS)

Notewriter II®, Notewriter is a registered Trademark of Passport Designs, 625 Miramontes Street, Suite 103, Half Moon Bay, CA 94019. Phone (415) 726–0280

Professional Composer®, Professional Composer is a registered trademark of Mark of the Unicorn, 222 Third Street, Cambridge, MA 02142. Phone (617) 576–2760

IBM® (and IBM compatible) software. (IBM is a registered trademark of International Business Machines Corporation.)

Copyist®, Copyist is a registered trademark of Dr. T's Music Software, 220 Boylston Street, Chestnut Hill, MA 02167. Phone (617) 244–6954 (also for Atari ST and Amiga computers)

Finale®, Finale is a registered trademark of Coda Music Software, 1401 East 79th Street, Bloomington, MN 55425–1126. Phone (612) 854–1288

The Laser Music Processor®, The Laser Music Processor is a registered trademark of Teach Services, 182 Donivan Road, Bruhton, NY 12916. Phone (518) 358–2125

MusicPrinter Plus®, MusicPrinter Plus is a registered trademark of Temporal Acuity Products, Inc., 300 120th Ave. N.E., Bldg. 1, Suite 200, Bellevue, WA 98005. Phone (800) 426–2673

Music Writer®, Music Writer is a registered trademark of Pygraphics, P.O. Box 639, Grapevine, TX 76051. Phone (800) 222–7536

The Note Processor®, The Note Processor is a registered trademark of Thoughtprocessors, 584 Bergen Street, Brooklyn, NY 11238. Phone (718) 857–2860

Theme®, Theme is a registered trademark of The Music Editor, Theme Software Company, P.O. Box 8204, Charlottesville, VA 22906. Phone (804) 973–6919

2 Preparation of Scores and Parts

The Score   As an instrumental arranger, you will be required to produce a full score and a set of parts, one part for each instrument in the ensemble. The score is usually transposed, showing each instrument as it will be written in the part. The order of instruments on the score is fairly well standardized, but some variations do exist. The usual order of instruments in the orchestra and concert bands are shown on the following page.

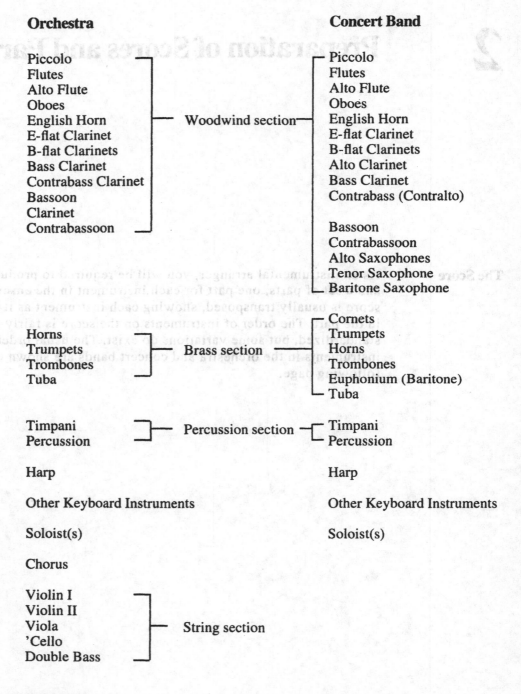

Orchestra		Concert Band
Piccolo Flutes Alto Flute Oboes English Horn E-flat Clarinet B-flat Clarinets Bass Clarinet Contrabass Clarinet Bassoon Clarinet Contrabassoon	Woodwind section	Piccolo Flutes Alto Flute Oboes English Horn E-flat Clarinet B-flat Clarinets Alto Clarinet Bass Clarinet Contrabass (Contralto) Bassoon Contrabassoon Alto Saxophones Tenor Saxophone Baritone Saxophone
Horns Trumpets Trombones Tuba	Brass section	Cornets Trumpets Horns Trombones Euphonium (Baritone) Tuba
Timpani Percussion	Percussion section	Timpani Percussion
Harp		Harp
Other Keyboard Instruments		Other Keyboard Instruments
Soloist(s)		Soloist(s)
Chorus		
Violin I Violin II Viola 'Cello Double Bass	String section	

Some common variations are:

1. The piccolo may be listed below the flute.
2. The bassoon may be listed immediately after the oboe, or even after the baritone saxophone in band scores.

The score orders listed above can be adapted to accommodate any instrumental ensemble. Figure 2.1 shows the first page of score for an orchestral work from the classical period.

Figure 2.1

Haydn: Symphony No. 101 in D Major (the Clock) Hob. I:101, First Movement, m. 1–8.

Figure 2.2 shows the position of a solo piano (or other solo instrument) in an orchestral score.

Figure 2.2

Mozart: Piano Concerto in C Major, K. 503, I (Allegro maestoso), m. 110–117.

Fundamentals

Figure 2.3a shows the first page of full score for a band work and figure 2.3b shows a somewhat condensed score for an elementary band work.

Figure 2.3

a. White: Afton Water, m. 1–2.

b. White: Cherry Tree Carol, m. 1–3.

Figure 2.4 is an example of the score for a standard jazz ensemble. (See figure 11.5 on p. 204 for another example.)

Figure 2.4

Nestico: Hay Burner, m. 1–7.

Fundamentals

Figure 2.5 shows two standard layouts for marching band scores.

Figure 2.5

a. Ponchielli: Dance of the Hours, m. 1–3.

b. Cichy: Gimme Some Lovin', m.1–3.

Take careful note of the brackets and bar lines on these scores (figures 2.1–2.4) and follow the same pattern in your scores. The brackets and bar lines generally are used to separate the woodwinds, brass, percussion, and string sections. They are an aid to the eye in reading the score.

Vertical Alignment in Scores

Vertical alignment must be strictly observed over the entire score page. All notes that sound at the same time must be directly over each other. To aid the eye in aligning notes over the page, it is best if you plan the number and spacing of measures first and draw the bar lines with a wide seethrough ruler (C-Thru® No. B-85 or equivalent). These vertical lines will then be a guide as you fill in the notes. If bar lines are far apart, you may need the ruler to line up the notes on the beginning of each beat.

Rehearsal Numbers/Letters

In instrumental arrangements, rehearsal numbers should be placed in both scores and parts. Several systems are in common use, including: letters (A, B, C, etc.) placed at important points in the score, measure numbers at the beginning of each system, measure numbers at important points in the score, and measure numbers on each measure. Your instructor will advise you as to the proper form for class assignments, but whatever system is used must be consistent between the score and parts.

Using measure numbers is highly recommended. It simplifies proofreading by making it easier to check parts for missing measures. To place rehearsal numbers, begin by counting the first full measure and mark a measure number in the score above each section (woodwind, brass, percussion, strings) at the proper points. These letters or numbers are generally placed in boxes to make them stand out on the page. There should be a rehearsal number or letter every 10–16 measures to allow performers to find starting places in rehearsal without having to count large numbers of measures.

Tempo and Dynamic Indications in Scores

General tempo indications are placed above each section (woodwind, brass, percussion, strings) in the score. These indications must be large enough to be easily seen by the conductor. It is not necessary to show general tempo indications on each part in the score, but all other indications must appear on each line. This includes dynamic levels, indications of articulation and phrasing, and momentary changes in tempo (including fermatas). If momentary changes of tempo (including fermatas) occur in the score, they must be carefully shown in precisely the same location in all lines. It may be necessary to break up whole rests into a number of shorter rests in order to accomplish this. The standard practice for rehearsal numbers as well as tempo and dynamic indications is illustrated in figure 2.6.

Figure 2.6

White: Afton Water, m. 53–58.

AFTON WATER by Gary C. White. Copyright © Neil A. Kjos Music Co., Distributor, San Diego, CA. Used by Permission 1991.

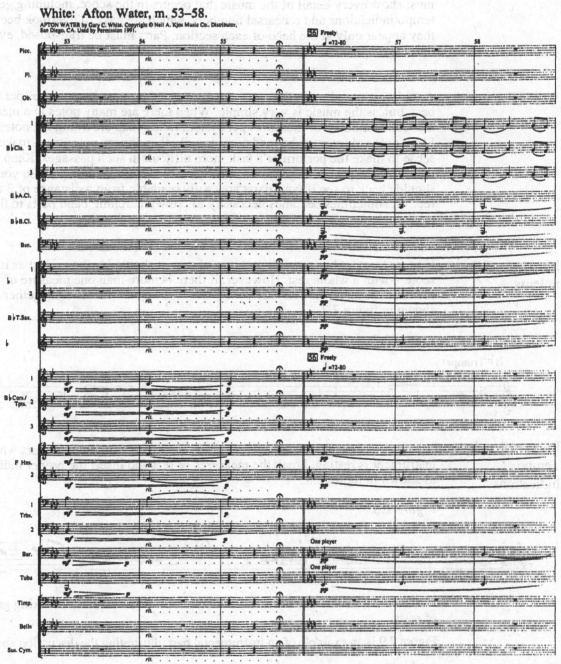

The Parts

A separate part must be extracted for each instrument in the ensemble. The parts must show every detail of the music that occurs in the score, including general tempo indications and rehearsal numbers, which are easy to overlook because they appear only at the head of each section. Parts must be transposed, even if the score is in concert pitch.

Avoid overcrowding in the parts. An average of four to six measures per line is best, unless the music is very simple. When there are many notes in a measure, reduce the number of measures per system rather than crowding the notes in. Short note values must be read more rapidly than longer notes, so it makes no sense to make the performer's task more difficult in such passages. Keep in mind that the player's eyes are normally several feet from the part, so you should check to see if your parts are easily readable from a distance of 3 to 4 feet. (It sometimes becomes necessary to crowd marching band parts to fit them on a single page of quickstep part paper.)

Measures of Rest in Parts

If an instrument has one full measure of rest, it should be shown just as in the score—with a whole rest. However, if there is more than one measure of consecutive rests, the standard practice is to group the measures together as shown in figure 2.7.

Figure 2.7

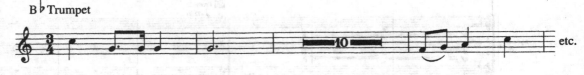

Rehearsal and Tempo Indications

If a rehearsal number, a change of meter, or a change of tempo occurs while an instrument is resting, break the measures of rest and insert the proper indication as shown in figure 2.8.

Figure 2.8

Even momentary ritardandos and accelerandos are a cause for breaking groups of rests.

Figure 2.9 is an example of an instrumental part, illustrating the discussion above.

Fundamentals

Figure 2.9

White: Afton Water, m. 1–40.

AFTON WATER by Gary C. White. Copyright © Neil A. Kjos Music
Co., Distributor, San Diego, CA. Used by Permission 1991

Headings in Score and Parts

A title should be centered on the first page of both score and parts. The composer's name appears on the right above the first system of music, with the arranger's name directly below (the designation: "Arr. by (name)" should be used). If there is a lyricist, his/her name appears to the left, above the first system of music and above the tempo indication.

The name of the instrument appears in the upper left-hand corner of each part. The instrument name should be fairly large and clear, since it will be used in sorting and filing the music.

Proofreading

Proofread *all* your work. This is a painstaking and time-consuming process, but it pays dividends in rehearsal. It is much easier to see errors in another's work than in your own. For this reason, it is strongly recommended that you pair off with another student and correct each other's work. Make sure that the score and parts agree in every way. This should be obvious, but there is a tendency to correct the part and not the score, or vice versa. Failure to resolve inconsistencies between score and parts wastes valuable rehearsal time. Check both score and parts for each of the following:

Accidentals
Double bars
Dynamics
Key signatures
Number of beats per measure
Phrasings
Rehearsal numbers (or letters)
Repeat signs
Tempo changes
Total number of measures
Transpositions
Word spellings

Automatic extraction of parts in computer notation programs is a great convenience, but it does not relieve you from careful proofreading, since the programs may leave out certain elements of the music, particularly those indications that appear at the head of each section. Also, programs differ in the way they deal with multiple measures of rest, particularly in situations where rehearsal numbers require that they be broken. If the program produces a separate computer file that can be edited, there is little problem, but if the part extraction is done from the original file, it can be difficult or nearly impossible to edit the parts into usable form. In such cases, it may be better to simply copy the individual instrument line into a new file that can be edited.

Workbook: Assignments A–C, pp. 13–42

Suggestions for Further Study

Most orchestration texts contain sections dealing with the layout of scores and parts. Of particular interest are:

Adler, Samuel. *The Study of Orchestration*. 2nd ed. New York: W. W. Norton & Company, Inc., 1989, 1982. (Chapter 18, p. 604)

Blatter, Alfred. *Instrumentation/Orchestration*. New York: Longman, Inc., 1980.

Burton, Stephen Douglas. *Orchestration*. Englewood Cliffs, N.J.: Prentice Hall, Inc., 1982. (Chapter 26, p. 278, Chapter 31, p. 408)

Kennan, Kent, and Donald Grantham. *The Technique of Orchestration*, 4th edition. Englewood Cliffs, NJ: Prentice Hall, Inc., 1990, 1983, 1970, 1952. (Chapter 20, p. 365)

Notation manuals such as the following often include a section on score and part layout:

Harder, Paul O. *Music Manuscript Techniques: A Programmed Approach*, Part II. Newton, Mass.: Allyn and Bacon, Inc. 1984.

Read, Gardner. *Music Notation*. 2nd ed. Boston: Crescendo Publishers, 1969.

Stone, Kurt. *Music Notation in the Twentieth Century*. New York: W. W. Norton & Company, Inc., 1980.

3 An Arranger's Introduction to Musical Textures

Texture

The term *texture* is often used rather loosely to describe the vertical aspects of music. We will consider texture more specifically and precisely, as the way the melodic, rhythmic and harmonic materials are woven together in a composition. As an arranger, it is important for you to know what texture type you are dealing with and how the various parts of the musical texture relate to each other to make sensible decisions about scoring.

Density

The density of texture is often described with terms such as "thick" or "thin," depending on whether there are many or few voices or parts (figure 3.1a–b).

Figure 3.1

a. **Thin Texture**

Haydn: Sonatina in G Major, Hob. XVI: 11.

b. Thick Texture

Taylor Made Piano, Roost, LP2222 from Jazz Piano, page 158, Wm. C. Brown, Inc.

Range	The range of a texture is often described with such terms as "wide" or "narrow," depending on the interval between the lowest and highest tones (figure 3.2a–b).

Figure 3.2

a. Wide texture

Berlioz: Requiem, X, *Agnus Dei.*

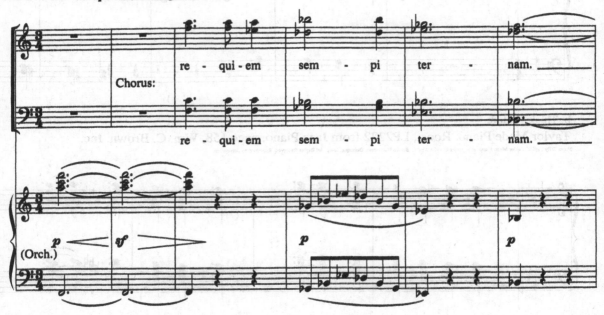

b. Narrow texture

Elliott Carter: Eight Etudes and a Fantasy for Woodwind Quartet, III.

Fundamentals

Texture Types

While density and range are usually described in relative terms, the description of texture type is much more precise and useful. There are a number of texture types that occur from time to time, but the most common are: monophonic, polyphonic, homophonic, and homorhythmic.

Analysis of Texture

The analysis of texture involves the identification of texture type and the recognizing and labeling of the principal elements of the texture. You may be able to identify the texture type rather quickly by careful listening or visual inspection of the score. If not, a reliable method is to identify first the textural elements, which are as follows:

1. **Primary Melodies (PM)** are the most important melodic lines in a musical texture.
2. **Secondary Melodies (SM)** are other melodies that are not equal in significance to the primary melody or melodies.
3. **Parallel Supporting Melodies (PSM)** are melodies that are similar in contour with a PM or SM.
4. **Static Support (SS)** are sustained tones or chords or repeated melodic and rhythmic figures or ostinati.
5. **Harmonic Support (HS)** is an element of accompaniment texture that provides a harmonic background to the melody.
6. **Rhythmic Support (RS)** is an element of accompaniment texture that provides a rhythmic background to the melody.
7. **Harmonic and Rhythmic Support (HRS)** is a combination of HS and RS in the same part.

Monophonic Texture

Monophonic texture is the simplest texture type in music. It consists of a single melodic line (PM) as shown in figure 3.3. (CD 4. cut 1)

Figure 3.3

Moussorgsky-Ravel: Pictures at an Exhibition, Promenade I, m. 1–2.

Monophonic textures can be expanded by doubling in octaves (figure 3.4a) or at other intervals (figure 3.4b).

Figure 3.4

  a. Sousa: Washington Post March, m. 1–7.

  b. Debussy: Sarabande *(Pour le Piano)*, m.1–2.

      Fundamentals

Monophonic textures are often split up among several instruments, as shown in the following excerpt from Bizet's *Jeux d'Enfants* (figure 3.5). (CD 1, cut 23)

Figure 3.5

Bizet: *Jeux d'Enfants*, op. 22, III (Impromptu), m. 31–36.

Polyphonic Texture

Polyphonic textures consist of more than one line moving independently (figure 3.6a) or in imitation of each other (figure 3.6b). The lines may be equal in significance (PM) or of unequal significance (PM vs. SM).

Figure 3.6

a. Mozart: Requiem

b. Bach: Invention no. 4 in D Minor, BWV 775, m. 1–4.

The various lines may be similar (figure 3.7a) or contrasting in character (figure 3.7b).

Figure 3.7

a. Josquin des Prés: *Tu Solus Facis Mirabilia*

b. Bach: *Fuga canonica* from The Musical Offering, BWV 1079.

Homophonic Texture

Homophonic texture is the most common texture in Western music. It is made up of a melody (PM) and an accompaniment that typically provides rhythmic support (RS) and harmonic support (HS), as shown in figure 3.8. (CD 1, cut 26) Harmonic and rhythmic support are often combined in the same parts (HRS).

Figure 3.8

Bizet: *Jeux d'Enfants,* op. 21, V (Galop), m. 1–6.

There are often separate harmonic supporting lines in ensemble music (figure 3.9). (CD 5, cut 33)

Figure 3.9
Weber: Overture to Oberon, m. 169-173.

The following excerpt from Holst's First Suite for Military Band has a separate rhythmic support (RS) part (figure 3.10). (CD 3, cut 13)

Figure 3.10

Holst: First Suite in E-flat for Military Band, op. 28, no. 1, III (March), m. 4–9.

FIRST SUITE IN E-FLAT FOR MILITARY BAND © Copyright 1921 by Boosey & Co., Ltd.; Copyright Renewed. Reprinted by permission of Boosey & Hawkes, Inc.

The accompaniment in the following passage from Bartók's Hungarian Sketches (figure 3.11) (CD 1, cut 3) features static supporting parts (SS) in the form of ostinati and sustained notes.

Figure 3.11

Bartók: Hungarian Sketches I (An Evening in the Village), m. 30–33.

HUNGARIAN SKETCHES © Copyright 1932 by Karl Rozsnyai and Rozsavolgyi & Co., Copyright Renewed. Copyright and Renewal assigned to Boosey & Hawkes, Inc. Reprinted by permission.

Homorhythmic Texture

Homorhythmic texture is a texture with similar rhythmic material in all parts. This texture is often referred to as "hymn style" or "chordal texture", depending on the presence or absence of melodic material. Homorhythmic texture usually has a melody (PM), often in the top voice, accompanied by several (usually three) harmonic supporting parts (HS) in similar rhythm. Figure 3.10 is an example of homorhythmic texture with a clearly defined upper melody. (CD 4, cut 2)

Figure 3.12

Moussorgksy-Ravel: Pictures at an Exhibition, Promenade I, m. 3–4.

PICTURES AT AN EXHIBITION © Copyright 1929 by Edition Russe de Musique; Copyright Renewed Copyright and Renewal assigned to Boosey & Hawkes, Inc. Reprinted by permission.

Fundamentals

Composite Textures

The fundamental texture types described above form the basis of most Western music, but more complex textures sometimes occur. Most of these textures can be described as composites of two of the fundamental textures. Figure 3.13 shows an example of such a composite texture, where the choral parts form a clear polyphonic texture, while the instrumental parts create an accompaniment texture; a clear example of polyphonic texture combined with homophonic texture. While not all textures can be neatly defined in general terms, it is the identification of the textural elements that will be most important for your work as an arranger.

Figure 3.13

Bach: Crucifixus from Mass in B minor, BWV 232, m. 3–41.

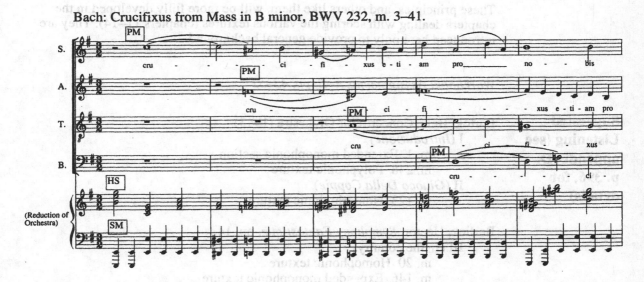

Summary

An understanding of musical texture is valuable for arrangers. In later chapters, we will learn general principles for scoring the various textural elements, but the following are several examples:

1. Primary melodies (PM) are scored in such a way that they will be the most prominent element in the texture. This can be accomplished by giving the PM to the strongest instrument in the texture, or by raising the dynamic of that part (usually two dynamics above the background).

2. Secondary melodies (SM) are clearly subordinate to primary melodies, but need to be heard clearly.

3. Parallel supporting melodies (PSM) are generally given to an instrument that blends well with the instrument playing the melody (PS or SM) they are supporting.

4. Static support (SS) and harmonic support (HS) should be subordinate to the melodic materials of the texture. These parts are generally scored so that they blend together.

5. Rhythmic support (RS) is generally balanced with the SS and HS elements, but may be contrasting in sound.

These principles, and others like them, will be more fully developed in the chapters dealing with scoring the various textures (chapters 11–14). They are introduced here only to provide general background.

Workbook: Asssignments A–B, pp. 43–51

Suggested Listening (see appendix D, p. 396, for details)

Bartók, Béla. Concerto for Orchestra (1943).
  I (*Introduzione*)
      m. 1 Extended monophonic section
      m. 248 Polyphonic texture
  II (*Giuoco Della Coppie*)
      m. 123 Homorhythmic texture

Berlioz, Hector. *Symphony Fantastique*, op. 14.
  III (In the country)
      m. 20 Homophonic texture
      m. 146 Expanded monophonic texture
  V (A witches' sabbath)
      m. 86 Monophonic texture

Bizet, George. *L'Arlésienne* Suite no. 1.
  I (Prelude)
      m. 1 Monophonic texture
      m. 90 Homophonic texture
      m. 113 Homophonic texture
  II (Minuetto)
      m. 29 Homophonic texture

Debussy, Claude. Prelude to "The Afternoon of a Faun."
   m. 1 Monophonic texture
   m. 63 Homophonic texture
   m. 107 Homorhythmic texture

Grainger, Percy. Lincolnshire Posy.
   I (Lisbon)
      m. 1 Expanded monophonic texture
      m. 60 Composite texture (homorhythmic and expanded monophonic)
   II (Horkstow Grange)
      Most of the movement is in homorhythmic texture
   III (Rufford Park Poachers)
      m. 1 Contrapuntal texture with unusual doubling

Holst, Gustav. Second Suite in F for Military Band, op.28, no. 2.
   I (March)
      m. 3 Homophonic texture
      m. 136 Homophonic texture
   II (Song Without Words)
      m. 1 Homophonic texture
   III (Song of the Blacksmith)
      m. 1 Homorhythmic texture
   IV (Fantasia on the 'Dargason')
      m. 1 Monophonic texture
      m. 177 Homophonic texture

Vaughan Williams, Ralph. Folk Song Suite.
   III (March)
      m. 1 Monophonic texture
      m. 5 Homophonic texture

Suggestions for Further Study

The subject of musical texture has not been fully developed in the literature. However, a number of authors recognize its importance to the arranger. The following orchestration books contain specific information about scoring in various texture types:

Adler, Samuel. *The Study of Orchestration*. 2nd ed. New York: W. W. Norton & Company, Inc., 1989, 1982. (Chapter 15, p. 459)

Burton, Stephen Douglas. *Orchestration*. Englewood Cliffs, N.J.: Prentice Hall, Inc., 1982. (Chapter 27, p. 338, Chapter 28, p. 348)

Kennan, Kent, and Donald Grantham. *The Technique of Orchestration*, 4th ed. Englewood Cliffs, N.J.: Prentice Hall, Inc., 1990, 1983, 1970, 1952. (Chapter 16, p. 291, Chapter 17, p. 329)

Piston, Walter. *Orchestration*. New York: W. W. Norton & Company, Inc., 1955. (Chapters 19–25, p. 355–405)

Rogers, Bernard. *Art of Orchestration: Principles of Tone Color in Modern Scoring*. Greenwood Press, 1970, reprint of 1951 edition. (Chapter 8, p. 93)

B Instrumentation

Music arranging requires an in-depth knowledge of the instruments or voices that make up the chosen ensemble. Each of the instruments has unique capabilities that a skilled arranger can take advantage of—and limitations that need to be considered if the arrangement is to be successful. For this reason, we will examine the most common members in each family of the orchestral and band instruments, taking note of the ranges, transpositions (if any), the division of the range into registers, any technical limitations that the arranger needs to be aware of, and special techniques that the arranger can utilize. In addition, where appropriate, we will include limited range and transposition information for some less-common instruments.

Ranges will be listed for four levels of performing experience: college/professional, high school, junior high school, and elementary school. They represent practical, if somewhat conservative, limits that you should observe in scoring for various levels of experience. The ranges have been chosen with the technical limitations of younger musicians in mind and the likelihood that the part can be consistently performed with good tone and intonation. This information has been collected from many sources, including: suggested ranges promulgated by publishers of educational music, interviews with conductors and instrumentalists, other orchestration and instrumentation books, and my experience as the composer of works for musicians from elementary age through professional levels. In most cases, the given range doesn't represent the highest or lowest possible note that a younger musician can play, but the notes that can be depended upon. The upper limits may be occasionally exceeded by a note or two without serious damage to the arrangement. The following chart summarizes the system used throughout the book to indicate the various levels. (Single noteheads below or above the normal ranges are optional notes, only available on some models of an instrument.)

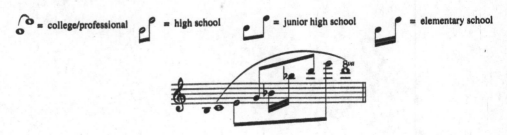

The graphs below register charts have been added to indicate the dynamic range within each register (see sample below). The top of the graph indicates the loudest sound available on the given instrument (not the loudest sound available from any instrument). The bottom of the graph indicates the softest sound available on the instrument, and the shaded area represents the dynamic range over various registers. Thus, an area that is shaded from the top of the graph to the bottom indicates that the total dynamic range of the instrument is available in that register. These charts, while representing the collective judgments of a number of professionals, are not based on scientific measurements. They should be viewed as subjective judgments of experienced musicians rather than scientific facts.

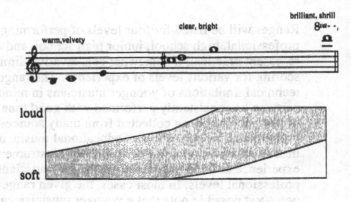

For wind instruments, the *tessitura* is often as important as the range and, in such cases, will be noted in the text. Tessitura is defined as the area of the total range in which the majority of the part is written. Tessitura is usually described in general terms: *high, middle,* and *low*. In the following two examples, the range is identical, but the tessitura is different.

When specific pitches are referred to in the text, it will sometimes be necessary to identify the specific note by the octave in which it appears. In such cases, the following system of octave designation will be used:

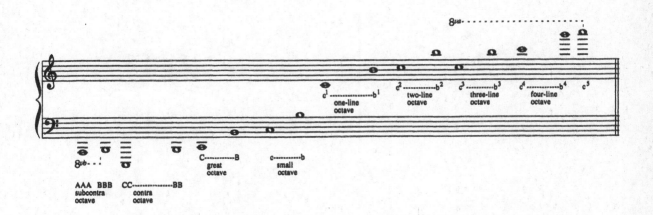

The instrumentation section has been kept intentionally brief, including only the most vital information. Further study in one of the instrumentation books listed at the ends of the chapters will give you more depth of knowledge, but consulting with performers on each of the instruments is perhaps the best way to gain an intimate understanding of an instrument and its unique capabilities.

The study of instrumentation is a continuing process for the arranger. New insights can be gained with each musical experience. The assignments that accompany the following chapters will provide opportunities for you to increase your knowledge and awareness of the instruments, but I urge you to consider every performing, listening, or other musical experience as an opportunity to learn more about instrumentation. In particular, I hope you will spend time listening to recordings and live performances while studying the score. When you hear a particularly striking effect in orchestration, try to find out, either by repeated listening or by examination of the score, exactly how it was achieved.

4 The Woodwinds: *Intimate Colors*

The woodwind family includes those wind instruments (sometimes called *aerophones*) in which the air within a hollow tube is set in motion by a vibrating reed or, in the case of the flute and piccolo, by air blown against the edge of a hole in the side of the instrument. Modern models of these instruments may be made of wood, metal, plastic, or other materials, and thus the "wood" in the family name has become a bit of a misnomer. These instruments have a wide range of timbres, offering some of the more diverse colors in the arranger's pallet. They are also, for the most part, instruments of more intimate character than the brass and percussion families, including some of the more interesting solo colors in an ensemble. The wide diversity of tone color can create problems of blend within the section, but these problems can be solved by careful selection of instruments and registers.

The Flute and Piccolo	French	German	Italian
	flûte	Flöte	flauto
	petite flûte	kleine Flöte	flauto piccolo

Figure 4.1

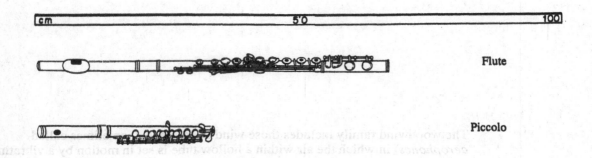

Flute

Piccolo

Ranges (written)   *Figure 4.2*

Piccolo   Flute

Transposition   The piccolo is written an octave below its sounding pitch to avoid extensive ledger lines.

Figure 4.3

Piccolo   Flute

written   sounding   written   sounding

Register Characteristics	The primary register division on the flute occurs between c-sharp^2 and d^2, with the fundamental producing the pitches in the lower register and the second partial producing those immediately above. A noticeable change in tone occurs at this point in the range, with the lower register being darker in color than the upper register. The piccolo is extremely weak in its lower register. The instrument is most used in the middle and upper register, where its tone is silvery to brilliant. Figure 4.4 provides more detailed information on the various registers of the flute and piccolo.

Figure 4.4

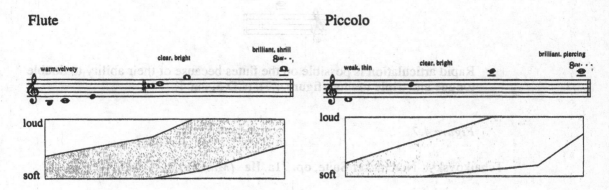

Flute   Piccolo

Technical Limitations	The flutes are flexible and agile instruments capable of playing nearly any melody. However, because the flutist expends a great amount of air in producing the tone, occasions to breathe must be provided at regular intervals. Figure 4.5 shows a few trills and tremolos that are impossible, or very difficult to play on the flute.

Figure 4.5

difficult or impossible trills and tremolos

Special Techniques

Harmonics are possible on pitches above c². The sound of the harmonic is thinner than the normal flute tone and is generally used as a special effect for single tones. A small circle is placed above the note to be played as a harmonic as shown in figure 4.6. (You should notate the pitch that you want to hear. The performer will finger a note an octave or more below the notated pitch and overblow to play the written harmonic.)

Figure 4.6

harmonic notation

Rapid articulation is possible on the flutes because of their ability to double tongue and triple tongue (figure 4.7). (CD 5, cut 4)

Figure 4.7

Tchaikovsky: Nutcracker Suite, op. 71a, IIa *(Marche)*, m. 41–43.

Musical Examples

The agility of the flute is demonstrated in the Danse Chinoise from Tchaikovsky's Nutcracker Suite (figure 4.8). (CD 5, cut 5)

Figure 4.8

Tchaikovsky: Nutcracker Suite, op. 71a, IIe *(Danse Chinoise)*, m. 1–4.

The following excerpt from Bizet's *Jeux d'Enfants* is a typical example of middle-range writing for the flute (figure 4.9). (CD 1, cut 28)

Figure 4.9

Bizet: *Jeux d'Enfants V (Galop),* m. 65–74.

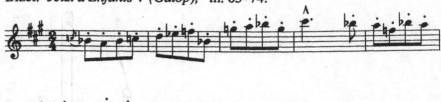

The piccolo is used effectively in Bartok's Hungarian Sketches (figure 4.10). (CD 1, cut 3)

Figure 4.10

Bartók: Hungarian Sketches, I (An Evening in the Village), m. 30–37.

HUNGARIAN SKETCHES © Copyright 1932 by Karl Rozsnyai and Rozsavolgyi & Co., Copyright Renewed. Copyright and Renewal assigned to Boosey & Hawkes, Inc. Reprinted by permission.

Perhaps the best-known example of piccolo writing occurs in the trio of Sousa's The Stars and Stripes Forever march (figure 4.11).

Figure 4.11

Sousa: The Stars and Stripes Forever (trio), m. 93–96.

The Oboe and English Horn	French	German	Italian
	hautbois	Hoboe	oboe
	cor anglais	Englischhorn	corno inglese

Figure 4.12

Oboe   English Horn

Ranges (written)   *Figure 4.13*

Oboe   English horn

Transposition   The English horn transposes down a perfect fifth.

Figure 4.14

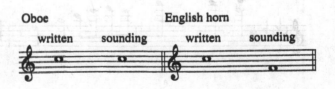

Oboe   English horn

written   sounding   written   sounding

Register Characteristics

The lower register of the oboe presents the greatest problems for the arranger. The tone is very strong and somewhat difficult to control. It tends to dominate in a woodwind ensemble texture. From d¹ to g¹ the tone becomes much more manageable, and the next register (from g¹ to g-sharp²) is the most characteristic oboe sound. In the extreme upper register, the tone becomes successively thinner and more piercing and the technique more and more difficult. Figure 4.15 summarizes the characteristics of the various registers of the oboe.

Figure 4.15

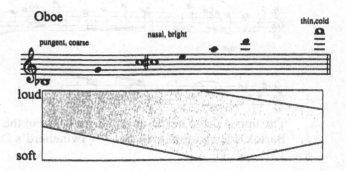

Technical Limitations

The oboe is quite flexible, if somewhat less agile than the flute. Most trills are possible, except for the half-step trill on the low a-sharp.

Figure 4.16

Impossible trill

Musical
Examples

An excellent illustration of the technical ability of the oboe in its middle register is the statement of the fugue subject in the final section of Britten's The Young Person's Guide to the Orchestra (figure 4.17). (CD 2, cut 19)

Figure 4.17

Britten: The Young Person's Guide to the Orchestra, op.34, m. 463–469.

THE YOUNG PERSON'S GUIDE TO THE ORCHESTRA © Copyright 1946 by Hawkes & Son (London) Ltd.; Copyright Renewed. Reprinted by permission of Boosey & Hawkes, Inc.

The upper range of the oboe can be heard in the following example from Bartok's Hungarian Sketches V (Swineherd's Dance) (figure 4.18). (CD 1, cut 15)

Figure 4.18

Bartók: Hungarian Sketches, V (Swineherd's Dance), m. 85–88.

HUNGARIAN SKETCHES © Copyright 1932 by Karl Rozsnyai and Rozzsavolgyi Co., Copyright Renewed. Copyright and Renewal assigned to Boosey & Hawkes, Inc. Reprinted by permission.

The following passage from Persichetti's Divertimento for Band is a typical example of the use of the English horn (figure 4.19). (CD 4, cut 12) This melodic line is doubled with flute at the octave.

Figure 4.19

Persichetti: Divertimento for Band, op. 42, II (Song), m. 1–12.

© 1951 Oliver Ditson Company. Used by permission.

The Clarinet Family	French	German	Italian
	clarinette	Klarinette	clarinetto
	clarinette basse	Bass Klarinette	clarinetto basso

Figure 4.20

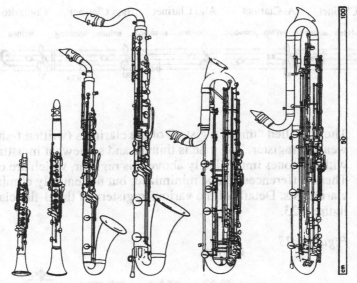

Eb Cl. Bb Cl. Alto Cl. Bass Cl. Contra-alto Cl. Contrabass Cl.

Ranges (written)   *Figure 4.21*

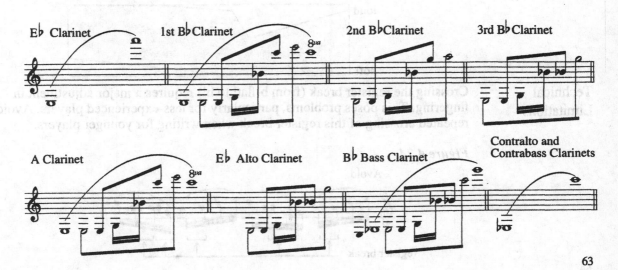

Eb Clarinet   1st Bb Clarinet   2nd Bb Clarinet   3rd Bb Clarinet

A Clarinet   Eb Alto Clarinet   Bb Bass Clarinet   Contralto and Contrabass Clarinets

Transposition	The clarinets are transposing instruments, most of them pitched in B-flat or E-flat.

Figure 4.22

Register Characteristics	The so-called "throat register" of the clarinets (written f-sharp^1 to b-flat^1) is their weakest register. The tone is thinner and somewhat indistinct, in sharp contrast with the tones immediately above this register, which are clear and penetrating. These differences can be minimized, but not entirely eliminated, by expert clarinetists. Details of the various registers of the B-flat clarinet are shown in figure 4.23.

Figure 4.23

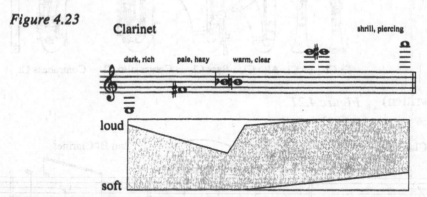

Technical Limitations	Crossing the register break (from b-flat^1 to b^1) requires a major adjustment in fingering. This poses problems, particularly for less-experienced players. Avoid repeated crossing of this register break when writing for younger players.

Figure 4.24

Musical Examples

The fluent nature of the clarinet in all registers is amply demonstrated by the following duet from The Young Person's Guide to the Orchestra (figure 4.25). (CD 2, cut 4)

Figure 4.25

Britten: The Young Person's Guide to the Orchestra, m. 107–110.

THE YOUNG PERSON'S GUIDE TO THE ORCHESTRA © Copyright 1946 by Hawkes & Son (London) Ltd.; Copyright Renewed. Reprinted by permission of Boosey & Hawkes, Inc.

The characteristic sound of the throat register can be heard in a passage from Tchaikovsky's *Valse des Fleurs* (figure 4.26). (CD5, cut 9)

Figure 4.26

Tchaikovsky: The Nutcracker Suite, op. 71a, III *(Valse des Fleurs)*, m. 97–106.

The lyric quality of the clarinet and bass clarinet are evident in the following passage from Holst's First Suite for Military Band (figure 4.27). (CD 3, cut 8) The bass clarinet line is supported in the low register by the bassoon and in the upper register by the B-flat clarinet.

Figure 4.27

Holst: First Suite in E-flat for Military Band, op. 28, no 1, II (Intermezzo), m. 67–72.

FIRST SUITE IN E-FLAT FOR MILITARY BAND © Copyright 1921 by Boosey & Co., Ltd.; Copyright Renewed. Reprinted by permission of Boosey & Hawkes, Inc.

Later in the same movement, the upper line of figure 4.27 is transferred to the bass clarinet, doubled with euphonium, tenor saxophone, and baritone saxophone (Figure 4.28). (CD 3, cut 11)

Figure 4.28

Holst: First Suite in E-flat for Military Band, op.28, no. 1, II (Intermezzo), m. 123–127.

FIRST SUITE IN E-FLAT FOR MILITARY BAND © Copyright 1921 by Boosey & Co., Ltd.; Copyright Renewed. Reprinted by permission of Boosey & Hawkes, Inc.

The Saxophone Family	**French**	**German**	**Italian**
	saxophone	Saxophon	sassofono

Figure 4.29

Soprano Alto Tenor Baritone
Saxophone Saxophone Saxophone Saxophone

Ranges (written) *Figure 4.30*

Soprano Saxophone   E♭ Alto Saxophone   B♭ Tenor Saxophone   E♭ Baritone Saxophone

Transposition *Figure 4.31*

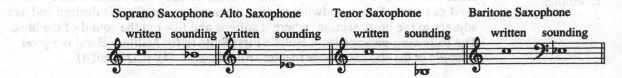

Soprano Saxophone   Alto Saxophone   Tenor Saxophone   Baritone Saxophone

written   sounding   written   sounding   written   sounding   written   sounding

| Register Characteristics | The saxophones are the strongest sounding instruments of the woodwind family. Their tone nearly balances that of the brass instruments, and they are often used in conjunction with brass. There is a tendency for the saxophones to predominate when used with other woodwinds. Details of the various registers for the alto saxophone are shown in figure 4.32. |

Figure 4.32

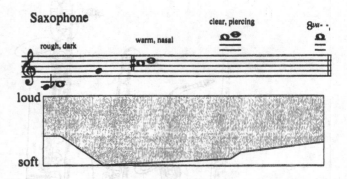

| Technical Limitations | The lower part of the saxophone's range (below written e¹) is somewhat coarse and difficult to control, particularly at soft dynamic levels. In the altissimo register (above f³) there is a general loss of agility, which makes trills, tremolos, and rapid melodic passages very difficult to produce. |

Figure 4.33

| Musical Examples | The saxophone family is the most important woodwind group in the jazz ensemble and a standard part of concert and marching band instrumentation. It is used as a part of the woodwind section when a heavier effect is desired and as an adjunct to the brass section, where it softens and fills out the sound of the brass. The following passage from Holst's First Suite in for Military Band is a good example of the alto saxophone in a solo role (figure 4.34). (CD 3, cut 4) |

Figure 4.34

Holst: First Suite in E-flat for Military Band, op. 28, no. 1, I, *(Chaconne)*, m. 64–72.

Alto Saxophone

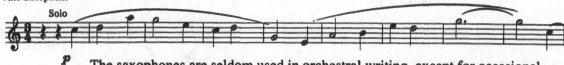

The saxophones are seldom used in orchestral writing, except for occasional solos. Ravel makes use of the plaintive quality of the alto saxophone in this well-known solo from Pictures at an Exhibition (figure 4.35). (CD 4, cut 7)

Figure 4.35

Moussorgsky-Ravel: Pictures at an Exhibition, II *(il Vecchio Castello)*, m. 7–12.

The tenor saxophone is quite prominent in the following excerpt from Hindemith's Symphony in B-flat (Figure 4.36). (CD 2, cut 23) The tenor saxophone is joined by the alto saxophone doubling in octaves later in the passage.

Figure 4.36

Hindemith: Symphony in B-flat for Concert Band, II (Andantino grazioso), m. 21–30.

The Bassoon and Contrabassoon	French	German	Italian
	basson	Fagott	fagotto
	contrebasson	Kontrafagott	contrafagotto

Figure 4.37

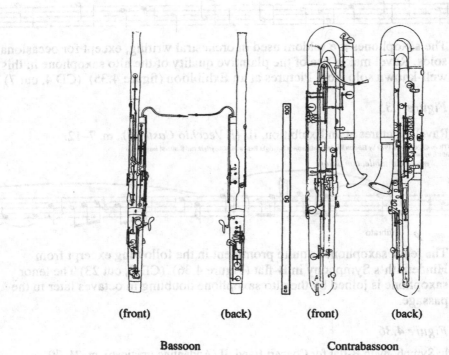

(front)	(back)	(front)	(back)
Bassoon		Contrabassoon	

Range (written)

Figure 4.38

Bassoon

Notice that the bassoon uses the tenor clef for its upper register.

Transposition   The bassoon is not a transposing instrument, but the contrabassoon is written an octave above its sounding pitch to avoid extensive ledger lines.

Figure 4.39

Register Characteristics   The dynamic range of the bassoon is somewhat more restricted than that of the other woodwind instruments, which may tend to make the instrument predominate in soft passages and be subordinated in extremely loud passages. Details of the various registers of the bassoon are shown in figure 4.40.

Figure 4.40

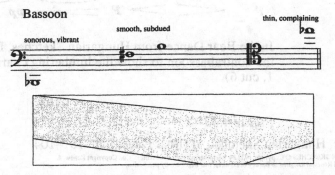

Technical Limitations   The complicated fingering system of the bassoon in the lower and upper registers causes difficulty for younger players, and the instrument is generally less agile in these areas. You should consult a fingering chart before writing trills and tremolos in the upper or lower register (figure 4.41).

Figure 4.41

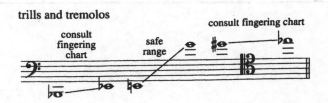

71

The middle and lower registers of the bassoon are shown to good advantage in the following passage from Tchaikovsky's Symphony No. 6 (figure 4.42). (CD 5, cut 20)

Figure 4.42

Tchaikovsky: Symphony No. 6 *(Pathétique),* op. 74, in B minor, IV (Finale), m. 30–36.

In the Bear Dance from Hungarian Sketches, Bartók contrasts the bassoon and the contrabassoon to show the lumbering character of the bear (figure 4.43). (CD 1, cut 6)

Figure 4.43

Bartók: Hungarian Sketches, II (Bear Dance), m. 101–104.

HUNGARIAN SKETCHES © Copyright 1932 by Karl Rozsnyai and Rozsavolgyi Co., Copyright Renewed.
Copyright and Renewal assigned to Boosey & Hawkes, Inc. Reprinted by permission.

The bassoon is an important accompanying instrument in the woodwind section. It excels in light staccato passages like the following from the Nutcracker Suite by Tchaikovsky (figure 4.44). (CD 5, cut 5)

Figure 4.44

Tchaikovsky: Nutcracker Suite, op. 71a, IIe *(Danse Chinoise)*, m. 1–3.

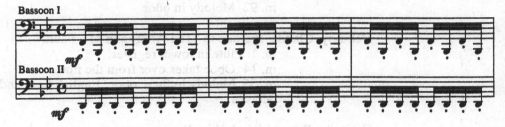

Workbook: Assignments A–G, pp. 53–70.

Suggested Listening (see appendix D, p. 396, for details)

Bartók, Béla. Concerto for Orchestra (1943)
    I *(Introduzione)*
        m. 30 Flute solo
        m. 154 Melody in oboe
        m. 174 Clarinets in octaves
        m. 192 Melody in flutes and oboe
        m. 272 Melody in clarinet
    II *(Giuoco Della Coppie)*
        m. 9 Bassoon duet
        m. 25 Oboe duet
        m. 45 Clarinet duet
        m. 60 Flute duet
        m. 165 Bassoon trio
        m. 198 Flutes and clarinets

Berlioz, Hector. *Symphony Fantastique*, op. 14
    III (In the country)
        m. 1 English horn solo
        m. 113 Flutes and oboes (joined later by clarinets)
    V (A witches' sabbath)
        m. 7 Flute, oboe, piccolo in octaves
        m. 40 Melody in E-flat clarinet, other woodwinds in accompaniment. (A striking use of the woodwinds)

Bizet, George. *L'Arlésienne* Suite, no. 1.
    I (*Prelude*)
        m. 17 Quintet consisting of flute, English horn, clarinet, and two bassoons
        m. 83 Flute, clarinet, and bassoon in octaves
        m. 90 Alto saxophone solo
    II (*Minuetto*)
        m. 29 Melody in clarinet and alto saxophone in octaves
        m. 92 Melody in oboe

Debussy, Claude. Prelude to "The Afternoon of a Faun."
        m. 1 Flute in lower register.
        m. 14 Oboe takes over from the flute.
        m. 55 Melody in flute, oboe, English horn and clarinet in octaves

Grainger, Percy. Lincolnshire Posy.
    I (Lisbon)
        m. 18 Full woodwind section of the band
        m. 34 Melody in clarinet accompanied by other woodwinds
    III (Rufford Park Poachers)
        m. 1 Piccolo, E-flat clarinet, clarinet, and bass clarinet
        m. 18 Clarinet section with other woodwinds in background
        m. 85 Piccolo, E-flat clarinet, oboe, and bassoon

Suggestions for Further Study

A number of books specializing on single members of the woodwind family are available including:

Dick, Robert. *The Other Flute*. New York: Multiple Breath Music Company, 1989.

Howell, Thomas. *The Avant-Garde Flute*. Berkeley, Calif.: University of California Press, 1974.

Langwill, Lyndesay G. *The Bassoon and Contrabassoon*. Rev. ed. New York: W. W. Norton & Company, Inc., 1965.

Rehfeldt, Phillip. *New Directions for Clarinet*. Berkeley, Calif.: University of California Press, 1978.

Spencer, William. *The Art of Bassoon Playing*. Princeton, N.J.: Summy-Birchard, 1958.

Sprenkle, Robert, and David Ledet. *The Art of Oboe Playing*. Princeton, N.J.: Summy-Birchard Music, 1961.

Toff, Nancy. *The Development of the Modern Flute*. New York: Taplinger Publishing Co., Inc., 1979.

Books on the woodwind family as a whole include:

Baines, Anthony. *Woodwind Instruments and Their History*. 3rd ed. New York: W. W. Norton & Company, Inc., 1967.

Bartolozzi, Bruno. *New Sounds for Woodwind*. Translated by Reginald Smith Brindle. 2nd ed. New York: Oxford University Press, 1981.

Westphal, Frederick William. *Guide to Teaching Woodwinds*. Dubuque, Iowa: Wm. C. Brown Publishers, 1990.

General treatises on instrumentation that contain extensive treatment of the woodwind section include:

Stiller, Andrew. *Handbook of Instrumentation*. Berkeley, Calif.: University of California Press, 1985, (Chapter 2, p. 13).

Berlioz, Hector, and Richard Strauss. *Treatise on Instrumentation*. Translated by Theodore Front. New York: Edwin F. Kalmus, 1948, (pp. 163–243 and p. 400).

5   The Brass: *Heroic Expression*

The brass family is a group of wind instruments (aerophones) that consist of hollow tubes in which an air column is set in motion by the player's vibrating lips placed against a mouthpiece. Most modern versions of these instruments are made of metal (usually brass), but types made from other materials (such as fiberglass) do exist. The brass family is much more unified in tone color than the woodwind section. The section is divided into two broad colors: the "bright" brass (trumpet and trombone) and the "mellow" brass (cornet, horns, euphonium, and tubas). Even these two groups blend together well, creating a solid section sound with a wide dynamic range and heroic color. The brass are second only to the percussion in power and can easily overwhelm the woodwinds and strings. For this reason, and for reasons of stamina, the brass are used intermittently in most musical contexts.

The Horn

French	German	Italian
cor	Horn	corno

Figure 5.1

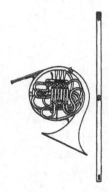

Range of Modern Horn (written)

Figure 5.2

Horn

The range of the horn is extensive. For this reason, there is some specialization in the horn section, with the higher parts being taken by the first and third horns and the lower parts by the second and fourth horns. This peculiar exception to the normal practice of scoring chords in order from top to bottom is well established in tradition, although the practice is gradually being phased out, particularly in concert band scoring. The third horn has traditionally been scored above the second horn in harmonic writing.

Figure 5.3

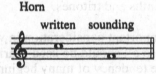
1-2 Horns in F

3-4 Horns in F

Transposition

The modern horn is a transposing instrument pitched in F.

Figure 5.4

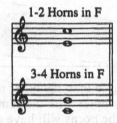
Horn

written   sounding

Many earlier scores call for natural horns that were pitched in various keys. Figure 5.5 shows the transpositions for these older parts. This information will be necessary for score study, but modern horns are never written with these transpositions.

Figure 5.5

Natural Horns

written   sounding

Bb-Alto   A   Ab   G   F   E   Eb   D   C   Bb-Basso

Register
Characteristics

The horn is capable of intense and exciting sounds in its upper register, which is quite a contrast with the soft and indistinct sound of the lower register. The dynamic range of the horns is smaller than the other brass instruments. A good rule of thumb is that two horns are required to balance one of the other brass instruments if the dynamic level is above *mf*. At the highest dynamic levels, more than two horns will be needed to balance the other brass instruments, and the four horn parts are often written in unison is such situations.

Figure 5.6

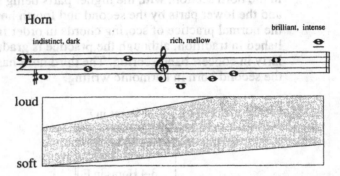

Technical
Limitations

The horn is much less agile than the other members of the brass family, due to close proximity of many notes with the same fingering and the wide range of the instrument. In general, the horns will have difficulty playing angular melodic lines with many leaps. Melodic leaps with intervals that are simple (octaves, perfect fifths, and perfect fourths) are much easier to play accurately than those that involve sevenths and tritones.

Tessitura is an important consideration in writing for the horn. The upper register (from c² to c³) should be used sparingly and for dramatic effects only. Guard against the tendency of many beginning orchestrators to write too high for the horns. The instrument should be thought of as an alto or tenor (rather than soprano) instrument.

Special
techniques

The tone of the horn can be modified in several ways:

1. Muted (*sourdine, Dämpfer, sordino*) A metal or cardboard mute is placed in the bell of the instrument. This diminishes the dynamic range of the instrument and creates a more pointed, "metallic" sound.
2. Stopped (*bouché, gestopft, chiuso*) The hand is inserted far enough into the bell to close the tube entirely, resulting in a further muting and even more metallic sound. Stopped notes are unreliable below written middle c (c¹). A plus sign ("+") is written above all stopped notes and a "o" is used to let the player know when to return to normal following a stopped tone.

3. Brassy (*cuivré, schmetternd, suoni metallici*) This is an exaggerated and forced sound that makes the instrument buzz.

4. Bells in the air (*pavillon en l'air, Schalltrichter, campana in aria*) The horn is normally played with bell pointed away from the player and the hand placed in the bell, creating the characteristic mellow horn sound. When the instrument is raised into horizontal position and the hand is removed ("bells in the air") the tone becomes much less refined, and the instrument takes on the character of a "hunting horn."

Figure 5.7 shows the proper notation for the four special effects listed above.

Figure 5.7

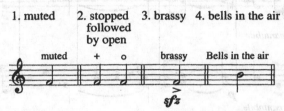

It is important to write "open" or "remove mute" in the part, to let the player know when to remove the mute.

Musical Examples

The middle register of the horn is shown to good advantage in the opening of Promenade II of Pictures at an Exhibition (figure 5.8). (CD 4, cut 3)

Figure 5.8

Moussorgsky-Ravel: Pictures at an Exhibition, Promenade II, m. 1–3.

The opening of the Overture to Oberon is a good example of the beauty of the horn tone in a higher register (figure 5.9). (CD 5, cut 32)

Figure 5.9

Weber: Overture to Oberon, m. 1–6.

The horn section often plays in four-part harmony, as shown in the theme from the Waltz of the Flowers from the Nutcracker Suite (figure 5.10). (CD 5, cut 8) Notice that the second horn plays consistently below the third horn in the traditional configuration for the horn section.

Figure 5.10

Tchaikovsky: Nutcracker Suite, op.71a, III *(Valse des Fleurs)*, m. 38–44.

The Trumpet and Cornet	French	German	Italian
	trompette	Trompete	tromba
	cornet à pistons	Kornett	cornetta a pistoni

Figure 5.11

Bb Trumpet

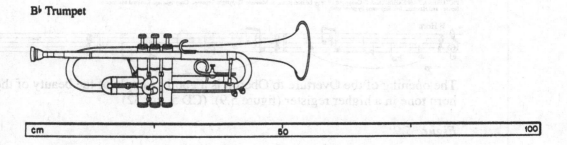

Instrumentation

Ranges (written)   *Figure 5.12*

1st B♭ Trumpet (Cornet)   2nd B♭ Trumpet (Cornet)   3rd B♭ Trumpet (Cornet)

Transposition

Trumpets are pitched in a several keys, but the B-flat and C trumpets are by far the most common.

Figure 5.13

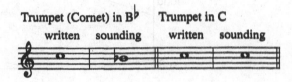

Trumpet (Cornet) in B♭   Trumpet in C
written   sounding   written   sounding

Earlier scores call for natural trumpets, usually pitched in the key of the composition or a nearly related key. Figure 5.14 shows the transpositions for these older trumpet parts. This information will be necessary for score study of earlier music, but modern valve trumpets are usually pitched in B-flat or C.

Figure 5.14

Natural Trumpets

written   sounding

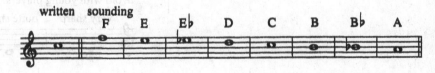

F   E   E♭   D   C   B   B♭   A

Register Characteristics

The trumpets are overpowering and brilliant in their upper register. The middle register, which is much more flexible in tone and dynamics, is generally preferred for brass section writing. The cornet was originally an instrument with a softer and mellower sound, but modern cornets have taken on the characteristics of the trumpets, so there is little difference between the instruments other than the external shape.

Figure 5.15

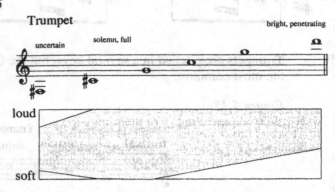

Technical Limitations

In the middle register the trumpet is the most agile of the brass instruments, capable of technical feats approaching those of the woodwinds. In the upper register (above g^2,) the agility of the instrument rapidly diminishes. The flexibility of the instrument also diminishes quickly below c^1, where intonation is also likely to cause problems. Several notes in the lower register are quite sharp in pitch and should be avoided in writing for young players. More-experienced players learn to compensate for these intonation difficulties.

Figure 5.16

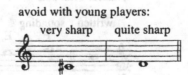

Tessitura is an important consideration in writing for the trumpet. Extended writing in the upper register (above g^2) will quickly tire the player, and it is best to provide opportunities to rest after each high register passage. This is particularly critical when writing for younger players.

Special Techniques	The tone of the trumpets can be modified by using a variety of mutes. The more common are listed below:

1. Straight mute (*sourdine droite, gerader Dämpfer, sordina diritta*) The most common mute for the trumpet, which decreases the dynamic range of the instrument and creates a more "pointed" sound. If you write "muted" in the trumpet parts, this will be the mute that will be chosen.
2. Cup mute (*sourdine cup, Cup-Dämpfer, sordina cup*) This is a more intimate and mellow sounding mute. Its tone is often associated with jazz and popular music.
3. Harmon mute ("wah-wah") (*sourdine harmon, Harmon-Dämpfer, sordina harmon*) This mute, which was developed for jazz performance, has found its way into concert music. The mute can be closed by placing fingers over a small bell-shaped tube (called the "stem") on the front of the mute and opened to produce the characteristic "wah-wah" effect. (Several other effects are available by extending or removing the stem.)

Figure 5.17 shows the proper notation for the three mutes above.

Figure 5.17

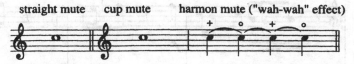

It is important to write "open" or "remove mute" in the part, to let the player know when to remove the mute.

Musical Examples	The characteristic sound of the middle register of the trumpet is shown in this excerpt from Promenade I from Pictures at an Exhibition (figure 5.18). (CD 4, cut 1) (Notice the trumpet section in a typical scoring in measures three and four.)

Figure 5.18

Moussorgsky-Ravel: Pictures at an Exhibition, Promenade I, m. 1–4.

The agility of the trumpet is amply demonstrated in the following example from
The Young Person's Guide to the Orchestra (figure 5.19). (CD 2, cut 11)

Figure 5.19

Britten: The Young Person's Guide to the Orchestra, op. 34, m. 306–313.

The sound of the trumpet section in the band is illustrated in the following
passage from the march from Holst's First Suite in E-flat for Military Band
(figure 5.20). (CD 3, cut 15)

Figure 5.20

Holst: First Suite in E-flat for Military Band, op. 28, no. 1, III (March), m. 109–116.

The Trombone and Bass Trombone	French	German	Italian
	trombone	Posaune	trombone
	trombone basse	Bass Posaune	trombone basso

Figure 5.21

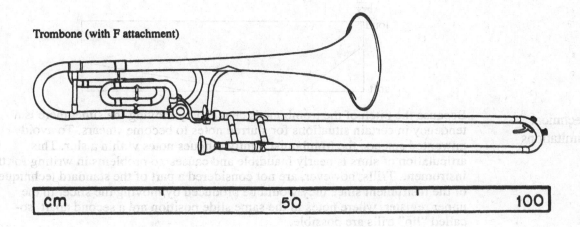

Trombone (with F attachment)

| cm | 50 | 100 |

Ranges   *Figure 5.22*

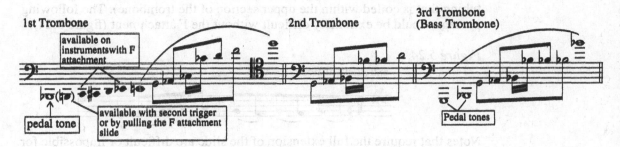

1st Trombone

available on instruments with F attachment

available with second trigger or by pulling the F attachment slide

pedal tone

2nd Trombone

3rd Trombone (Bass Trombone)

Pedal tones

The bass and tenor trombones have the same range. The lower notes that are easily produced on the bass trombone are much more difficult on the tenor, and the larger size of the bass trombone makes playing in the upper register much more difficult. Notice that, in the upper register, the trombone is written in tenor clef. The trombones are not transposing instruments.

Register
Characteristics

Figure 5.23

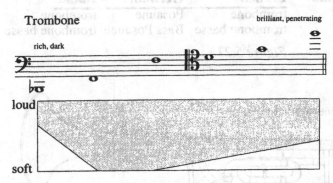

Trombone

rich, dark

brilliant, penetrating

loud

soft

Technical
Limitations

Because the pitch of the trombone is changed by moving the slide, there is a tendency in certain situations for slurred notes to become smears. To avoid unwanted smears, the trombonist lightly tongues notes within a slur. This articulation of slurs is nearly inaudible and causes no problems in writing for the instrument. Trills, however, are not considered a part of the standard technique of the instrument since they would be produced by moving the slide. In the upper register, where notes in the same slide position are a second apart, so-called "lip" trills are possible.

Rapid movement from B-flat to B is difficult for a tenor trombone without the F attachment mechanism on the upper part of the instrument (see figure 5.21-the F attachment consists of a trigger that operates a circular valve opening the extra tubing that is coiled within the upper section of the trombone). The following passage would be extremely difficult without the F attachment (figure 5.24).

Figure 5.24

extremely difficult

Notes that require the full extension of the slide are difficult or impossible for young players, whose arms may not be long enough to reach the 7th position. For this reason, the notes shown in figure 5.25 should be avoided when writing for younger players.

Figure 5.25

avoid

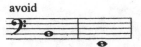

Special Techniques	The mutes for the trombone are similar to those for the trumpet. They include the straight mute, cup mute, and harmon mute. The notation for muting is shown in figure 5.17.

The trombone is capable of a true smear in certain areas. Figure 5.26 shows the available ranges for some of the common glissandos for the trombone. These ranges (covering a diminished 5th in each case) should not be exceeded, but any smear within the given ranges is quite easily accomplished.

Figure 5.26

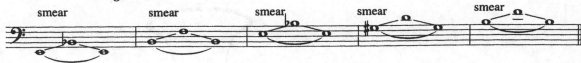

Musical Examples	The power and excitement that trombones can generate is illustrated in the following example from The Young Person's Guide to the Orchestra (figure 5.27). (CD 2, cut 12)

Figure 5.27

Britten: The Young Person's Guide to the Orchestra, op. 34, m. 347–352.

THE YOUNG PERSON'S GUIDE TO THE ORCHESTRA © Copyright 1946 by Hawkes & Son (London) Ltd.: Copyright Renewed. Reprinted by permission of Boosey & Hawkes, Inc.

The trombones can blend perfectly with the trumpets, as shown in the following excerpt from the march from the Nutcracker Suite (figure 5.28). (CD 5, cut 3)

Figure 5.28

Tchaikovsky: Nutcracker Suite, op. 71a, IIa *(Marche)*, m. 17–18.

The Tuba and Euphonium

French	German	Italian
tuba	Basstuba	tuba
tuba ténor	Tenortuba	tuba tenore

Figure 5.29

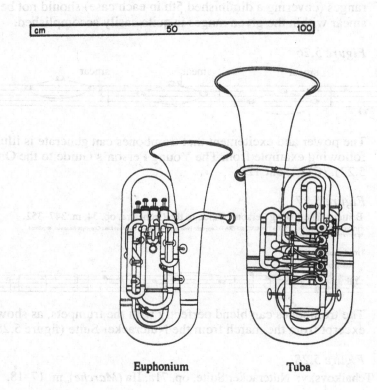

Euphonium   Tuba

Ranges

The tuba family includes several sizes of bass tubas and the euphonium (or baritone horn).

Figure 5.30

Euphonium (Baritone)

Tuba (Sousaphone)

Pedal tone

(Lower limit of range without a fourth valve)

Transposition

The tuba and euphonium are usually written in the bass clef as nontransposing instruments. However, in band arrangements for school groups, a separate treble clef part should be provided for those euphonium players who have converted from trumpet. This "treble clef baritone" part is transposed to B-flat (figure 5.31).

Figure 5.31

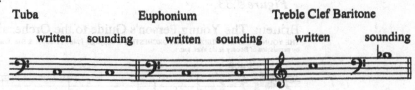

Register Characteristics

Figure 5.32

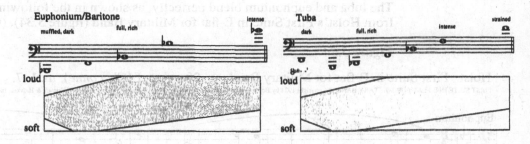

Technical Limitations

The tuba and, to a lesser extent, the euphonium require large quantities of wind. For this reason, when writing for either of these instruments, it is important to keep phrases fairly short or provide for opportunities to breathe within phrases.

The tuba is quite agile in the range from BB-flat to f, but the lower range is quite ponderous and should be used only for slow-moving parts. The range above f is quite intense in sound, but the instrument quickly loses agility in this register.

Tessitura is quite important in writing for the tuba. The upper and lower reaches of the range should be used sparingly and a medium tessitura is recommended.

The tuba is seldom used in a solo role, so examples that show the instrument in isolation are rare. The following short solo from The Young Person's Guide to the Orchestra provides an excellent opportunity to hear the tuba alone (figure 5.33). (CD 2, cut 13)

Figure 5.33

Britten: The Young Person's Guide to the Orchestra, op. 34, m. 353–357.

THE YOUNG PERSON'S GUIDE TO THE ORCHESTRA © Copyright 1946 by Hawkes & Son (London) Ltd.; Copyright Renewed. Reprinted by permission of Boosey & Hawkes, Inc.

The tuba and euphonium blend perfectly, as shown in the following passage from Holst's First Suite in E-flat for Military Band (figure 5.34). (CD 3, cut 1)

Figure 5.34

Holst: First Suite in E-flat for Military Band, op. 28, no. 1, I *(Chaconne)*, m. 1–7.

FIRST SUITE IN E-FLAT FOR MILITARY BAND © Copyright 1921 by Boosey & Co., Ltd.; Copyright Renewed. Reprinted by permission of Boosey & Hawkes, Inc.

Later in the same work, the euphonium has a solo based on the same melodic idea (figure 5.35). (CD 3, cut 10)

Figure 5.35

Holst: First Suite in E-flat for Military Band, op. 28, no. 1, II *(Intermezzo)*, m. 100–105.

FIRST SUITE IN E-FLAT FOR MILITARY BAND © Copyright 1921 by Boosey & Co., Ltd.; Copyright Renewed. Reprinted by permission of Boosey & Hawkes, Inc.

Workbook: Assignments A–I, pp. 71–84.

Suggested Listening (see appendix D, p. 396, for details)

Bartók, Béla. Concerto for Orchestra (1943).
I (*Introduzione*)
m. 35 Three trumpets in harmony
m. 134 Melody in trombone
after m. 313 Extended fugato in brass
m. 514 Melody in full brass
II (*Giuoco Della Coppie*)
m. 90 Muted trumpet duet
m. 123 Bright brass
m. 147 Mellow brass

Grainger, Percy. Lincolnshire Posy
III (Rufford Park Poachers)
m. 18 Flügelhorn solo
m. 64 Short motives in trombones, trumpets, horns and baritone

Holst, Gustav. Second Suite in F for Military Band
I (March)
m. 3 Traditional "brass band" sound
m. 46 Melody in euphonium, accompanied by horns, trombones, and tuba
III (Song of the Blacksmith)
m. 1 Full brass band
m. 15 Melody in cornet, accompanied by brass section
IV (Fantasia on the 'Dargason')
m. 97 Melody in cornet, accompanied by remaining bright brass

Mahler, Gustave. Symphony No. 4 in G Major (1900).
I (*Moderato*)
m. 110 Melody in horn is quite striking
m. 150 Muted trumpet trio (note stopped horn in m. 154)
m. 203 Trumpet solo
m. 224 Trumpet in the low register

Suggestions for Further Study

A number of books specializing on single members of the brass family are available including:

Bate, Philip. *The Trumpet and Trombone*. New York: W. W. Norton & Company, Inc., 1966.

Gregory, Robin. *The Horn*. New York: Praaeger, 1969.

Morley-Pegge, Reginald. *The French Horn*. 2nd ed. New York: W. W. Norton & Company, Inc., 1973.

Schuller, Gunther. *Horn Technique*. New York: Oxford University Press, 1962.

Books on the brass family as a whole include:

Baines, Anthony. *Brass Instruments and Their History and Development*. London: Faber and Faber, 1976.

Hunt, Norman, and Daniel Bachelder. *Guide to Teaching Brass*. 4th ed. Dubuque, Iowa: Wm. C. Brown Publishers, 1991.

General treatises on instrumentation that contain extensive treatment of the brass section include:

Berlioz, Hector, and Richard Strauss. *Treatise on Instrumentation*. Translated by Theodore Front. New York: Edwin F. Kalmus, 1948, pp. 247-347.

Stiller, Andrew. *Handbook of Instrumentation*. Berkeley, Calif.: University of California Press, 1985, chapter 3, p. 63.

6 Percussion: *An Orchestra in Itself*

General Considerations

The percussion section consists of a wide variety of instruments (several hundred) that are struck, plucked, or rubbed. These instruments are sometimes referred to as "membranophones" or "idiophones," depending on the presence or absence of a drum head. A complete treatment of the percussion family is beyond the scope of this book. We will concern ourselves only with those instruments that are commonly found in high school percussion sections. (For a more complete treatment of the percussion, refer to one of the specialized books on percussion listed at the end of the chapter.)

The dynamic range of the percussion section exceeds that of any other section of the orchestra or band. It is capable of extremely soft effects that would be covered by any other instrument and sounds that will drown out the largest ensemble. Great care must be taken in writing dynamics for the percussion instruments. These instruments are most colorful and effective when they first enter, and the effect of any one instrument will quickly pale if overused. For this reason, it is normal to expect a percussionist to change from one instrument to another and play several instruments in the course of a composition.

The percussion will be divided into two broad categories: the "indefinite-pitch percussion" and the "definite-pitch percussion". This distinction is more a matter of notation than sound, since nearly all percussion instruments have some more-or-less definite pitch. A percussion instrument will be called "indefinite" in pitch if specific pitches are not usually written for it in percussion parts.

Each category will be further divided into three groups on the basis of *decay* (the length of time for a single stroke on the instrument to die away). Instruments with a "short decay" die away in .5 seconds or less, while instruments of "medium decay" may last from .5 seconds to approximately 3 seconds. The instruments of "long decay" require more than 3 seconds to decay, and some of these instruments have decay times of 30 seconds or more. Some instruments, particularly the keyboard percussion, have varying decay times depending on the pitch that is struck. In such cases the decay time of the lowest and highest pitches are indicated and a line drawn between the two, indicating a continuous variation of decay between the extremes (see figure 6.9, for example).

Of course, the sound of any percussion instrument will decrease gradually during a decay and may be soft enough to be unnoticed in most circumstances, but the full decay times must be considered when a total silence occurs within the decay times listed. Decay times for each instrument will be expressed in note values assuming the quarter note equals one second.

Notation for
Short-decay
Instruments

Instruments of short decay will not need to be choked, even for the shortest notes. Note values from a quarter note to thirty-second note will all have the same duration, and may be written freely to indicate single strokes. It makes very little sense to write note values of a half note or greater for single strokes. In such cases, rests should be inserted to fill out time between events. Needless to say, tied notes are seldom used for single strokes on these instruments. If the sound of an instrument of short decay is to be sustained, it is necessary to play a "roll" on the instrument. A roll is a rapid reiteration of single (or multiple) strokes that keeps the instrument sounding for any required duration. The proper notation for a roll is shown in figure 6.1.

Figure 6.1

Although it was a standard practice in earlier music, the trill sign should never be used for a roll.

The short-decay instruments that will be covered in this chapter include: xylophone (p. 96), snare drum (p. 107), tambourine (p. 109), wood block (p. 110), claves (p. 112), and maracas (p. 112).

Notation for
Medium-decay
Instruments

Instruments of medium decay will seldom need to be choked unless there is a total silence in the music. It is necessary, in such cases, to write the duration of the choked note quite accurately and also to write "choke" at the point where silence is required (figure 6.2).

Figure 6.2

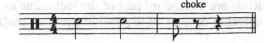

Since these instruments may have decay times several times longer than the short-decay instruments, single strokes may be written as half notes, whole notes, or tied notes. Rolls are a part of the standard technique for medium-decay instruments, even in cases where the tone would sustain for the full duration. The roll in this case is used to provide stress on certain notes.

Medium-decay instruments included in the chapter are: marimba (p. 98), timpani (p. 99), bass drum (p. 113), tom-toms (p. 114), triangle (p. 115), cowbell (p. 117), and hi-hat (p. 118).

Notation for Long-decay Instruments

The instruments with long decay often require choking to avoid blurring and confusion. The instruments of definite pitch will generally be choked whenever there is a chord change to avoid excessive dissonance. Care must be taken to choke even the indefinite-pitch instruments if a silence is desired within the range of their decay (which may be as long as 30 seconds). If a long-decay instrument is to be allowed to decay without choking, an open tie is added to the note (figure 6.3). The abbreviation "l. v." (*laissez vibrer*) is sometimes placed after the open tie to indicate that the note is to be left to vibrate .

Figure 6.3

The following measures may be filled with rests (figure 6.3) or notes to be played on other instruments (figure 6.4).

Figure 6.4

Since the decay times may extend over many measures, the point of choking may be indicated as in figure 6.5.

Figure 6.5

Rolls are a standard part of the technique of these instruments and are used as coloring devices or to provide stress on particular notes.

Long-decay instruments discussed in this chapter include: chimes (p. 101), orchestra bells (p. 102), vibraphone (p. 104), crash cymbals (p. 119), suspended cymbals (p. 120), and tam-tam (p. 121).

The Definite-pitch Percussion

The definite-pitch percussion is written on the standard five-line staff in concert pitch. (Some of the instruments transpose by octaves to avoid ledger lines.) In general, the standard notational practices are used (with the additions described above).

The only short-decay instrument of definite pitch that we will discuss is the xylophone. The medium-decay instruments include the marimba and timpani, while the long-decay instruments include the chimes, orchestra bells, and vibraphone.

The Xylophone

French	German	Italian
xylophone	Xylophon	xilofono

Figure 6.6

Range (written)   *Figure 6.7*

Transposition   *Figure 6.8*

Decay   *Figure 6.9*

Mallets

The xylophone is normally played with hard rubber mallets to produce the characteristic cutting sound. If an extremely brittle sound is desired, plastic or wood mallets may be used. The lower range of the instrument can be played with soft rubber or yarn mallets to simulate the sound of the marimba. Soft mallets are totally ineffective in the middle and upper registers.

Technical Limitations

The xylophone is often played with two mallets (one in each hand). This enables extremely rapid melodic work, if the intervals are not too large. Successive wide leaps increase the level of difficulty and passages with constant leaps can become nearly impossible unless one hand can be kept on one note while the other moves about (figure 6.10).

Figure 6.10

The noisy clatter of the xylophone is very effective for melodic and rhythmic effects, but harmonic effects are less clear, unless softer mallets are used (which effectively limits such passages to the lower register).

The Marimba	**French**	**German**	**Italian**
	marimba	Marimbaphon	marimba

Figure 6.11

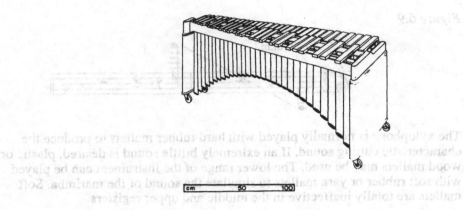

Range   *Figure 6.12*

Decay   *Figure 6.13*

Mallets

The marimba is normally played with medium or soft yarn mallets, which bring out the tone of the instrument with relatively little impact noise. These mallets are most effective in the lower half of the instrument's range. Soft or medium rubber mallets provide a good tone with much more impact noise. These mallets are effective over the entire range of the instrument. *Under no circumstances* should plastic or metal mallets be used on the marimba, since they will permanently damage the bars.

Technical Limitations

The marimba is normally played with either two, three, or four mallets. The limitations on melodic writing are similar to those for the xylophone; and these limitations extend to harmonic writing, as well. Chord progressions that require all four tones to move are generally more difficult than those that allow for common tones (figure 6.14). The difficulty of chord progressions should not be judged by playing them on the piano. Some progressions that are difficult on the piano are easy on the marimba and some easy progressions on the piano are impossible on the marimba.

Figure 6.14

The Timpani

French	**German**	**Italian**
timbales	Pauken	timpani

Figure 6.15

Ranges   *Figure 6.16*

Decay

Figure 6.17

Mallets

The timpani are normally played with special felt mallets, which vary from hard to soft. The harder mallets are best for rhythmic definition, while the softer are best for smooth rolls. Wooden mallets are also available for hard marcato effects.

Technical Limitations

The timpani must be tuned in advance of playing, and approximately 3–5 seconds are required to tune each drum (longer for less-experienced players). This means that timpani writing should normally be limited to four distinct pitches at a time, with rests provided for each change of pitch. A notation for tuning and retuning of the timpani is shown in figure 6.18.

Figure 6.18

Tuning gauges can improve the time necessary to tune the timpani, and experienced players can perform melodic passages requiring constant retuning. However, the recommendations listed above should be strictly observed when dealing with younger players.

Rapid passages involving many changes in pitch are effective rhythmically, but the pitches will tend to be obscured due to the relatively long decay times for each drum. Repeated pitches, on the other hand, will sound quite clear (figure 6.19).

Figure 6.19

Special Techniques

The timpani can be retuned while sounding to produce a portamento (glissando). Such portamentos must be within the range of one drum and are notated as shown in figure 6.20.

Figure 6.20

The Chimes

French	German	Italian
cloche tubes	Röhrenglocken	campane tubolari

Figure 6.21

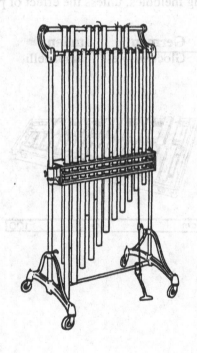

Range

Figure 6.22

Decay

Figure 6.23

♩ = 60 m.m.

Mallets

The chimes are played with hammer-shaped mallets made from rawhide or plastic.

Technical
Limitations

The pitch of the chimes is much more complex than other definite pitch percussion instruments, due to the presence of several "inharmonic" partials. For this reason, the chimes will not generally blend well with other instruments. Unison doubling of chime notes by other orchestral instruments will produce surprisingly dissonant effects. Also, the rather long decay of each tube will tend to obscure rapid melodic writing. The instrument is most effective on single notes or slow-moving melodies, unless the effect of pealing bells is desired.

The Orchestra Bells

French	German	Italian
jeu de timbres	Glockenspiel	campanelli

Figure 6.24

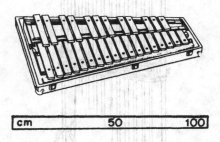

Range   *Figure 6.25*

Transposition   *Figure 6.26*

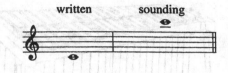

Decay   *Figure 6.27*

Mallets

The normal mallets for the orchestra bells are made of brass or plastic, both of which produce the characteristic sparkling sound. The brass mallets are more brilliant. Softer mallets, such as hard or medium rubber, produce a subtle, more celestalike tone.

Technical Limitations

The long decay times of the orchestra bells produce confusion in rapid melodic writing. This effect is not unpleasant; but if a clear melody is desired, it will be necessary for the player to hand-damp the previous note while playing each successive note, thus limiting the speed of performance considerably. The general statements about wide leaps that were made about the xylophone (p. 97) apply to the orchestra bells as well.

The Vibraphone (vibe)	French	German	Italian
	vibraphone	Vibraphon	vibrafono

Figure 6.28

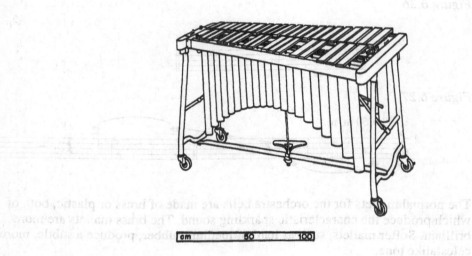

Range

Figure 6.29

Decay

Figure 6.30

Mallets

The mallets used on the vibraphone are usually medium or soft yarn mallets. The medium mallets produce good definition for melodic effects, while the soft mallets excel in legato styles and harmonic effects. Special "jazz mallets" are available for jazzlike effects.

Technical Limitations

The long decay times of the vibraphone bars have made necessary the addition of a damper pedal (much like the damper pedal on the piano.) The proper notation for pedaling is shown in figure 6.31.

Figure 6.31

In addition, performers regularly used some hand or mallet damping to clarify melodic and harmonic effects.

The volume of the vibraphone is surprisingly limited, and some instruments have electrical amplification systems to compensate for the lack of carrying power.

Special Techniques

Vibraphones are equipped with electrically driven fans in the resonator tubes that produce the characteristic tremolo (vibrato) sound for which the instrument is named. The speed of the tremolo can be varied from approximately 2 pulses per second to 8 pulses per second. Since the instrument is now usually played with the fans off, the tremolo sound is considered a special technique. Specify "fans off" if the tremolo sound is not desired; and "slow fans," "medium fans," or "fast fans" if the tremolo sound is to be used.

The Indefinite-pitch Percussion

The vast majority of percussion instruments are classified as "indefinite" in pitch, which means only that definite pitches are not usually written for them. These instruments are written on a staff of one to five lines, depending on the number of instruments each percussionist is expected to play. Each instrument is assigned to a particular line or space on the staff for the duration of a single composition. Since the number of instruments involved varies for piece to piece, there is little standardization in terms of staff assignment, except that higher-pitched instruments are usually assigned to higher lines or spaces than lower-pitched instruments. Figure 6.32 shows an example of proper notation for indefinite-pitched percussion.

Figure 6.32

An alternative to the notation system above uses the standard five-line staff with the same instrument assignment system. The practical advantage to the arranger of being able to use standard manuscript paper for score and parts is the primary reason for this system. With the advent of computer notation programs, there is less need for this system. Figure 6.33 shows the excerpt in figure 6.32 notated in the five-line system.

Figure 6.33

On the five-line staff, the snare drum is written on the third space and the bass drum on the first space (figure 6.34).

Figure 6.34

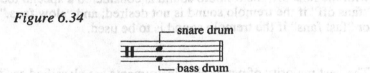

Players will, of course, read either staff system equally well; but they tend to prefer the former over the latter, since it makes less clutter on the page.

In general, the standard notational practices are used (with the additions described on p. 94-95), with a few additions for special effects that will be described for each instrument.

The short-decay instruments of indefinite pitch include the snare drum, tambourine, woodblock, temple blocks, claves, and maracas. The medium-decay instruments are bass drum, tom-toms, triangle, cow bell, and hi-hat, while the long-decay instruments include crash cymbals, suspended cymbals, and tamtam. This list barely scratches the surface of a very large family of percussion instruments.

The Snare Drum	**French**	**German**	**Italian**
	claisse claire	kleine Trommel	tamburo militare

Figure 6.35

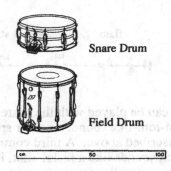

Snare Drum

Field Drum

Sizes

Snare drums come in a variety of sizes from the smallest, called a piccolo snare drum, through the standard concert snare drum to the largest, or field drum. The smaller instruments are crisp and clear in sound, while the larger are deeper, more resonant, and slightly longer in decay.

Decay

Figure 6.36

Sticks

The snare drum is usually played with snare drum sticks, which come in a variety of sizes and weights. Players will generally choose sticks for a passage based on the dynamic levels and general character of the passage, but it is possible to specify the sticks desired. A second common "stick" is actually a pair of wire or plastic brushes, which can be used for the standard jazz sound or as a distinctive effect in themselves. Single strokes and simple rolls are possible with brushes, but the most common jazz technique, called "stirring," involves rubbing the brushes on the drum head to produce a soft, swishing sound.

Technical Limitations

The snare drum produces a sharp buzz with each stroke when the snares (tightly coiled metal wires or gut cables that are stretched across the bottom head) are engaged, and the snare sound limits the lower dynamic range of the drum considerably. The snare sound will cut through soft textures and make the snare drum tend to predominate, regardless of the written dynamic. (Consider using "snares off" if the dynamics are very soft.)

Several grace-note-like decorations are standard technique on the snare drum (and any percussion instrument that uses snare drum sticks). These decorations are used to create various degrees of stress on important notes. They are often more effective than simple accents, since they have the effect of lengthening the note. Figure 6.37 shows four of the most common decorations.

Figure 6.37

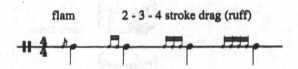

flam   2 - 3 - 4 stroke drag (ruff)

The snare drum can be played with the snares disengaged (call for "snares off") to produce a tom-tom-like sound. Another special technique is the "stirring" with brushes, described above. A third common special technique, the so-called "rim shot," which sounds like a pistol-shot, is produced by striking the head and the rim of the drum simultaneously (or striking a stick that is in contact with both the head and the rim). The proper notation for the rim shot is shown in figure 6.38.

Figure 6.38

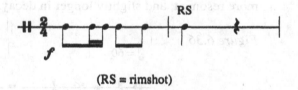

(RS = rimshot)

The Tambourine	**French**	**German**	**Italian**
	tambour de basque	Tambourin	tamburo basco

Figure 6.39

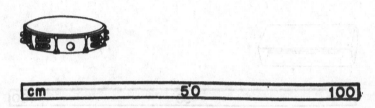

Sizes

Tambourines vary in size from approximately 6 inches to approximately 15 inches in diameter, with a normal concert instrument being approximately 10 inches in diameter. The metal jingles, which are suspended in slots in the shell of the instrument, also vary in size, composition, and number, which causes a wide variation in the sound of the instrument. The performer is usually trusted to choose the proper sound for any given musical situation, but the arranger who wishes to contrast two different tambourine sounds could specify the general size as "small," "medium," or "large."

Decay

Figure 6.40

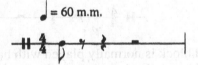

Strikers

The traditional mode of playing the tambourine is with the hands and fingers. Light strokes are generally performed with the fingers and accented notes with a knuckle, fist, or the knee. Snare drum sticks and yarn or cord mallets may also be used. The head is sometimes damped and rhythms performed on the rim with the open fingers. This produces a light jingle without the characteristic drum sound.

Technical Limitations

The tambourine is a highly colored and distinctive sound that will quickly lose effect if overused. For this reason, it should be used sparingly.

Special Techniques

Several types of rolls are available, including the "shake" roll, which is used for long rolls at higher dynamic levels; the "thumb" roll, which is limited to short bursts; and rolls on the rim with the fingers, which are more delicate than the other types.

The Wood Block	**French**	**German**	**Italian**
	block de bois	Holzblock	blocco di legno

Figure 6.41

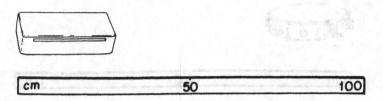

Sizes   Wood blocks vary in size from approximately 1.5 x 6.25 inches, to 4 x 12 inches. The larger are generally lower in pitch, but the pitch is also controlled by the position and size of the slit that is cut into the side of the block. Specify "small," "medium," or "large" wood blocks and leave the details of choice to the performer.

Decay   Figure 6.42

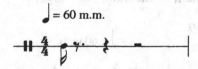

Sticks   The wood block is normally played with hard rubber mallets, although snare drum sticks and plastic or yarn mallets are sometimes used. Plastic mallets are the harshest in sound, while yarn mallets produce a smooth sound that is excellent at softer dynamics.

The Temple Blocks	French	German	Italian
	temple blocks	Tempelblocks	temple blocks

Figure 6.43

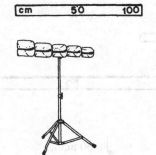

Sizes

The normal set of temple blocks consists of five hollow blocks that are tuned to a rough pentatonic scale. Because its tuning is not standardized, the instrument is treated as an indefinite-pitch instrument.

Decay

Figure 6.44

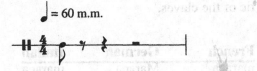

Sticks

The normal sticks are rubber, yarn, or cord mallets. Harder sticks (plastic, metal, or wood) are generally not used, since they will damage the instrument.

Technical Limitations

Because of the layout and size of the temple blocks, rapid passages are often difficult and should be planned with an instrument at hand.

The Claves

French	German	Italian
claves	Claves	claves

Figure 6.45

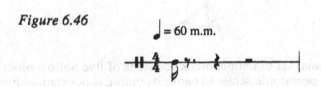

Decay

Figure 6.46

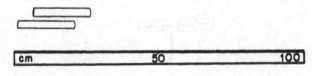

$\quad = 60$ m.m.

Technical Limitations

Since the claves are played by striking the two bars together, rhythms are limited to single strokes (sixteenth notes at a moderate tempo). Rolls are not characteristic of the claves.

The Maraca

French	German	Italian
maraca	Maraca	maraca

Figure 6.47

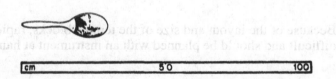

Decay

Figure 6.48

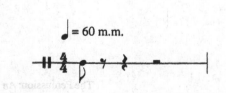

$\quad = 60$ m.m.

Technical Limitations	Since the maracas are hollow gourd rattles, there is some difficulty in playing extremely short notes, but players adopt methods such as striking a maraca on the hand to achieve dry effects. Maracas are generally used for Latin American rhythms, but their use should not be limited to those effects. They contribute an effective and unique color to the percussion section.

The Bass Drum	French	German	Italian
	grosse caisse	grosse Trommel	gran cassa

Figure 6.49

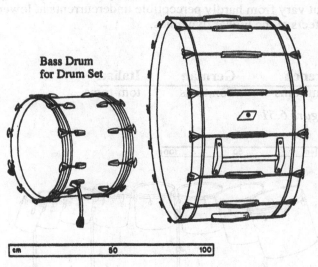

Concert Bass Drum

Bass Drum
for Drum Set

Sizes	Bass drums vary in size from 6 by 18 inches up to 18 by 40 inches (occasionally even larger). The pitch of the drum is generally related to the size, but the tension on the head can be varied to change the pitch over a limited range.

Decay   *Figure 6.50*

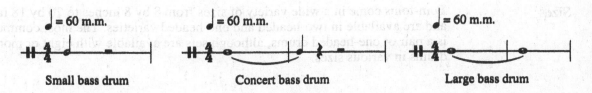

♩ = 60 m.m.   ♩ = 60 m.m.   ♩ = 60 m.m.

Small bass drum   Concert bass drum   Large bass drum

Sticks

Bass drums are normally played with special lamb's wool beaters with cork, yarn, or wood cores; but hard felt or wood mallets are used for louder and marcato playing. Snare drum sticks and yarn mallets may also be used, but these are not considered standard.

Technical Limitations

The rather long decay time makes complicated rhythmic material sound rather confused unless hard mallets are used.

Special Techniques

The "cannon shot" is a hard blow struck dead-center on the drum. This effect is strong enough to produce a noticable impact on the body, as well as a extremely loud sound. The bass drum is also capable of producing beautiful sustained rolls that vary from hardly perceptible undercurrents at lower dynamics to thunderous effects at the higher dynamics.

The Tom-toms

French	German	Italian
tom-toms	Tomtoms	tom-toms

Figure 6.51

Sizes

Tom-toms come in a wide variety of sizes from 8 by 8 inches to 20 by 18 inches and are available in two-headed and one-headed varieties. The most common set is a pair of one-headed drums, although sets are available with eight or more drums in various sizes.

Decay

Figure 6.52

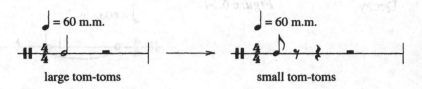

large tom-toms   small tom-toms

Sticks

The tom-toms are normally played with felt or yarn mallets; but snare drum sticks, rubber mallets, and brushes may also be used, depending on the sound desired.

Technical Limitations

With large sets of tom-toms, care should be taken to avoid drum-change patterns that are awkward to execute.

Special Techniques

The tom-toms are played in much the same way as the snare drum when snare drum sticks are employed. Rim shots are a standard part of the technique with snare drum sticks.

The Triangle	**French**	**German**	**Italian**
	triangle	Triangel	triangolo

Figure 6.53

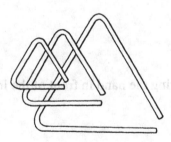

cm   50   100

Sizes

Triangles come in various sizes from 5 to 14 inches on the side, and the pitch is related both to the size and the diameter of the metal rod. (Thicker rods are higher in pitch than thinner rods). It is best to specify "high," "medium," and "low" pitches in writing for sets of triangles, since pitch can not be predicted from the size alone.

Decay

Figure 6.54

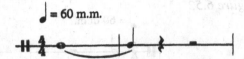

Beaters

The triangle is normally played with a length of metal rod called a triangle beater. These beaters come in various thicknessess, with the thinner beaters used for softer, more delicate effects. (Specify "thin," "medium," or "thick" beaters.) Plastic mallets and snare drum sticks are also used. These beaters remove most of the "sparkle" from the tone of the triangle.

Technical Limitations

Due to the long decay time, complicated rhythmic patterns will not come out clearly. The instrument is best for single strokes or rolls.

Special Techniques

The triangle can be muted with the hand to produce shorter sounds. Muting can be combined with open strokes to produce interesting rhythmic effects (figure 6.55).

Figure 6.55

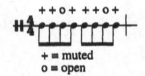

+ = muted
o = open

A delicate vibrato can be produced by waving the hand in front of the instrument after it is struck.

The Cowbells

French	German	Italian
cencerros	Cencerros	cencerros

Figure 6.56

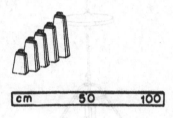

| cm | 50 | 100 |

Sizes

Cowbells come in many sizes, and the pitch is directly related to the size of the bell. (Specify "small," "medium," and "large.")

Decay

Figure 6.57

muted   open

Sticks

Cowbells are normally played with snare drum sticks (often reversed), but rubber and yarn mallets are also good for more delicate effects.

Special Techniques

Cowbells are played in two places: the top surface (specify "on the top") and the edge, or mouth (specify "on the mouth"). The mouth sound is more resonant than the top sound. In Latin American rhythms, the two sounds are used in rapid alternation. Muting is possible, either by placing the instrument on a soft cloth, for slight muting; or by hand or body muting, to produce a rather dead sound. Hand muting is also a part of Latin American playing style.

The Hi-hat

French	German	Italian
hi-hat	Hi-hat	hi-hat

Figure 6.58

Decay

Figure 6.59

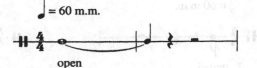

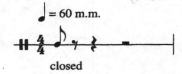

Sticks

The hi-hat is usually played with snare drum sticks or brushes, but it is also possible to use yarn mallets.

Technical Limitations

In the open position, the long decay makes rapid rhythmic patterns ineffective; but when closed, nearly any rhythm can be articulated.

Special Techniques

A wide variety of sounds is available from the hi-hat, and this variety is much exploited in popular music and jazz. The cymbals can be closed after striking in open position or opened after striking in closed postion. The notations for closed versus open hi-hat are the "+" and "o," as shown in figure 6.55. The hi-hat is normally played on the surface (the "bow"), but playing near the raised center "bell" produces a more distinct pitch.

The Crash Cymbals (Hand Cymbals)	**French** cymbales de concert	**German** Schlagbecken	**Italian** piatti da concerato

Figure 6.60

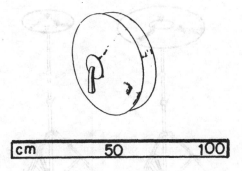

Sizes

Crash cymbals come in many sizes and thicknesses from 16 inches to 24 inches, but the 18-inch medium weight cymbals are fairly standard. The player will choose the size depending on the character of the music; but "small," "medium," and "large" sizes can be specified.

Decay

Figure 6.61

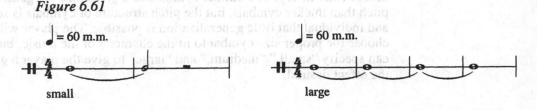

Technical Limitations

Since the crash cymbals are played by striking them together, it is difficult to play repeated notes much faster than eighth notes in march time (120 m.m.). A limited roll is available (specify "plate roll"), but it is difficult to control, and sustained effects are generally superior on the suspended cymbal.

Special Techniques

The normal effect is the single loud crash, which is used to support major climaxes in the music; but soft crashes are effective in quiet passages. If a short sound is desired, the cymbals are choked against the body (specify "choke"). A soft swish is performed by scraping the edge of one cymbal across the face of the other (specify "swish"). A rather raucous short sound may be produced by holding the cymbals together on impact (specify "choke and hold together").

The Suspended Cymbals	**French**	**German**	**Italian**
	cymbale suspendue	Becken freihängend	piatto sospeso

Figure 6.62

Sizes

Cymbals vary in size from 6 to 28 inches in diameter and in weight from very thin to extra heavy. The thinner cymbals of a given size are generally lower in pitch than thicker cymbals, but the pitch structure of cymbals is so complicated and individual that little generalization is possible. The player will generally choose the proper size cymbal to fit the character of the music; but the arranger can specify "small," "medium," and "large" to give the player a general idea of the effect desired.

Decay

Figure 6.63

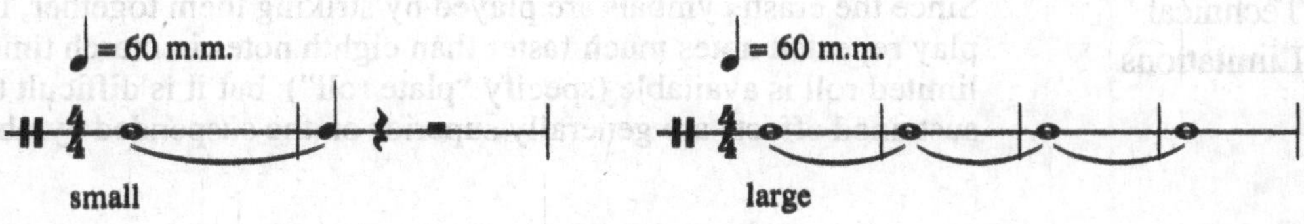

$\quad$ ♩ = 60 m.m. $\qquad\qquad\qquad\qquad$ ♩ = 60 m.m.

small $\qquad\qquad\qquad\qquad\qquad\qquad$ large

Sticks	Suspended cymbals are normally played with yarn mallets to produce a smooth roll or with snare drum sticks for definite rhythmic patterns. Wire brushes produce a delicate, shimmering sound and triangle beaters a rather harsh, metallic sound.

Sticks

Suspended cymbals are normally played with yarn mallets to produce a smooth roll or with snare drum sticks for definite rhythmic patterns. Wire brushes produce a delicate, shimmering sound and triangle beaters a rather harsh, metallic sound.

Technical Limitations

The long decay times make complicated rhythmic patterns ineffective, but complicated patterns can be clearly played on the bell with snare drum sticks. The highly colored sound of the suspended cymbal adds luster to many musical textures, but the sound will pall if overused. Use the suspended cymbal for a few carefully chosen places, but remember that it is equally effective at loud and soft dynamics.

Special Techniques

Many special effects are possible on the suspended cymbal. Two of the more common are: scraping across the face with a coin or light triangle beater to produce a swishing sound (specify "coin across face") and laying a circular length of light chain across the face to produce a sizzle cymbal effect.

The Tam-tam

French	German	Italian
tam-tam	Tam-tam	tam-tam

Figure 6.64

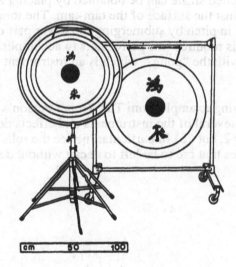

Sizes

Tam-tams vary in size from 20 to 60 inches in diameter, but the standard size is approximately 30–36 inches. Organizations rarely own more than two tam-tams.

Decay

Figure 6.65

$\quad \downarrow = 60$ m.m.

large

Beaters

The standard beater is a special heavy lamb's wool or yarn mallet called a tam-tam beater. In addition the instrument can be struck with yarn or felt mallets, snare drum sticks, triangle beaters, and wire brushes.

Technical Limitations

The tam-tam has the longest decay of any of the percussion instruments. This makes it impossible to play rhythmic patterns with the standard tam-tam beater. (Rhythmic patterns may be played with snare drum sticks or triangle beaters, but these beaters are not heavy enough to set the entire instrument in motion.) The sound of the tam-tam "blooms" after it is struck, unless the instrument is "warmed up" by striking it softly in advance of the stroke. Also, complete damping of a large tam-tam is quite difficult and rather ugly in sound. The instrument should generally be used in situations where it can be allowed to decay normally. The long decay can be shortened somewhat by moving the beater around the surface to damp various areas of the instrument.

Special Techniques

A high-pitched sizzle can be obtained by placing a length of chain or a triangle beater against the surface of the tam-tam. The tone of the tam-tam can be "bent" downward in pitch by submerging the lower part of the instrument in a tub of water. (This requires two performers to accomplish.) The tam-tam should not be confused with the "gong," which is an instrument of definite pitch.

Musical Example

The following example from The Young Person's Guide to the Orchestra illustrates several of the instruments and effects described in this chapter (figure 6.66). (CD 2, cut 16) In particular, notice the rolls to sustain tones and the half-ties on notes that are to be left to decay without damping.

Figure 6.66

Britten: The Young Person's Guide to the Orchestra, op. 34, m.419–429.

THE YOUNG PERSON'S GUIDE TO THE ORCHESTRA © Copyright 1946 by Hawkes & Son (London) Ltd.: Copyright Renewed.
Reprinted by permission of Boosey & Hawkes, Inc.

Specialized Percussion Instruments

In addition to the standard concert percussion instruments listed in this chapter a number of specialized sets of instruments are available for particular purposes. The "trap set" that is used in popular music and jazz is described in chapter 19, and the instruments used in the marching band are described in chapter 20.

Workbook: Assignments A–E, pp. 85–95.

Suggested Listening (see appendix, D p. 396, for details)

Berlioz, Hector. *Symphony Fantastique*, op. 14.
    III (In the country)
        m. 175 Timpani "chords"
    IV (Procession to the Stake)
        m. 1 Timpani tuned in thirds.
    V (A witches' sabbath)
        m. 102 Two large bells back stage.
        m. 363 Bass drum roll with long crescendo

Copland, Aaron. *El Salon Mexico* (1936).
    The analysis in appendix D concentrates on the use of percussion.

Grainger, Percy. Lincolnshire Posy.
    II (Horkstow Grange)
        The entire movement should be studied for the role of the percussion in building for and achieving climax.

Holst, Gustav. Second Suite in F for Military Band, op. 28, no. 2.
    III (Song of the Blacksmith)
        m.1 Snare drum
        m. 19 Anvil and cymbals
        m. 23 Snare drum, anvil, and cymbals
    IV (Fantasia on the 'Dargason')
        m. 33 Triangle
        m. 41 Tambourine
        m. 49 Triangle
        m. 105 Tambourine
        m. 137 Crash cymbals and bass drum
        m. 185 Bass drum roll as a background texture

Mahler, Gustave. Symphony No. 4 in G Major (1900).
    I (Moderato)
        m. 1 Sleighbells
        m. 209 Timpani, triangle, tam-tam

Suggestions for Further Study

A number of books have been written on the percussion family, including:

Adato, Joseph, and George Judy. *Percussionist's Dictionary*. Melville, N.Y.: Belwin-Mills Publishing Corporation, 1984.

Blades, James, and Jeremy Montagu. *Early Percussion Instruments*. London: Oxford University Press, 1976.

Brindle, Reginald Smith. *Contemporary Percussion*. New York: Oxford Universiity Press, 1970.

Holland, James. *Percussion*. London: McDonald and Jane's, 1978.

Holloway, Norman, and Daniel Bachelder. *Guide to Teaching Percussion*. 4th ed. Dubuque, Iowa: Wm. C. Brown Publishers, 1984.

Lang, Morris, and Harry Spivack. *Dictionary of Percussion Terms*. Rev. ed. New York: Lang Percussion Co., 1988.

Peinkofer, Karl, and Fritz Tannigel. *Handbook of Percussion Instruments*. London: Schott, 1976.

General treatises on instrumentation that contain information on the percussion section include:

Stiller, Andrew. *Handbook of Instrumentation*. Berkeley, Calif.: University of California Press, 1985, (chapter 5, p. 118, chapter 6, p. 140, chapter 7, p. 172).

7 Strings: *Lyric Voices*

The string family is divided into two groups: the "bowed" strings and the "plucked" strings, so named because of their normal playing technique. The bowed strings form a highly unified ensemble that is the center of the orchestra. The string section is capable of a wide range of expression, wonderful blend in accompaniment textures, and tireless performance. The string sound never seems to pall on the ear as does the sound of most other orchestral instruments, and more or less continuous string sound is characteristic of orchestral writing.

Two common members of the plucked string family (harp and guitar) will be discussed in the next chapter.

The Bowed Strings

This chapter will deal with the common bowed string instruments: the violin, viola, 'cello, and bass. These instruments share many common performance techniques that will be introduced before the individual instruments are discussed.

Bowing

The tone of the bowed strings is normally produced by drawing the bow across one or more of the strings. When the bow is drawn away from the instrument it is referred to as a down bow, and when it is drawn toward the instrument it is called an up bow. The symbols for down bow and up bow are shown in figure 7.1.

Figure 7.1

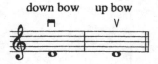

Players are taught to start a passage down bow when it begins on an accented beat (particularly the first beat of a measure) and to start up bow when an unaccented note (or notes) precedes an accented beat (see figure 7.2).

Figure 7.2

Passages that observe this normal pattern do not need up bow and down bow symbols. If the normal pattern is to be reversed, alert the player by drawing the up or down bow above the first note of the passage (see figure 7.3).

Figure 7.3

The bow has a similar function to the air in wind instruments, and there are many parallels:

1. The bow is limited in length, just as the supply of air is limited for wind players.
2. The duration that can be played on a single bow (or breath) varies with the dynamic level. Much more bow is required for loud playing than for soft.
3. String players use the bow to produce phrasing and articulation just as wind players use their breath.

An important difference is that the bow can be used in both directions, whereas the wind player must stop to breathe. This means that the strings can be played for long periods of time without stopping.

The slur is used in string parts to show groups of notes that are to be played under a single bow (figure 7.4).

Figure 7.4

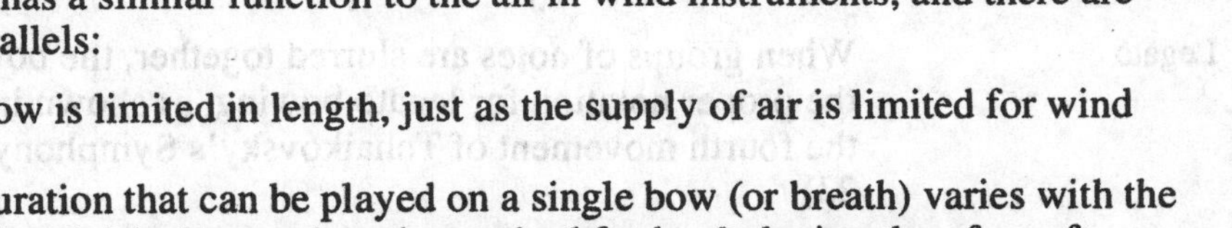

Bowing Styles	There is little agreement among string players as to the names for the various styles of bowing. The following list of common bowing styles is not at all exhaustive, and the names are not to be considered definitive; but the notation symbols, at least, are standardized.
Détaché	In détaché bowing the bow direction changes with each note, with no silence between notes. This bowing is assumed in the absence of any of the special bowing indications listed below. Détaché bowing may involve a very smooth connection between notes, or the notes may be accented. The following passage from Pictures at an Exhibition is an illustration of détaché bowing (figure 7.5). (CD 4, cut 10)

Figure 7.5

Moussorgsky-Ravel: Pictures at an Exhibition, Promenade III, m. 3–5.

PICTURES AT AN EXHIBITION © Copyright 1929 by Edition Russe de Musique; Copyright Renewed. Copyright and Renewal assigned to Boosey & Hawkes, Inc. Reprinted by permission.

Legato	When groups of notes are slurred together, the bowing is legato. The slur sign is the proper notation for legato bowing, as shown in the following passage from the fourth movement of Tchaikovsky's Symphony No. 6 (figure 7.6). (CD 5, cut 23)

Figure 7.6

Tchaikovsky: Symphony No. 6 *(Pathétique)*, op. 74, in B minor, IV, m. 108–111.

Staccato	There are two types of string staccato: "on the string," in which the bow actually stops on the string to make the space between notes; and "off the string" or spiccato, in which the bow bounces off the string. In both cases, the bow direction changes with each note. The *staccato* dot is the proper indication for both types, and the player normally chooses the type that is appropriate for the given passage. The following passage from The Nutcracker Suite is an illustration of "off the string" staccato (figure 7.7). (CD 5, cut 7)

Figure 7.7

Tchaikovsky: Nutcracker Suite, op. 71a, IIa, *(Marche),* m. 41–44.

**Slurred Staccato
(Group Staccato)**

Several staccato notes (generally no more than three or four) can be slurred together. This means that the player takes them in the same bow, but makes a slight separation between the notes. This is a favorite bowing for repeated-note figures in accompaniments, as shown in the following example from The Nutcracker Suite (figure 7.8). (CD 5, cut 7)

Figure 7.8

Tchaikovsky: Nutcracker Suite, op. 71a, III, *(Valse des Fleurs),*   m.34–41.

Pizzicato

An alternate method of playing the bowed string instruments is to pluck the string with the finger, an effect that is called pizzicato. A beat or two of rest is normally required for the string player to shift from bowed (arco) to plucked (pizzicato). The proper notation for pizzicato is the abbreviation "pizz." and the return to bowing should be indicated by "arco," as shown in the following example from Bizet's *Jeux d'Enfants* (figure 7.9). (CD 1, cut 24)

Figure 7.9

Bizet: *Jeux d'Enfants* , op. 22, III (Impromptu), m. 62–66.

Tremolo	Two distinct types of tremolo are available on the bowed string instruments: "bowed tremolo," in which the bow is moved back and forth as fast as possible; and "fingered tremolo," which is an expanded trill covering the interval of a third or fourth.
Bowed Tremolo	Bowed tremolo is a device that produces a rustling effect at softer dynamic levels (see figure 7.10a from Bartók's Hungarian Sketches). (CD 1, cut 9) It produces energy and excitement at higher dynamic levels (see figure 7.10b from Tchaikovsky's Symphony No. 6). (CD 5, cut 24)

Figure 7.10

a. Bartók: Hungarian Sketches III (Melody), m. 32–35.

HUNGARIAN SKETCHES © Copyright 1932 by Karl Rozsnyai and Rozsavolgyi & Co., Copyright Renewed. Copyright and Renewal assigned to Boosey & Hawkes, Inc. Reprinted by permission.

b. Tchaikovsky: Symphony No. 6 *(Pathétique)*, op. 74, in B minor, IV, m. 116–120.

(Notice that there must be three strokes across the stem of quarter and half notes, but only two on eighth notes.)

Fingered Tremolo

The fingered tremolo is a rapid alternation of two notes on the same string, in the manner of a trill, with the notes taken under a single bow. The effect is somewhat similar to that of the bowed tremolo, as illustrated in the following passages from Bartók's Hungarian Sketches (figure 7.11a) (CD 1, cut 14) and Britten's The Young Person's Guide to the Orchestra (figure 7.11b) (CD 2, cut 10).

Figure 7.11

a.   Bartók: Hungarian Sketches, V (Swineherd's Dance), m. 66–70.

(Notice the notation of the fingered tremolo. Each note is given full value, on the theory that they are both sounding for the entire duration.)

Harmonics   If a string is lightly touched at precisely its mid-point, the fundamental pitch is suppressed and the second partial sounds. This effect, which is available on all string instruments, is known as a natural harmonic. It is possible to touch the string in several places so that any one of the first four (or even more) partials will sound. On the violin's open G string, the following pitches will result (figure 7.12):

Figure 7.12

open string   (2nd partial)   (3rd partial)   (4th partial)   etc.

The proper notation for the harmonic is shown in figure 7.13.

Figure 7.13

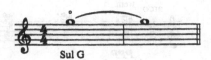

Sul G

The following passage from The Young Person's Guide to the Orchestra uses several natural harmonics (figure 7.14). (CD 2, cut 15) Roman numerals serve to indicate the string to be used, with "I" assigned to the highest string and "IV" to the lowest string.

Figure 7.14

Britten: The Young Person's Guide to the Orchestra, op. 34, m. 392–394.

In addition to the natural harmonics described above, the violin and viola are sometimes asked to play artificial harmonics. These are produced by fingering any note and touching the string to bring out the fourth partial, a pitch two octaves higher than the fingered note. The notation for artificial harmonics shows the note to be fingered, the note to be touched (a diamond shape note a perfect fourth above the fingered note), and usually, but not always the pitch that results (a cue-sized note two octaves above the fingered note) as shown in figure 7.15.

Artificial harmonic

Figure 7.15

Artificial harmonics are relatively rare in orchestral writing, since they are more difficult to produce. The following passage from The Young Person's Guide to the Orchestra illustrates a single artificial harmonic with a bowed tremolo on the violin (figure 7.16). (CD 2, cut 17)

Figure 7.16

Britten: The Young Person's Guide to the Orchestra, op. 34, m. 429–434.

THE YOUNG PERSON'S GUIDE TO THE ORCHESTRA © Copyright 1946 by Hawkes & Son (London) Ltd., Copyright Renewed. Reprinted by permission of Boosey & Hawkes, Inc.

Muting

A small wood, metal, or plastic mute can be placed on the bridge of a bowed string instrument to produce a veiled and softer tone quality (specify con sordino or "muted"). The effect of muting an entire string section is quite lovely, as the opening of Bartók's Hungarian Sketches illustrates (figure 7.17). (CD 1, cut 1)

Figure 7.17

Bartók: Hungarian Sketches, I (An Evening in the Village), m. 1–6.

HUNGARIAN SKETCHES © Copyright 1932 by Karl Rozsnyai and Rozsavolgyi & Co., Copyright Renewed. Copyright and Renewal assigned to Boosey & Hawkes, Inc. Reprinted by permission.

When the mutes are to be removed, specify *senza sordino* or "remove mutes" (see figure 7.18).

Multiple Stops

It is possible to play on two strings at the same time, producing an effect called a double stop. Chords can be played in arpeggio on three or four strings (triple stop, quadruple stop). A complete treatment of multiple stops is beyond the scope of this book. You may refer to one of the orchestration or instrumentation manuals at the end of the chapter for more information. Multiple stops are relatively rare in orchestral writing, since it is usually better to divide a string section rather than have them try to play a multiple stop in tune. However, figure 7.18 from Bartók's Hungarian Sketches (CD 1, cut 17) clearly calls for a quadruple stop in the violins, and a triple stop in the violas and 'cellos.

Figure 7.18

Bartók: Hungarian Sketches, V (Swineherd's Dance), m. 115–120.

The Violin

French	German	Italian
violon	Geige	violino
violons	Geigen	violini

Figure 7.19

Ranges

Figure 7.20

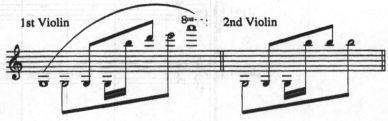

Register Characteristics

The individual tone colors of the four strings make the primary distinction in sound on the violin. Figure 7.21 is a summary of the violin's open strings and register characteristics.

Figure 7.21

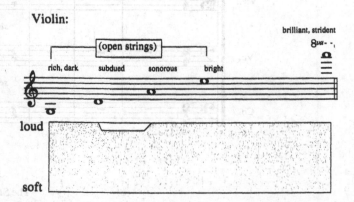

Technical Limitations	The violin is the most agile of the bowed string family. It is capable of playing nearly any melodic line, although extreme chromaticism presents a challenge. The pizzicato is quite resonant on the G and D strings, but the upper strings are much weaker in sound, and notes above the treble staff are generally disappointing. The fingered tremolo is limited in range to a fourth, (the normal reach between the first and fourth fingers.) Natural harmonics should be limited to the second through the fourth partials, as shown in figure 7.22.

Figure 7.22

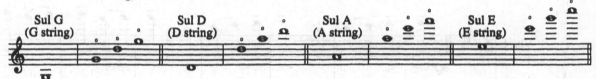

Musical Examples	The violins in their lower register are capable of great warmth and feeling, as can be heard in the following example from Bartók's Hungarian Sketches (figure 7.23). (CD 1, cut 7)

Figure 7.23

Bartók: Hungarian Sketches, III (Melody), m. 1–8.

HUNGARIAN SKETCHES © Copyright 1932 by Karl Rozsnyai and Rozsavolgyi & Co., Copyright Renewed. Copyright and Renewal assigned to Boosey & Hawkes, Inc. Reprinted by permission.

The light staccato style is illustrated in Bizet's *Jeux d'Enfants* (figure 7.24). (CD 1, cut 26)

Figure 7.24

Bizet: *Jeux d'Enfants*, op. 22, V (Galop), m. 1–6.

When melodic material is placed in the upper register of the first violins, it is often supported in octaves by the second violins. This produces a powerful effect, as can be heard in this example from Tchaikovsky's Symphony No. 6 (figure 7.25). (CD 5, cut 21)

Figure 7.25

Tchaikovsky: Symphony No. 6 *(Pathétique)*, op. 74 in B Minor IV, m. 55–60.

The Viola

French	German	Italian
alto	Bratsche	viola
altos	Bratschen	viole

Figure 7.26

Range

Figure 7.27

Viola

Notice that the viola is normally written in the alto clef, except for the upper register, where it shifts to the treble clef to avoid ledger lines. The alto clef should be used for all passages that don't involve more than two or three ledger lines. Players are accustomed to parts that shift from clef to clef, but you should try not to use more than one clef per measure.

Register Characteristics

The individual tone colors of the four strings make the primary distinction in sound on the viola. Figure 7.28 is a summary of the viola's open strings and register characteristics.

Figure 7.28

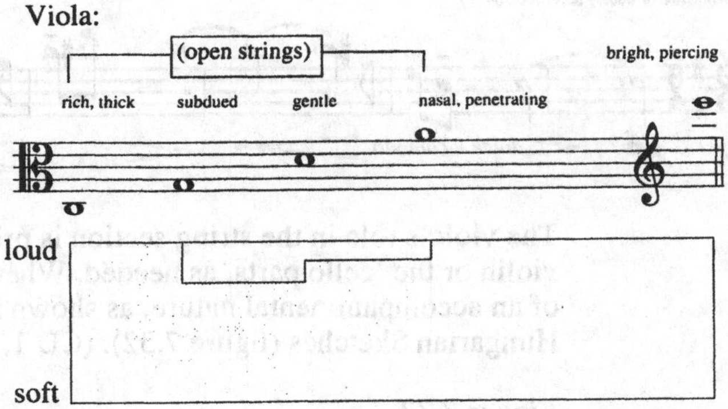

Viola:

(open strings)

rich, thick   subdued   gentle   nasal, penetrating   bright, piercing

loud

soft

Technical Limitations

The viola is not as agile as the violin, but its capabilities are similar to those of the violin in many ways. The pizzicato is quite effective on all strings, although the best effect is obtained in the range of an octave above each open string. The fingered tremolo is limited (as on the violin) to the range of a fourth, and the second through fourth partials may be used effectively for natural harmonics (figure 7.29).

Figure 7.29

Sul C (C string)   Sul G (G string)   Sul D (D string)   Sul A (A string)

The lyrical qualities of the viola section are in evidence in the following excerpt from Bizet's *Jeux d'Enfants* (figure 7.30). (CD 1, cut 20)

Figure 7.30

Bizet: *Jeux d'Enfants*, op. 22, II (Berceuse), m. 22–26.

Britten explores all of its registers in the passage that introduces the viola in The Young Person's Guide to the Orchestra (figure 7.31). (CD 2, cut 6)

Figure 7.31

Britten: The Young Person's Guide to the Orchestra, op. 34, m. 182–188.

THE YOUNG PERSON'S GUIDE TO THE ORCHESTRA © Copyright 1946 by Hawkes & Son (London) Ltd.; Copyright Renewed. Reprinted by permission of Boosey & Hawkes, Inc.

The viola's role in the string section is primarily that of doubling either the violin or the 'cello parts, as needed. When it has an independent role, it is often of an accompanimental nature, as shown in the following excerpt from Bartók's Hungarian Sketches (figure 7.32). (CD 1, cut 12)

Figure 7.32

Bartók: Hungarian Sketches, V (Swineherd's Dance), m. 5–8.

HUNGARIAN SKETCHES © Copyright 1932 by Karl Rozsnyai and Rozsavolgyi & Co., Copyright and Renewal assigned to Boosey & Hawkes, Inc. Reprinted by permission.

The Violoncello ('Cello)	French	German	Italian
	violoncelle	Violoncell	violoncello
	violoncelles	Violoncelle	violoncelli

Figure 7.33

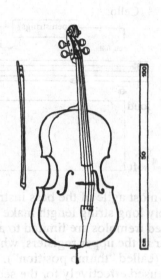

Range   *Figure 7.34*

'Cello

The range of the 'cello is extensive. The lower part of the range is written in the bass clef, while the upper middle area uses the tenor clef. Finally, the extreme upper range is written in the treble clef. You should judge the general tessitura of a given passage in deciding which clef to use. In general, you should use the clef that will result in the fewer ledger lines.

Register Characteristics

The individual tone colors of the four strings make the primary distinction in sound on the 'cello. Figure 7.35 is a summary of the 'cello's open strings and register characteristics.

Figure 7.35

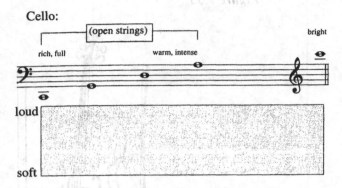

Technical Limitations

The 'cello is the most agile of the bass instruments of the orchestra. Its resonant tone and relatively long string length make the pizzicato very effective in all registers. Fingered tremolos are limited to a major third in the lower registers, but may be wider in the upper registers, where the cellist can stop the string by using the thumb (called "thumb position"). The natural harmonics speak quite well and may be used effectively for the second through fifth or sixth partial, as shown in figure 7.36.

Figure 7.36

Musical Examples

The 'cello has two functions in the orchestra, the primary bass instrument of the string section and a melodic instrument in its own right. In most orchestral textures, the 'cello carries the bass part, with the double basses doubling on heavier or louder sections. The doubling of 'cello and bass parts is so common that they are often written on the same staff (of course the bass will sound an octave lower), as shown in the following excerpt from the Nutcracker Suite (figure 7.37). Notice the effective use of the pizzicato in this passage. (CD 5, cut 2)

Figure 7.37

Tchaikovsky: Nutcracker Suite, op. 71a, IIa *(Marche)*, m. 5–7.

As a melodic instrument, the 'cello is second to none. Its intense tone enhances any tenor-range melody (figure 7.38). Notice the use of the tenor clef in this passage. (CD 2, cut 7)

Figure 7.38

Britten: The Young Person's Guide to the Orchestra, op. 34, m. 203–208.

The Double Bass (Bass)	**French**	**German**	**Italian**
	contre basse	Kontrabass	contrabasso
	contre basses	Kontrabässe	contrabassi

Figure 7.39

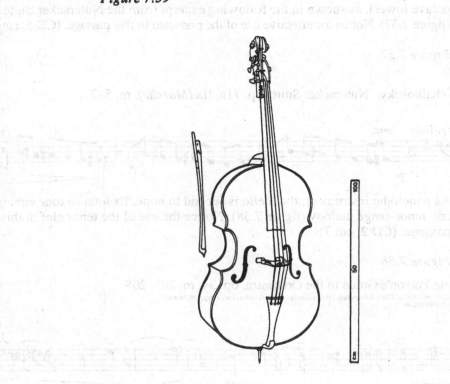

Range (written)

Figure 7.40

Double Bass

Some basses have a fifth string that is tuned to CC, while others may have an extension on the E string to reach the CC. Basses without the fifth string or extension must either tune the E string down to CC or move the part an octave higher.

Transposition	The double bass is the only transposing member of the bowed string family. It transposes an octave to avoid ledger lines.

Figure 7.41

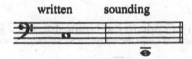

Register Characteristics	The individual tone colors of the four strings make the primary distinction in sound on the bass. Figure 7.42 is a summary of the bass's open strings and register characteristics.

Figure 7.42

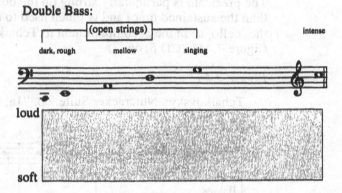

Technical Limitations	The tone of the double bass is surprisingly weak and must be supported by the 'cello section or the wind basses (bassoon, trombone, tuba). The instrument is much less agile than the 'cello and sometimes plays simplified versions of the cello's bass part (figure 7.43). (CD 1, cut 13)

Figure 7.43

Bartók: Hungarian Sketches, V (Swineherd's Dance), m. 56–60.

HUNGARIAN SKETCHES © Copyright 1932 by Karl Rozsnyai and Rozsavolgyi & Co., Copyright Renewed. Copyright and Renewal assigned to Boosey & Hawkes, Inc. Reprinted by permission.

Musical Examples	As discussed above, the basses rarely have a truly independent part, but Britten does give the section a solo role in The Young Person's Guide to the Orchestra (figure 7.44). (CD 2, cut 9)

Figure 7.44

Britten: The Young Person's Guide to the Orchestra, op. 34, m. 240–247.

The pizzicato is particularly strong on the double bass (actually more resonant than the sustained tone) and is much used to underline accompaniment figures in the 'cello, as in the accompaniment to Tchaikovsky's Waltz of the Flowers (figure 7.45). (CD 5, cut 7)

Figure 7.45

Tchaikovsky: Nutcracker Suite, op. 71a, III *(Valse des Fleurs)*, m.34–38.

Workbook: Assignments A–E, pp. 97–104.

Suggested Listening (see appendix D, p. 396, for details)	Bartók, Béla. Concerto for Orchestra (1943) 　　I (*Introduzione*) 　　　　m. 1 Cellos and basses alone, muted upper strings in m. 6. 　　　　m. 51 Melody in violins I-II in octaves (with woodwind doubling). 　　　　m. 76 Melody in violins unison. Berlioz, Hector. Symphony Fantastique, op. 14 　　IV (Procession to the Stake) 　　　　m. 1 Four-part pizz. chords in double basses. 　　　　m. 25 Melody in lower strings.

V (A witches' sabbath)
> m. 1 Pianissimo bowed tremolo chords in muted upper strings.
> m. 444 Col legno in violins and violas.

Bizet, George. *L'Arlésienne* Suite no. 1.
> I (Prelude)
>> m. 113 Melody in octaves for viola and violin I.
>> m. 119 Melody in octaves for violin I-II, violas, and cellos.
>> m. 138 Bowed tremolo
> II (Minuetto)
>> m. 45 Melody in octaves for violin and cello.
>> m. 77 More extensive doubling of melody in upper strings.
>> m. 101 Melody in violin I, with diminuendo emphasized by gradually reducing the number of stands playing.
> III (Adagietto) The entire movement is for muted string orchestra.

Debussy, Claude. Prelude to "The Afternoon of a Faun" (1892–94)
> m. 11 Bowed tremolo sur la touche in divided, muted strings. A very subtle rustle.
> m. 40 Violins in octaves.
> m. 63 Melody extensively doubled in violins, violas, and cellos with woodwind and harp background.
> m. 75 Solo violin.
> m. 94 Combination of fingered and bowed tremolo.

Mahler, Gustave. Symphony No. 4 in G Major (1900)
> I (Moderato)
>> m. 38 Melody in high 'cellos, above the upper strings.
>> m. 71 Double basses alone (reduced to single instrument later)
>> m. 326 First violins gradually rise to extreme upper register.

Suggestions for Further Study

A number of books specializing on single members of the string family are available, including:

Nelson, Sheila M. *The Violin and Viola*. New York: W. W. Norton & Company, Inc., 1973.

Turetzky, Bertram. *The Contemporary Contrabass*. Berkeley, Calif.: University of California Press, 1974.

Yampolsky, I. M. *Principles of Violin Fingering*. Translated by Alan Lumsden. New York: Oxford University Press, 1967.

Books on the string family as a whole includes:

Lamb, Norman. *Guide to Teaching Strings*. 5th ed. Dubuque, Iowa: Wm. C. Brown Publishers, 1990.

General treatises on instrumentation that contain an extensive treatment of the string section include:

Adler, Samuel. *The Study of Orchestration*. New York: W. W. Norton and Company, 1989, 1982, chapter 2, p. 8, chapter 3, p. 55, chapter 4, p. 94, chapter 5, p. 109.

Berlioz, Hector, and Richard Strauss. *Treatise on Instrumentation*. Translated by Theodore Front. New York: Edwin F. Kalmus, 1948, pp. 2–137.

Forsyth, Cecil. *Orchestration*. New York: Dover Publications, Inc., 1982, No. 46–57, pp. 303–486.

Kennan, Kent, and Donald Grantham. *The Technique of Orchestration*, 4th edition. Englewood Cliffs, NJ: Prentice-Hall, 1990, 1983, 1970, 1952, chapter 2, p. 7, chapter 3, p. 32, chapter 4, p. 52.

Stiller, Andrew. *Handbook of Instrumentation*. Berkeley, Calif.: University of California Press, 1985, chapter 9, p. 311.

8 Keyboard Instruments, Harp, and Guitars

The keyboard instruments and harp are generally considered peripheral to the orchestra and band. They are, however, included often enough to merit some consideration in this book. The harp was well established as a member of the orchestra by the middle of the 19th century, and the piano has been used occasionally in the 20th century. The celesta is usually thought of as a member of the percussion section, although it is nearly always played by a pianist rather than a percussionist. Furthermore, the piano has a central role in the beginning orchestra, where it is regularly used to fill out incomplete and weak sections in the ensemble.

The guitar has never had a regular place in the orchestra, but appears from time to time as a solo instrument. In the 20th century, the guitar has been an important instrument in the development of jazz and popular music, and electric guitars are primary instruments in rock ensembles.

The Piano

	French	German	Italian
	piano	Klavier	pianoforte

Figure 8.1

Reprinted by permission of the publishers from The New Harvard Dictionary of Music by Don Michael Randel, Cambridge. Mass.: Harvard University Press, Copyright © 1986 by the President and Fellows of Harvard College.

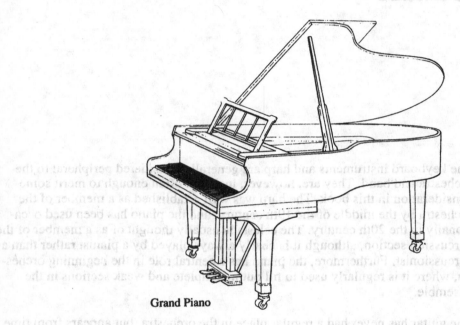

Grand Piano

Range

Figure 8.2

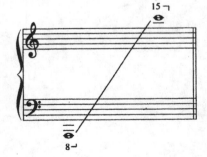

Register Characteristics

The lower register of the piano has been used to add definition to the bass line or as a percussion effect faintly reminiscent of a low bell or gong. The middle register has relatively little use as a color effect, but is used regularly in beginning orchestra music to strengthen and support the texture. The upper register adds a brittle and sparkling quality to high melodic lines and a harplike effect in arpeggiated chordal textures.

Figure 8.3

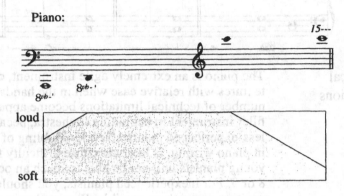

Piano:

The Pedals

The typical grand piano is equipped with three pedals, which are named (from left to right) the *una corda* or soft pedal, the *sostenuto* pedal, and the damper pedal. The damper pedal, which lifts the dampers from all the strings and allows them to ring freely, is used regularly, both for its practical value in allowing notes to continue to sound while the hands move to new locations on the keyboard—and as a coloring device, where the added resonance of strings that have not been struck colors the sound in many interesting ways. Space does not permit a complete exposition of the nature and notation of the coloristic effects created by pedaling. In general, however, the points where the damper pedal is to be depressed and released are marked in piano music in one of several ways (figure 8.4).

The *una corda* pedal on the grand piano shifts the entire piano action slightly to the right, so that hammers strike only two of the three strings. (The term *una corda*, which translates as "one string" is thus a misnomer with the modern piano.) On an upright piano, the hammers are moved closer to the strings. The effect is a slight softening and muting of the sound. This pedal is seldom used in orchestral writing.

The *sostenuto* pedal is rarely used. On a grand piano, it can be depressed while one or more dampers are raised, causing only those dampers to remain up. In other words, it is a selective damper pedal. On upright pianos, it may be a partial damper pedal that raises only the dampers in the lower register.

Figure 8.4

damper pedal   *una corda* pedal   *sostenuto* pedal

Technical Limitations

The piano is an extremely agile instrument, capable of playing complicated textures with relative ease when in the hands of an experienced pianist. A number of technical limitations become apparent when the piano is used as a filler instrument in beginning orchestra, because it is likely to be played by a less-experienced pianist. Octave doubling of melodic lines, a standard technique in piano writing, is likely to cause difficulty for young pianists. In fact, many young pianists will not be able to reach an octave comfortably before the age of 8 or 9. For inexperienced pianists, you should try to keep the hands in one position as much as possible. Pianists begin with what is called "five-finger" position, in which the fingers of each hand are assigned one note for the entire composition. You need not be so restricted in writing orchestra filler parts, but accompaniment figures that cause rapid left-hand movements should be avoided.

Figure 8.5

easy accompaniment figures

difficult accompaniment figures

The Celesta

French	German	Italian
célesta	Celesta	celesta

Figure 8.?

Figure 8.6

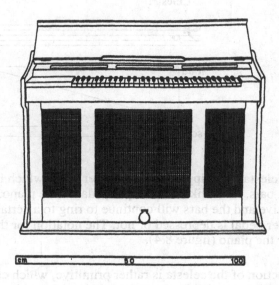

Range

Figure 8.7

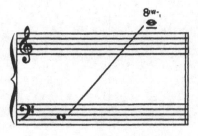

Transposition

Figure 8.8

written   sounds

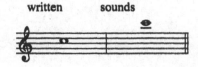

Register Characteristics

The dynamic range of the celesta is extremely limited, making it one of the instruments most likely to be covered in any but the lightest textures. The upper register has more carrying power than the lower register.

Figure 8.9

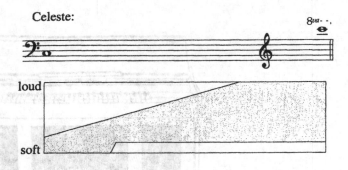

Celeste:

The Pedal

The celesta is equipped with a damper pedal which lifts the dampers from all the metal bars, much like the damper pedal of the piano. This pedal is only partially effective and the bars will continue to ring to a certain extent whether the damper pedal is depressed or not. The notation for the damper pedal is the same as for the piano (figure 8.4).

Technical Limitations

The action of the celesta is rather primitive, which causes the instrument to be difficult to play. While the standard piano figurations are possible, parts for the celesta should be kept relatively simple.

The Harp	**French**	**German**	**Italian**
	harpe	Harfe	arpa

Figure 8.10

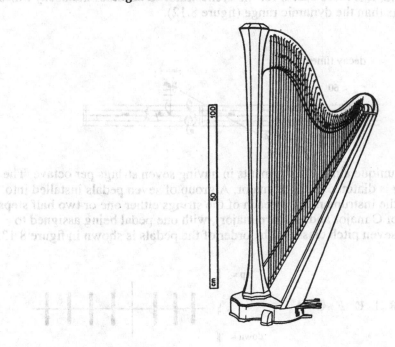

Range   *Figure 8.11*

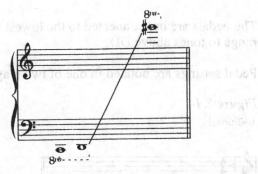

Register
Characteristics

The harp is quite consistent in dynamic range over its entire compass, but the lowest bass tones do not have as much carrying power as do the upper tones. Since the strings, once plucked, will continue to sound until damped by the player's hand, it is more useful for the orchestrator to consider the decay times of the strings than the dynamic range (figure 8.12).

Figure 8.12

The pedals

The harp is unique among instruments in having seven strings per octave. The basic tuning is diatonic in C-flat major. A group of seven pedals installed into the base of the instrument raises each of the strings either one or two half steps (to the key of C major and C-sharp major), with one pedal being assigned to each of the seven pitch classes. The order of the pedals is shown in figure 8.13.

Figure 8.13

D C B | E F G A

up = ♭

♮

down = ♯

The pedals are not connected to the lowest C and D, which limits the chromatic range to tones above DD.

Pedal settings are notated in one of two ways, as shown in figure 8.14.

Figure 8.14

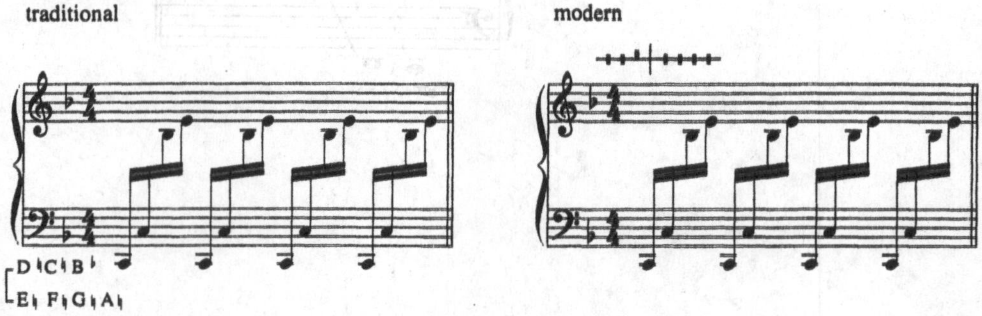

Instrumentation

In writing for the harp, it is important that you first consider the pedal setting, which establishes the seven pitches that will be available. Both diatonic and nondiatonic settings are commonly used and a number of chords can be set up by utilizing the enharmonic relationships possible between adjacent strings (figure 8.15).

Figure 8.15

Technical Limitations

The normal hand position on the harp precludes the use of the little finger, so chords should be limited to four notes per hand. Also, you should take note that the thumb is placed on higher strings than the three fingers in both the left and right hands, a fact that has an effect on the comfort of various chord spacings. It is more comfortable to have a wider interval between the upper and second note in a chord than between the lower two chord tones (figure 8.16).

Figure 8.16

comfortable   less comfortable

The harp is often used in arpeggiated chords to produce coloristic effects, as shown in the following passage from Tchaikovsky's Nutcracker Suite (figure 8.17). (CD 5, cut 6)

Figure 8.17

Tchaikovsky: Nutcracker Suite, op.71a, III *(Valse des Fleurs)*, m. 1–10.

Another standard effect is the glissando, as illustrated in the following passage from Britten's The Young Person's Guide to the Orchestra (figure 8.18). (CD 2, cut 10)

Figure 8.18

Britten: The Young Person's Guide to the Orchestra, op. 34, m. 276–278.

Instrumentation

Arpeggios are combined with glissandi in the following excerpt from Bartók's Hungarian Sketches (figure 8.19). (CD 1, cut 10)

Figure 8.19

Bartók: Hungarian Sketches, III (Melody), m. 53–60.

HUNGARIAN SKETCHES © Copyright 1932 by Karl Rozsnyai and Rozsavolgyi & Co., Copyright Renewed. Copyright and Renewal assigned to Boosey & Hawkes, Inc. Reprinted by permission.

The Acoustic Guitars

French	**German**	**Italian**
guitare	Gitarre	chitarra

Figure 8.20

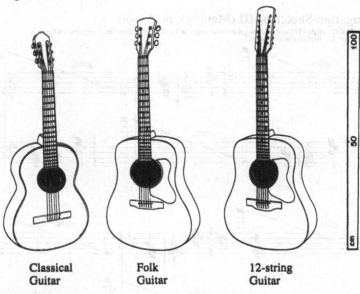

Classical Guitar   Folk Guitar   12-string Guitar

Ranges (written for acoustic guitars in standard tuning)

Figure 8.21

String: ⑥ ⑤ ④ ③ ② ①

Transposition

The guitars transpose down one octave, which allows them to be notated in the treble clef over their entire range.

Figure 8.22

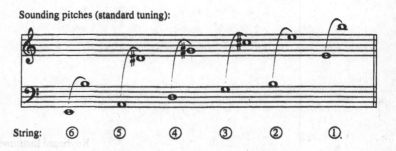

Sounding pitches (standard tuning):

String: ⑥ ⑤ ④ ③ ② ①

General Characteristics	The guitars are members of the plucked string family. The six (or twelve) strings pass over a fingerboard inlaid with raised metal bars called *frets*, which are used for stopping the strings. The frets provide security of intonation and allow the strings to vibrate more freely than the strings of the bowed string family. The fingers of the left hand are used to stop the strings by pressing just behind a fret. Fingerings are indicated with numbers, as shown in figure 8.23.

Figure 8.23

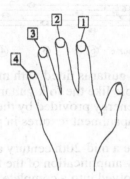

The strings are plucked with the fingers or nails of the right hand and with various plectrums (called *picks*).

The Classical Guitar	The classical guitar has a soft, mellow tone suitable for chamber music. It is slightly shorter than the other acoustic guitars and is strung with nylon (formerly gut) strings. The strings are plucked with the nails or flesh of the fingers of the right hand. The use of picks is not a part of the standard technique of the classical guitar. The classical guitar is the standard instrument for concert music and is seldom used in popular music.
The Folk Guitar	The folk guitar is slightly longer than the classical instrument, with a shorter body and longer, narrower neck. It is fitted with wire strings, giving it a brighter, more cutting tone. The folk guitar is generally played with picks rather than the fingernails. The folk guitar is the standard acoustical guitar for popular music.

The Twelve-string Guitar

The twelve-string guitar has two strings placed close together for each note. The pair of strings is called a *course*. The lower courses are tuned in octaves and the upper courses in unison.

Figure 8.24 open strings of the twelve-string guitar (sounding pitches)

course ⑥ ⑤ ④ ③ ② ①

The twelve-string guitar is fitted with metal strings and played with picks, giving it a tone that is more like the folk guitar than the classical guitar, but much fuller, due to the energy provided by the additional strings. It is used primarily for chordal accompaniment textures in popular music.

The Electric Guitars

Electric guitars are a mid-20th century addition to the guitar family. Developed originally to allow amplification of the folk guitar in popular music settings, the instrument has evolved into a complete family of instruments with unique tonal characteristics. The playing technique and ranges of the electric guitars (except the bass) are similar to that of the folk guitar.

Figure 8.25

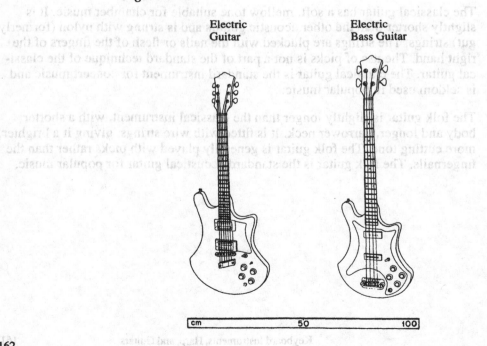

Electric Guitar

Electric Bass Guitar

cm   50   100

162

Hollow-body Electric Guitar	A hollow-body electric guitar is an amplified acoustic guitar of the folk or twelve-string type. The instrument is fitted with one or more (usually two or three) electrical sensors (called *pick-ups*) under each string that pick up the string's vibration. The body of the instrument contains a circuit that mixes the signals from the pick-ups and allows some control of the signal level and tone. The hollow body guitar has a switch that allows the player to select the pick-ups to be connected, a volume control, and treble and bass tone controls similar to those of stereo receivers. Some electric guitars have a built-in preamplifier that increases the range of control of the signal before it leaves the instrument. The instrument is connected to a power amplifier and speakers that are often contained in a single box.

Solid-body Electric Guitar

The solid-body electric guitar has a body made of a single piece of wood (or other material) instead of the hollow box of acoustic instruments. The body reflects the vibration of the strings rather than resonating it, and the tone quality is determined largely by the electronics. The instrument is fitted with pick-ups and controls that are similar to those of the hollow-body instrument, but the sound is much brighter with a longer decay time.

Electric Bass Guitar

The electric bass guitar is a four-string solid-body instrument tuned an octave below the other guitars. This places it in the same range as the double bass of the bowed string family. It is written in the bass staff with an octave transposition.

Figure 8.26

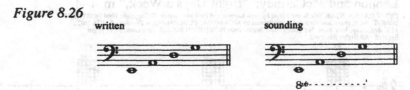

The playing technique is similar to the other guitars, but the larger size makes the instrument slightly less agile than the other members of the family.

Notation of Guitar Music

Several notation systems are in common use for the guitars. The notation of classical guitar music is quite similar to traditional notation, with a few special symbols to indicate the string and the fingering.

Figure 8.27

Specific frets are notated with roman numerals, with I indicating a half-step above the open string, II a whole-step, etc.

Several tabulature notations have been developed to notate popular music and jazz. The most common of these are the guitar symbols found in printed sheet music (figure 8.28).

Figure 8.28
Lennon and McCartney: "Eight Days a Week," m. 1–4.

EIGHT DAYS A WEEK Words and Music by John Lennon and Paul McCartney. © Copyright 1964 NORTHERN SONGS. All Rights Controlled and Administered by MCA MUSIC PUBLISHING, A Division of MCA INC., 1755 Broadway, New York, NY 10019 under license from NORTHERN SONGS. International Copyright Secured. All Rights Reserved.

Special Effects

Harmonics are available on both acoustic and electric guitars. Natural harmonics on the first through sixth partial are easily played, and some artificial harmonics are also available. (See chapter 7 for a more thorough discussion of harmonics.)

Alternative tunings are a standard effect for the guitar family. While the instrument can be tuned in nearly any way, the best results are obtained when strings are tuned lower than the standard tuning. Tuning strings above their usual levels may result in a broken string. The most common alternative tuning is the "dropped D" tuning, in which the lowest string is tuned down to D. Other common alternative tunings are the so-called "open" tunings, in which the open strings of the guitar produce a chord. The open tunings are named by the chord they produce. Figure 8.29 shows several of the common alternate tunings. For more detailed treatment of this subject, consult guitar methods.

Figure 8.29

Another approach to alternative tunings is a device called a *capo*, which fits on the neck of the guitar and depresses all strings at the same fret. The effect is to transpose the instrument, allowing the player to play in a variety of keys using a limited number of chord positions. The player considers the next fret above the capo to be the first fret and fingers a standard chord, which will be transposed according to the position of the capo. For example, with the capo on the first fret an E chord becomes an F chord.

Most electric guitars are fitted with a small handle attached to the bridge that allows the player to bend the pitch, particularly in a downward direction. These so-called *wiggle* or *whammy bars* (also misnamed *tremolo bar*) are used to produce vibrato and to bend the tone, a characteristic of much popular music.

Electric guitars will produce *feedback* when brought in close proximity to their speakers. These howling sounds are rather unpredictable, since they depend on the acoustics of the instrument, the speaker, and the room, but once produced they can be controlled to a certain extent by shifting the position of the guitar relative to the speakers. This effect has been much exploited in certain styles of rock music.

The sound of any electric guitar can be modified by electronic devices known by such names as "fuzz tone," "distortion," "reverb," "wah-wah," "delay," and "phaser." These devices are available in small boxes that can be controlled by the player's foot. A complete discussion of electronic modification of guitar sounds is beyond the scope of this book, but the effects are a standard part of rock and rock-oriented music.

Workbook: Assignments A–D, pp. 105–109

Suggested Listening (see appendix D, p. 396, for details)

Bartók, Bela. Concerto for Orchestra (1943)
    I (*Introduzione*)
       m. 154 Important figure in harp
       m. 438 Unusual harp effect: wooden or metal stick scraping strings

Debussy, Claude. Prelude to "The Afternoon of a Faun" (1892-94)
       m. 4 Harp glissando
       m. 63 Harp texture
       m. 108 Harp harmonics

Suggestions for Further Study

Books specializing in the keyboard instruments and harp include:

Bacon, Tony, ed. *Rock Hardware: The Instruments, Equipment and Technology of Rock*. New York: Harmony, 1981.

Inglefield, Ruth K., and Lou Anne Neill. *Writing for the Pedal Harp*. Berkeley, Calif.: University of California Press, 1984.

Ripin, Edwin M., ed. *Keyboard Instruments*. New York: Dover, 1977.

Salzedo, Carlos. *Modern Study of the Harp*. New York: G. Schirmer, Inc., 1948.

Schmeckel, Carl D. *The Piano Owner's Guide*. New York: Charles Scribner's Sons, 1974.

Books specializing in guitar include:

Denyer, Ralph. *The Guitar Handbook*. New York: Knopf, 1982.

Isherwood, Millicent. *The Guitar*. London: Oxford University Press, 1986.

Schneider, John. *The Contemporary Guitar*. Berkeley, Calif.: University of California Press, 1984.

Sors, Fernando. *Method for the Spanish Guitar*. Translated by A. Merrick. New York: Da Capo Press, 1971.

General treatises on instrumentation and orchestration containing information on the keyboard instruments, harp and guitar include:

Adler, Samuel. *The Study of Orchestration*. 2nd ed. New York: W. W. Norton & Company, Inc., 1989, 1982, chapter 4, p. 94 [harp and guitar]; chapter 13, p. 405; chapter 14, p. 419.

Berlioz, Hector, and Richard Strauss. *Treatise on Instrumentation*. Translated by Theodore Front. New York: Edwin F. Kalmus, 1948, pp. 137–161 and pp. 243–247.

Burton, Stephen Douglas. *Orchestration*. Englewood Cliffs, N.J.: Prentice Hall, Inc., 1982, chapter 6, p. 77; chapter 19, p. 212; chapter 23, p. 244.

Kennan, Kent, and Donald Grantham. *The Technique of Orchestration*, 4th edition. Englewood Cliffs, NJ: Prentice Hall, Inc., 1990, 1983, 1970, 1952, chapter 15, p. 273; chapter 18, p. 338.

Stiller, Andrew. *Handbook of Instrumentation*. Berkeley, Calif.: University of California Press, 1985, chapter 8, p. 255; chapter 9, p. 311.

9 Writing for Younger Musicians

The challenge of writing interesting music for younger musicians tests the skill of even the most-experienced arranger. Yet, the need for music that stimulates the imagination and challenges students to improve their musical understanding and performance is greater here than at any other level. To write effectively for young people, you need to understand the incremental way that musical skills are acquired by young instrumentalists and how they develop physically.

Physical Development

Young people typically begin their instrumental instruction in the period from six to ten years of age, when physical development is far from complete. Their motor control, while highly developed, is eight to ten years from reaching its peak. Physical size, strength, and stamina are limited, making performance on adult-sized musical instruments very difficult. This problem is alleviated to some extent in string ensembles by the availability of smaller-sized instruments, but this resizing is not possible with most wind instruments.

The Impact of Physical Size

The smaller size of young musicians impacts the instrumentation available in ensembles, particularly in the bass range. Because the bass instruments may be too large for children to handle, most beginning string ensembles have no double basses; and beginning bands often have no tubas, euphoniums, bassoons, bass clarinets, or baritone saxophones. Since most arrangements depend on a strong bass line, the arranger for beginning ensembles must make sure that the bass line is covered by instruments that are available in the ensemble. There is little problem in doing this for the beginning orchestra, since the 'cello has traditionally served the bass function. In the band, however, the bass part will need to be carried by the lower trombone, and sometimes the tenor saxophone. Parts for the double basses, tubas, euphoniums, bassoons, bass clarinets and baritone saxophones must be provided, but you should not assume that they will be played. They should double the lower trombone and tenor saxophone lines, either at the unison or the octave (figure 9.1).

Figure 9.1

White: Cherry Tree Carol

In the beginning orchestra, there may be no violas, which creates a gap in the middle of four-part textures. This problem is often solved by including a piano reduction that can be played to fill out the texture. It is also possible to write the viola part in such a way that it is not essential to the musical effect, for example, if the two violin parts move mostly in parallel thirds and sixths and the bass line is strong, the resulting three-part texture may be quite satisfying even if the viola is missing. Another alternative is to provide a third violin part that doubles the viola line (as long as it doesn't exceed the violin's range) to complete the four-part texture.

The winds and percussion are likely to be missing from beginning orchestras. These instruments should not be given a featured role unless you know they will be available.

Double reeds and horns are often weak in beginning ensembles. You should write no independent parts for these instruments. The oboe should double the cornet or clarinet part when these instruments have the primary melody (PM). The horns often double alto saxophone or trombone parts.

By the junior high school level, the instrumentation is more complete in both band and orchestra, and the ensembles can be scored in the usual way. However, it is best to provide fairly extensive cross-cueing or to double all important lines, since instrumentation is quite variable from one ensemble to another. The bass instruments may still be quite weak in relation to the treble instruments.

The young musician's smaller size limits performance in various ways on all musical instruments. For example, keyboard players may not be able to reach an octave with one hand before the age of eight, and most trombone players will not be able to reach the seventh position in the early years. These limitations are taken into consideration in the range charts for each of the instruments and do not need further explanation here.

The Impact of Strength and Stamina

Limitations of strength are felt most directly in pitch range and dynamic range. The range charts for the instruments take the limited strength of young performers into consideration, but the limitations on dynamic range must be addressed. Most beginning players will be limited both in the upper and lower parts of the adult dynamic range for their instruments, making extended crescendos and decrescendos beyond their power. They will be able to make a clear contrast between loud and soft, but bear in mind that the total dynamic range is quite small. (This need not limit the range of written dynamics. Players need to learn to make these distinctions.)

Limitations of stamina must be accounted for in several ways. Compositions for young musicians should be relatively short—from one to three minutes in duration. This provides for rest time between numbers that is essential to beginning players. It is also a good practice to provide frequent short rests in the parts for wind players. This is particularly essential in writing for the flute, oboe, and trumpet, since these instruments present the greatest challenge to the player in terms of stamina. Phrase length is also a major concern for wind players in general. Breathing places must be provided at frequent intervals, particularly for the larger, bass members of the wind family.

The Impact of Motor Control Limitations

A young person's incomplete motor control shows up in limitations on the performance of fast or rhythmically complex passages, long notes at slow tempos, and (on some instruments) in negotiating register changes. Register-change limitations have been dealt with for specific instruments in earlier chapters, so we will concentrate here on generalizations about speed and rhythmic complexity.

Speed

Elementary-level musicians on treble-range instruments should be asked to play no faster than eighth notes at a moderate tempo (100 to 120 beats per minute). Fluency increases by junior high level to include sixteenth notes at the same tempo, but you should not ask for continuous playing at this speed. High school musicians can play for short periods of time in thirty-second notes and more continuously in sixteenth. Because higher instruments are generally more fluent than lower instruments, and woodwinds and strings are more fluent than brass, the recommendations above must be tempered to take these differences into consideration. Drum parts should be no faster than sixteenth notes at the elementary levels and can include thirty-second by junior high school. Rolls are possible at the elementary levels; but, since longer rolls may sound rather uneven, it is best to restrict rolls to no more than a quarter note duration at a moderate tempo, unless they will be covered by a tutti ensemble.

Young musicians find it very difficult to control their instruments on slow, sustained material. The lack of vibrato and uncertain intonation make such passages cold and ineffective. In slower tempos, it is important that you keep an audible pulse and moving material going at all times.

Rhythmic Complexity

Elementary-level musicians generally find it difficult to change from one tempo to another, particularly if there isn't a moment of silence in which to prepare for the change. It is always best to provide such clear breaks at points of tempo change. Also, momentary changes of tempo (accelerandos, ritardandos, and tempo rubato) are difficult to control and should be avoided at the earliest levels, with the possible exception of a ritardando at the end of a section. These limitations gradually diminish during the junior high and high school years, and quite subtle changes of tempo can be asked of high school musicians.

Rhythms that contain a wide variety of patterns present difficulties to young musicians, even if the individual rhythmic patterns are well within their grasp. Again, it is the necessity to change patterns constantly that they find beyond their control. Generally, you will find that the best results are obtained when a few rhythmic patterns are established and repeated consistently throughout a section (figure 9.1). The range of rhythmic activity can be expanded during the junior high and high school years and becomes much less of a concern to the arranger.

The Incremental Development of Musical Skills

It goes without saying that music instruction must begin with a few patterns and concepts and gradually develop in an incremental way. It is not sound educational practice to attempt to introduce everything at once. During the elementary, junior high school, and high school years the young musician is gradually introduced to the many patterns of pitch and rhythm that characterize Western music. In order to write effective music that will be successfully performed by young musicians, you need to have some idea of what a student is likely to understand and be able to play at a given point. The proper sequential pattern for introducing musical skills is the subject of much study and considerable controversy, and the following material represents a few generalizations gleaned from the requirements of educational publishers, rather than the results of research.

Key Limitations

Wind players are started in the key of B-flat major (C major for the B-flat instruments that predominate in the band). Very early in their training (usually during the first year) they are introduced to the keys of F major and E-flat major. Most music for elementary school bands is written in these three keys (and their relative minors). By junior high school, a band should be able to play comfortably in the keys of C major and A-flat major; and by high school level, D-flat major and G major. However, even at the high school level, the original keys (F, B-flat, and E-flat) are still the most secure in intonation. In general, bands at all levels experience greater intonation difficulties in the sharp keys than the flat keys.

Figure 9.2

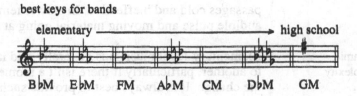

best keys for bands

elementary ⟶ high school

BbM   EbM   FM   AbM   CM   DbM   GM

Some chromaticism is possible at the earliest levels, particularly when the chromatic inflection is in the key signature of another key that is well established. (For example, as soon as F major is established, an E natural can be easily played in the keys of B-flat major and E-flat major.) Other accidentals may occasionally be introduced, but this might force the director to stop in the middle of a rehearsal to introduce new fingerings, which are better introduced in the lesson context so that other musicians are not kept waiting. (Directors who prepare all band music in lessons don't experience this difficulty.)

In the orchestra, the sequence of keys is considerably different. String instruments typically begin in the key of D (which they all have as an open string). The keys of G and A are added in the first year, and most elementary orchestra music is written in those three keys (and their relative minors). By junior high school, an orchestra will have added the keys of C major and F major; and, by high school, the keys of B-flat major, E-flat major and E major. Orchestras will generally play with greater confidence in the sharp keys than in the flat keys.

Figure 9.3

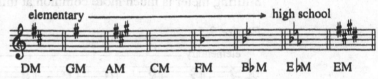

Best keys for orchestras:

elementary ⟶ high school

DM   GM   AM   CM   FM   B♭M   E♭M   EM

Since the fingering system of the string instruments is based around the diatonic scales, you should be careful of how chromaticism is introduced into the music for beginning string players. Passages in which chromatic notes are introduced in a diatonic pattern are easily played, while nondiatonic sequences will produce technical difficulties and intonation problems (figure 9.4).

Figure 9.4

easy   avoid

CM

Tuning Problems Playing in tune is a challenge for beginning performers, and some intonation problems are inevitable. A successful arrangement must take possible intonation difficulties into account. Young performers are likely to be confused by dissonance in the harmony, so a harmonic style that emphasizes triads and straightforward diatonic harmony will be most successful. Generally, thicker textures are more successful in hiding intonation difficulties than thin, more exposed textures. There is safety in numbers! However, the unrelieved tutti textures in much elementary band and orchestra music is boring and oppressive and gives the young performer no opportunity to develop self-confidence. Your challenge as an arranger is to provide a variety of textures and limited opportunities for sections and individuals to be featured, while maintaining the general safety net of the tutti texture for most of the arrangement. Intonation generally deteriorates at the upper and lower extremes of most instrument's ranges, so it would be safest to feature the middle of the range in exposed or solo parts.

Meter

Music instruction is usually begun with the most common simple meters: $\frac{4}{4}$, $\frac{2}{4}$, and $\frac{3}{4}$. For some reason, beginning musicians find triple meter more difficult than duple meters. When writing in $\frac{3}{4}$ meter for beginners you should make the rhythms very simple and repetitive. The first compound meter is $\frac{6}{8}$, and the first equivalents of the common simple meters: $\mathbf{C}$, and $\mathbf{\phi}$, are introduced early on. By junior high school, students should be able to play with confidence in those meters, and occasional shifting of meter among the simple meters will be possible. Other compound meters (such as $\frac{9}{8}$ and $\frac{12}{8}$) are introduced in high school along with equivalents to the common simple meters (such as $\frac{3}{2}$ and $\frac{4}{8}$). Shifting meter is much more common at this level.

Figure 9.5

Rhythmic Patterns

Any attempt to be absolute in categorizing a sequential order for the introduction of rhythmic patterns would be doomed to failure: rhythmic difficulty depends as much on the context in which the pattern occurs as it does on the pattern itself. In addition, students are capable of learning quite complex patterns (those that appear in popular music, for example) by rote. The following list contains some common rhythmic figures that students should be able to read at various stages in their musical development.

Figure 9.6
elementary

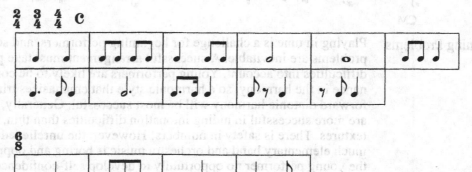

junior high school

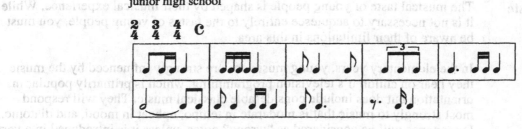

high school

(and other equivalent meters)

Musical Taste

The musical taste of young people is shaped by their musical experience. While it is not necessary to acquiesce entirely to the tastes of young people, you must be aware of their limitations in this area.

In the elementary years, young musicians are strongly influenced by the music they hear on children's television programming, which is primarily popular in orientation but does include considerable classical music. They will respond most strongly to music that is moderate in tempo, upbeat in mood, and diatonic. Dissonance will be considered as "wrong" notes, unless it is introduced in a very conventional way. Simple jazz and popular rhythms are appreciated, and repetitive patterns are the norm. Phrase structure should be clear-cut and conventional. Musical styles that deviate from these norms are likely to be confusing to young people.

In the junior high and high school years, a young person's taste is most strongly shaped by popular music, particularly the so-called "top forty" styles. There is, however, a growing maturity and broadening of taste during these years, and by the end of high school, some musicians are quite sophisticated in their appreciation of music. They will accept considerable chromaticism and dissonance if they have heard music of similar style. They are easily bored and will respond best to pieces that present a variety of tempos and moods.

As an arranger, you have an opportunity, particularly at the junior high and high school levels, to play a part in the development of young people's musical tastes. They are, however, more easily led than driven. If they understand what a piece of music is trying to communicate, they will tolerate even rather dissonant 20th-century styles. Programmatic references may be quite helpful in gaining acceptance.

Arranging Techniques

To provide maximum security for young musicians you should:

1. Reduce the number of different parts in each section. In beginning band there is normally only one flute, oboe, alto saxophone, and horn part. Two clarinet, trumpet, and trombone parts are usually provided. See figure 9.1 for a standard score layout.

2. Keep all like instruments on the same rhythm. There is safety in numbers.

3. Limit the number of independent rhythms to two (plus a percussion part) for elementary ensembles. Junior high school ensembles can handle three independent rhythms.

To provide interest and variety you should:

1. Change texture types from time to time. Two-part imitative counterpoint can be quite effective. Antiphonal effects between sections also provide interest. (Don't overlook the percussion in considering antiphonal effects.) Tutti monophonic textures are absolutely safe and provide an effective alternative to block-style writing.

2. Use special effects, such as pizzicato in the strings and mutes in both winds and strings occasionally. These techniques are fairly easily learned, and young musicians find them interesting and fun.

3. Make sure that each section of the ensemble has a chance to play an important part somewhere in the arrangement. This ensures that each player's part is interesting, and the color and register contrast creates interest for the listener as well.

4. Use a variety of percussion instruments in band scoring. While the timpani and larger mallet percussion may not be available at the elementary level, instruments such as bells, triangle, wood block, suspended cymbal, and tambourine are a good source of color and variety.

Summary

As you can see from the discussion in this chapter, writing for young musicians is a challenging (and rewarding) task. Technical limitations must be accommodated, and the music must fit into the educational sequence in a logical way. Of central importance, however, is the aesthetic quality of the music, since the development of appreciation for the art of music is the primary justification for including music in the school curriculum.

Workbook: Assignments A–B, pp. 111–118

Suggestions for Further Study

A few orchestration texts deal briefly with scoring for younger players. These include:

Burton, Stephen Douglas. *Orchestration*. Englewood Cliffs, N.J.: Prentice Hall, Inc., 1982, chapter 35, p. 454.

Cacavas, John. *Music Arranging and Orchestration*. Miami, Fla.: Belwin-Mills Publishing Corp., 1975, Keys and Ranges, p. 138.

Erickson, Frank. *Arranging for the Concert Band*. Miami, Fla.: Belwin-Mills Publishing Corp., 1983, chapter 19, p. 157.

Kennan, Kent, and Donald Grantham. *The Technique of Orchestration*, 4th edition. Englewood Cliffs, N.J.: Prentice Hall, Inc., 1990, 1983, 1970, 1952, chapter 19, p. 353.

A book that deals exclusively with writing for young musicians is:

Oboussier, Philippe. *Arranging Music for Young Players*. London: Oxford University Press, 1977. (This book emphasizes ensembles that are more common in Europe than the U. S.)

It is helpful to study method books for a more-complete picture of the skills that can be expected at each level. There are a many graded instrumental methods available that will provide an insight into the incremental nature of musical development.

The best sources of information continue to be guides from educational publishers that specify limitations on works for various grade levels. These guides are not available to the general public and are often considered proprietary information, available only to composers and arrangers writing for the publisher. Much of the material of this chapter was selectively adapted from these guides.

10 Balance, Blend, Masking, and Voice Crossing

The *New Grove Dictionary of Music and Musicians** (London: Macmillan, 1980) defines orchestration as "the art of combining the sounds of a large complex of instruments (an orchestra) to form a satisfactory blend and balance," thus identifying two of the central issues for anyone who scores music for instrumental ensembles.

Balance

Two instruments are said to be *in balance* if they are perceived to be playing with equal loudness. The critical word in this definition is *perceived*, since balance can only be judged by the ear, and no objective measurement of relative loudness is significant. If two like instruments are playing the same pitch, the subjective judgment of balance might be very close to an objective measurement. However, if the two instruments are of different timbre and are playing different pitches, the situation is much more complicated, due to a number of factors, including the nonlinearity of the ear's perception of loudness at different frequencies. Also, you cannot depend on achieving balance simply by writing the same dynamic level for the two instruments. Each instrument has its own dynamic range on each note (which is detailed in the charts in the "register characteristics" section of chapters 4–8), and the players may not be able to achieve a balance because of the limits of their instruments. In the final analysis, a sense of balance in scoring for instruments can only be developed by musical experience, but the following generalizations will get you started.

Balance of Sections in the Orchestra and Band

The chart in figure 10.1 presents a general view of the relative dynamic ranges of the four sections of the orchestra and band. This chart and others like it throughout this chapter are based on subjective judgments rather than objective measurements. You should concentrate not on the details, but on the general pattern.

Figure 10.1

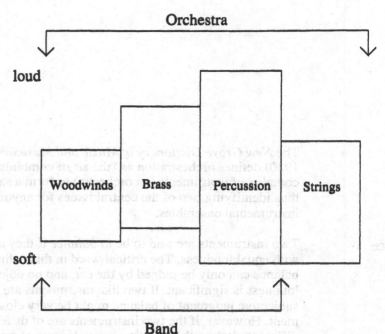

As you can see, the percussion section has the most extensive dynamic range and the woodwinds the least extensive. In the middle of the dynamic range, a balance of all the forces is possible, but as the dynamic levels rise, the woodwinds and then the strings will be gradually overbalanced by the brass and percussion. As they approach the lowest dynamic levels, the brass and woodwinds will reach a point where they can play no softer and must stop playing if a balanced effect is to be achieved. In the band, the woodwinds (with some light percussion) produce the softest effects. This will give you a general perspective on how to use the various sections of these ensembles.

Balance for Individual Instruments

A further refinement of the chart in figure 10.1 would show the relative dynamic range of some of the more common instruments in each of the sections of the orchestra, as shown in figure 10.2. (This chart deals with the dynamic range of a single instrument, and you should bear in mind that there are multiple instruments in most of the sections in the band and orchestra. However, it should be pointed out that multiple instruments playing in unison do not increase the perceived loudness of sound as much as you might assume, because they tend to cancel each other out.)

Figure 10. 2

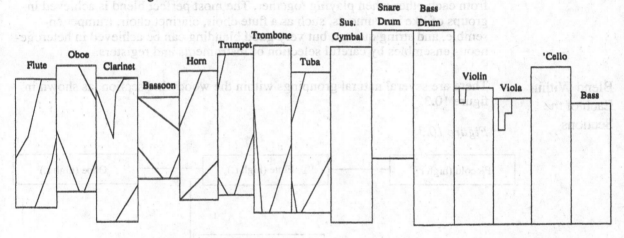

(The complete dynamic range will not be available on every note in an instrument's range, so the dynamic charts in chapters 4–7 have been compressed within the chart for each instrument.)

As you can see, achieving balance can be a difficult task, particularly at the high and low ends of the dynamic range. You can use the information in the charts to form a rough estimate of the likely balance of any instrumental combination, but only by hearing what you write can you refine your judgments. The assignments in the workbook will provide a number of opportunities to begin this process.

The Musical Context and Balance

You should not think of balance and imbalance in positive and negative terms. The musical context dictates whether balance or imbalance is desirable. For example, when an instrument has an important melodic line, we expect it to be somewhat louder than an accompaniment. Also, in harmonic writing, we expect certain chord members to be stronger than others. The "proper" balance for a chord may not be absolute equality of all chord members. The principles of doubling that you learned in four-part writing represent a rough attempt to codify these expectations.

The Performer and Balance	The final responsibility for achieving a proper balance lies with the performer (and the conductor). The experienced musician will sense the desired effect and adjust his or her performance to bring it about. Even questionable balance can be compensated for by professional musicians. However, because younger musicians do not have the skill and musical experience to make the adjustments, the onus is much more on the arranger to write the proper balance into the score. This is another example of the additional challenges that face the arranger when writing for the elementary and junior high school levels.

Blend

Two instruments are said to blend when they can not be clearly distinguished from each other when playing together. The most perfect blend is achieved in groups of like instruments, such as a flute choir, clarinet choir, trumpet ensemble, and string quartet, but very good blending can be achieved in heterogeneous ensembles by careful selection of instruments and registers.

Blend Within Each of the Sections

There are several natural groupings within the woodwind section, as shown in figure 10.3.

Figure 10.3

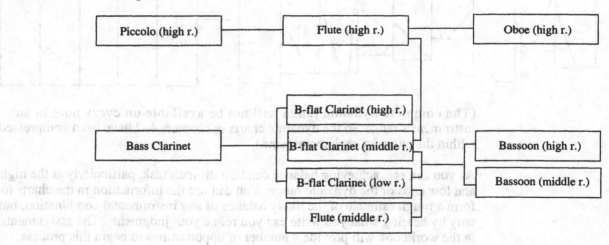

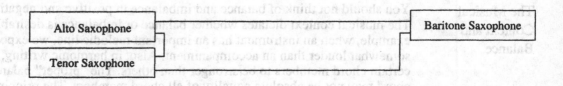

The pairing of the upper-register flute and piccolo in octaves is a natural and brilliant combination, while a pair of flutes and a pair of oboes make a good high-register quartet. Another standard quartet in the woodwind section is a pair of clarinets and a pair of bassoons, with the clarinets in the lower half of their range and the bassoons in the upper half of their range. Another standard quartet in the woodwinds is a pair of alto saxophones, a tenor saxophone, and a baritone saxophone.

Figure 10.4 shows the best groupings within the brass section.

Figure 10.4

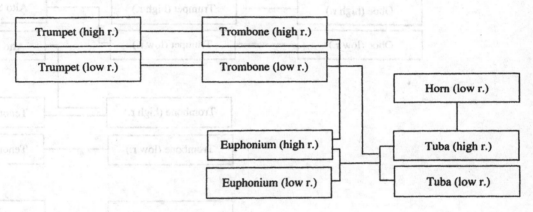

The standard bright brass quartet is a pair of trumpets and a pair of trombones, and octave doubling between a trumpet and trombone is very effective for melodic lines. The euphonium and tuba are a natural octave doubling, and perfect fifths between these two instruments are extremely resonant. The low register of the horn and trombone also combine well with the tuba. The euphonium can be used in the upper register to soften and mellow the sound of the trombone.

The string section is the most unified of all the sections of the orchestra, as shown in figure 10.5.

Figure 10.5

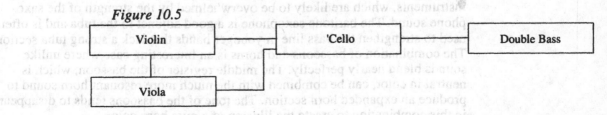

The standard string quartet is a pair of violins, a viola, and a 'cello. The orchestral string section is an expanded version of this quartet, with the addition of the double basses to strengthen the bass. You can be sure that any combination of these forces will blend very well.

Blend Between Sections

We will now consider the affinities in sound among the instruments in different sections, beginning with the woodwind and brass sections (figure 10.6).

Figure 10.6

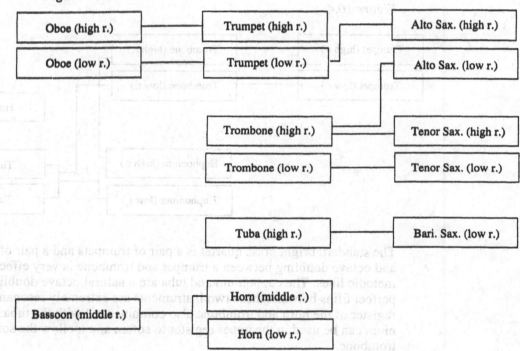

A good blend can be obtained in the combination of oboes and trumpets, particularly in the upper registers. The alto and tenor saxophone combine well with the bright brass and seem more at home there than with the other woodwind instruments, which are likely to be overwhelmed by the strength of the saxophone sound. The baritone saxophone is a good adjunct to the tuba and is often used to strengthen the bass line in younger bands that lack a strong tuba section. The combination of bassoons and horns is an interesting case where unlike sounds blend nearly perfectly. The middle register of the bassoon, which is neutral in color, can be combined with the much more resonant horn sound to produce an expanded horn section. The tone of the bassoons tends to disappear in this combination to create the illusion of a pure horn color.

Figure 10.7 shows some successful combinations involving the woodwinds and the strings.

Figure 10.7

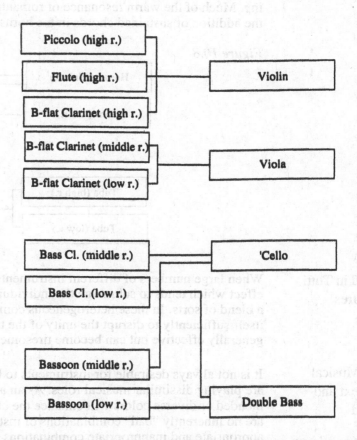

These combinations are largely the result of similarity of range. The addition of a single woodwind instrument doubling each of the string parts was a standard technique in the classical period orchestra, particularly in forte passages. The woodwind instrument adds body to the string sound without standing out in its own right. (In the early classical period, the oboe was used in doubling the violin, but Mozart substituted the clarinets, considering that combination to be superior.)

There are relatively few successful combinations of brass and strings, as shown in figure 10.8, but the combination of horns with the lower strings is outstanding. Much of the warm resonance of romantic period orchestration comes from the addition of sustained chords in the horns to the string texture.

Figure 10.8

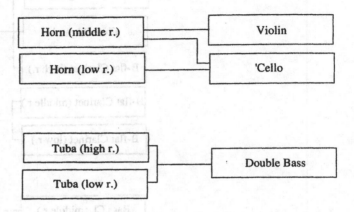

Blend in Tutti Textures

When large numbers of different instruments are combined, there is a leveling effect which tends to submerge the individual color of each instrument, creating a blend of sorts. In these heterogeneous combinations, no instrument can assert itself sufficiently to disrupt the unity of the texture. Such combinations are generally effective but can become tiresome if overused.

The Musical Context and Blend

It is not always desirable for instruments to blend or balance, particularly if they are playing dissimilar musical roles. As an arranger, you must judge whether blended or diverse colors will enhance the clear perception of the music. There are no inherently "bad" combinations of instruments, but there certainly are appropriate and inappropriate combinations for a given musical situation. In chapters 11–14, we will detail the need for balance and blend in the four major texture types.

The Performer and Blend

In this chapter, we have assumed that the sounds of the instruments are invariable; but as Robert Cogan observed in his book, *New Images of Musical Sound* (Cambridge, Mass.: Harvard University Press, 1984), "The sound of an instrument may not be infinitely malleable, but it is significantly malleable . . . ." A part of the performer's role is to modify the normal sound of the instrument to make it fit into the musical texture, and experienced players are remarkably flexible in adapting their instruments to different musical environments. The instrumental combinations we have recommended should produce an acceptable blend without Herculean effort on the part of the performer. This is especially important in writing for younger musicians who may not have the skill or sensitivity to make the adjustments.

Masking

The term *masking* is used by acousticians to describe the capacity of one sound to render another inaudible. This is a serious concern to the arranger, who may inadvertently obscure an important melodic line by masking it. Masking comes about when two sounds are at or near the same pitch or when the dynamic level of a lower-pitched sound is significantly greater than a higher-pitched sound. A typical example of masking occurs when background textures are placed at the same pitch level as melodic lines. In figure 10.9 (on the following page), the melodic line will be masked whenever it shares a note with the accompaniment, rendering it inaudible for the most part. As Holst actually scored this passage, the melody comes through clearly, since the repeated eighth note texture remains above the line (figure 10.10). (CD 3. cut 6) (Notice the partial masking of the top notes of the melody when they double the background eighth note texture. These notes come through due to the strength of the cornet's sound in that register.)

Figure 10.9

Holst: First Suite in E-flat for Military Band, op. 28, no. 1, II (Intermezzo), m. 1-6 (modified).

FIRST SUITE IN E-FLAT FOR MILITARY BAND © Copyright 1921 by Boosey & Co., Ltd.; Copyright Renewed. Reprinted by permission of Boosey & Hawkes, Inc.

Figure 10.10

Holst: First Suite in E-flat for Military Band, op. 28, no. 1, II (Intermezzo), m. 1-6.

FIRST SUITE IN E-FLAT FOR MILITARY BAND © Copyright 1921 by Boosey & Co., Ltd.; Copyright Renewed. Reprinted by permission of Boosey & Hawkes, Inc.

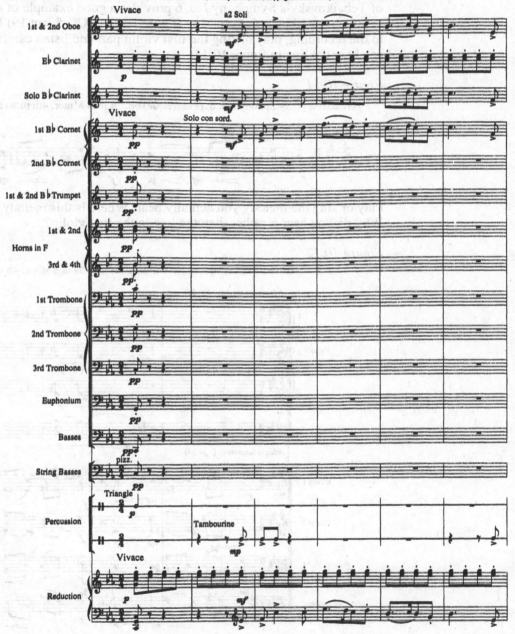

Voice Crossing

The traditional prohibition against crossing voices in four-part textures was motivated partly by considerations of masking and partly as an effort to avoid confusion in melodic connections. The opening phrase of the fourth movement of Tchaikovsky's Symphony No. 6 provides a good example of melodic lines being obscured by voice crossing (figure 10.12). (CD 5, cut 19) Before listening to the recording, play or sing the first violin part and listen carefully to see if you can hear the line in figure 10.11.

Figure 10.11

Tchaikovsky: Symphony No. 6 *(Pathétique)* op. 74 in B Minor, 4th movement, m. 1–4.

Play or sing the melody you actually hear. Where is this melody in the score? Why do you hear it rather than the line in the first violin?

Figure 10.12

Tchaikovsky: Symphony No. 6 (*Pathétique*), op. 74 in B Minor, 4th movement, m. 1–4.

Of course, Tchaikovsky knew what melodic line the listener would hear and presented it much more directly later in the same movement (figure 10.13). Why did he score it with crossing voices at the opening of the work?

Figure 10.13

Tchaikovsky: Symphony No. 6 (*Pathétique*), op. 74 in B Minor, 4th movement, m. 90–94.

You may wonder whether changing the dynamic levels (marking the second violin piano, for example) or changing the instruments involved so there was contrast in color (assigning the second violin part to the clarinet, for example) would allow the first violin line to come through. Experience shows that, while these measures might be partially effective if the texture is restricted to only two lines, they are largely ineffective as soon as other parts (the violas and 'cellos) are added. An inescapable conclusion is that the listener will tend to seek the "path of least resistance" in choosing melodic connections. That includes a preference for smaller over larger melodic intervals and an assumption that the melodic line remains in the same location within the texture (at the top, in this case). As an arranger, you run the risk of obscuring your melodic material every time you allow voice crossing.

Workbook: Assignments A–B, pp. 119–125

Suggestions for Further Study

Most orchestration texts deal with these topics. Among the more useful books are:

Del Mar, Norman. *Anatomy of the Orchestra*. Berkeley, Calif.: University of California Press, 1984.

Hopkins, Antony. *Sounds of Music*. London: J. M. Dent and Sons Ltd.,1982.

Piston, Walter. *Orchestration*. New York: W. W. Norton & Company, Inc., 1955, chapter 26-29, pp. 415–452.

Rimsky-Korsakov, Nicolai. *Principles of Orchestration*. New York: Dover Publications, Inc., 1964, 1922, 1912, chapter 2, p. 36; chapter 3, p. 63.

C Transcription

When music is scored for a medium other than the original, it is said to be *transcribed*. Examples of transcription include: band transcriptions of orchestral works, orchestral transcriptions of keyboard music, and keyboard transcriptions of orchestral works. The term *transcription* is often considered synonymous with *arrangement,* but in this book we will make a distinction: transcription involves rescoring a work with the intention of preserving, as nearly as possible, the original musical effect, while arranging involves the composition of certain elements such as introductions, transitions, and codas. Arranging also involves planning the overall form of the piece.

Transcription involves much more than simply assigning the notes of a score to new instruments. The timbre, range, and register characteristics of instruments differ, and some rewriting will be necessary to accommodate these differences. Many of the assignments in this section involve the transcription of keyboard music for instrumental ensembles, where the differences in character of the two media necessitates some rewriting to preserve the original musical effect.

Creating a Transcription Using Traditional Methods

The process of creating a transcription can be broken down into a logical, step-by-step process:

1. Study the composition to be transcribed. You should make an analysis of the work to understand the nature of the musical materials and how they function together to create the form of the work. Particular attention should be paid to textural analysis. This is also the time to note any writing that is so idiomatic to the original instruments that it may present problems in the transcription.

2. Examine the resources available in the new medium to see if a transcription is possible, given those resources. The range and the number of instruments within given ranges should be considered and compared with the original ensemble. This is the time to anticipate problems and work out solutions, before the actual writing begins.

3. Make a detailed plan of instrument assignments throughout the work. These assignments can be noted lightly in pencil on a photocopy of the original. You should work out all the details of blend and balance in this detailed plan and sketch out any passages that require rewriting on staff paper. The transcription takes shape during this phase of the work.

4. Produce a pencil score. This is largely a matter of transcribing the decisions arrived at in the third step onto score paper, but much polishing also takes place at this time. Unforeseen problems may require that prior decisions be reevaluated. This step is completed when you have written in all the editorial details (such as dynamics, tempo indications, and articulations) and have thoroughly proofread the score.

5. Study the completed score, observing instruments that may be overused or underused. Now is the time to consider the effect of the work as a whole and make any needed adjustments.

6. Copy a set of parts, one for each instrument. Part extraction is time-consuming work and should not be put off until the last minute. Make certain that you allow time for careful proofreading of the parts.

7. Have the work read and rehearsed. During the rehearsal stage you will learn whether your scoring decisions were good, or whether you will need to rewrite any passages that don't sound the way you thought they would. Many of these "rewrites" are simple and can be made directly in the parts, but it is important that you keep careful records and transfer all changes to the score. Many differences between score and parts arise due to carelessness in making corrections during the first rehearsals.

8. Bring your work to fruition with a performance. The excitement and satisfaction of hearing your work played in public is very rewarding, and you can learn how it comes across to an audience. This is the time for evaluation and a time to consider what you have learned that will make your next arrangement even more effective.

**Creating a
Transcription
Using a
Computer**

The personal computer is creating a revolution in the way musicians work, and the following scenario may be more appropriate if you have a computer available.

Steps 1–3 remain the same as in the traditional method preceding.

4. Enter a tentative score on the computer. This may involve entering the notes and rhythms from the computer keyboard (or mouse) or it may involve playing the lines in using a MIDI keyboard. (Programs vary in the methods available for note entry.) You may choose to enter the notes in concert pitch and have the computer transpose them for you, or you may choose to transpose the music as it is entered. Print out a copy of the tentative score and study it carefully to observe instruments that may be overused or underused. Now is the time to consider the effect of the work as a whole, and make any needed adjustments.

5. Edit the score carefully, checking for accuracy of the notation (particularly if automatic transposition has been used) and adding dynamics, tempo indications, and articulations. You may wish to use a printed copy of the score to sketch in editing, since it is easy to get lost when the score is only on-screen.

6. Produce a score and a set of parts using whatever means your notation program provides for part extraction. Do not assume that parts that have been extracted by a computer program are accurate. Allow time for careful proofreading of the parts.

7. Have the work read and rehearsed. During the rehearsal stage, you will learn if your scoring decisions were good, and can rewrite any passage that doesn't sound the way you thought it should. Many of the "rewrites" are simple and can be made directly in the parts; but it is important that all changes are entered into both score and parts on the computer.
8. The performance and evaluation phases are the same as for the traditional methods outlined above.

It is important that you develop an organized approach to transcription. The step-by-step outlines above were created to help you avoid wasted effort that often comes from starting a score without preliminary planning.

11 Scoring Monophonic Textures and Melodic Lines

In monophonic textures, the musical activity is concentrated in a single melodic line, which may be played by one instrument or doubled in a variety of ways. While this texture is relatively rare in ensemble literature and is typically a momentary phenomenon, the principles you will learn in this chapter apply to the scoring of melodic material in any texture type.

Range

In scoring a melodic line, you must first consider which of the available instruments have a range that will allow them to play the line—and, secondly, how the line will sound on each of those instruments. This initial choice of instrument may seem to be rather simple and somewhat mechanical, but it is an artistic decision that should not be taken lightly. As an arranger, you should look at the instruments as a group of beautiful sounds that you can use to color and shade a melodic line in many different ways. This musical equivalent of the "painter's eye for color" is a valuable tool, and you should begin to develop it in the early scoring projects.

The following charts summarize the ranges for elementary, junior high, high school, and college/professional levels for the most common instruments, as presented in chapters 4–7 (figure 11.1). You should have these ranges fairly well in mind at this point, even though you may need to consult the charts from time to time.

Figure 11.1a

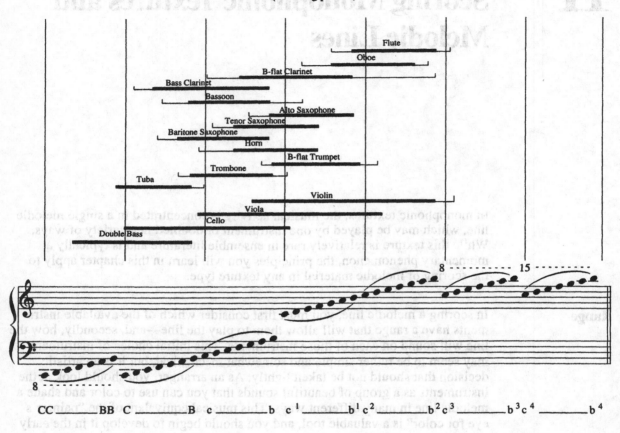

elementary (junior high school) ranges
(sounding pitches)

Figure 11.1b

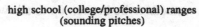

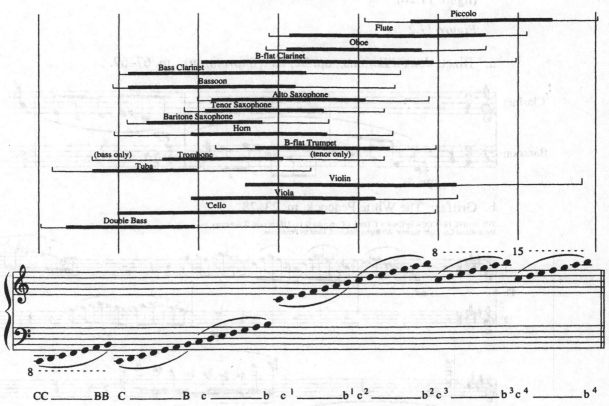

Division of Melodic Lines

When an instrument has been assigned to a melodic line, it will normally play at least one full phrase before the scoring is changed. It is sometimes necessary or desirable, however, to divide a melodic line between two instruments. This normally occurs when a melodic line goes out of the range of one instrument (figure 11.2a) or needs to be broken up to allow a player to rest or breathe (figure 11.2b).

Figure 11.2

a. Bizet: *Jeux d'Enfants,* op. 22, III *(Impromptu),* m. 67–69.

b. Griffes: The White Peacock, m. 23–28.

THE WHITE PEACOCK by Charles T. Griffes. Copyright © 1917 (Renewed) G. Schirmer, Inc. International Copyright Secured. All Rights Reserved. Used by Permission.

Study figure 3.5 on page 39, where Bizet divides a wide-ranging line among all the strings to create a continuous melody that moves from C-sharp to e³ without a significant change of color.

Transcription

The general principles for breaking melodic lines within a phrase are:

1. Each instrument must have logical musical units (motives or sets of motives). Breaking a line in any other way gives the players nonsensical music to perform, and the result will not be satisfactory.
2. The parts should be arranged so that the instruments share a note at the points of division. This covers the break and makes it invisible. There will always be some space at the point of division if this practice is not observed.

Notice how Bizet, Gershwin, and Griffes observed these two standard practices of all good orchestrators in the excerpts in figure 11.2 above and figure 3.5 on page 39.

Doubling

Doubling occurs when more than one instrument is assigned to play a melodic line at the same time. In such cases, the instruments chosen should blend and balance to create the best effect. The advantages of doubling are:

1. The line is stronger in sound.
2. A new color is created.
3. The players are more secure.

The disadvantages of doubling are:

1. The players lose freedom in interpretation when they must play together.
2. Doubling sometimes results in intonation problems.
3. The color of individual instruments is clearer and more vivid than the color of combinations of instruments.

Excessive doubling is to be avoided. In general, there are only three good reasons for doubling:

1. Double for strength.
2. Double for color.
3. Double for security (only when dealing with inexperienced players).

Unison Doubling

Unison doubling works well if the instruments blend perfectly. The wind sections of the band and the string sections of the orchestra are good examples of this kind of unison doubling. The "section sound" requires at least three players in unison to be effective, since there is an averaging of the slight differences in intonation and vibrato that doesn't take place when only two players are in unison. (In fact, the common practice of doubling pairs of instruments in unison is risky with younger players, whose intonation is less reliable.)

Doubling two instruments in unison strengthens the sound somewhat, but it doesn't double the volume. It requires an increase of several times the sound to create the effect of doubling in volume, since there is a logarithmic relationship between amplitude and loudness, and the instruments tend to cancel each other out through phase cancellation. In unison doubling of unlike instruments, it is best to use the recommendations for instruments that blend in chapter 10.

Octave and Multiple-octave Doubling

Octave doubling is stronger in sound than unison doubling, because a new pitch area is excited and the instruments don't mask each other. Again, you should use instruments that blend well together. As additional octaves are added, the weight increases until the air seems permeated with the melody. The effect of multiple-octave doubling in a large ensemble can be overwhelming. If not overused, it is one of the more powerful effects on the orchestrator's palette (figure 11.3).

Figure 11.3

Beethoven: Symphony No. 9 in D Minor, op. 125, I, m. 18–21

Gapped Octave Doubling

Gapped octave doubling occurs when there are two or more octaves between adjacent instruments. Gapped spacing tends to be hollow and rather impersonal. It is generally considered to be a special effect and occurs rarely.

Doubling at Other Intervals

Melodic doubling at various intervals is a standard practice in many styles of music. Even in music of the so-called "common practice period," which placed a premium on contrary motion between parts, melodic doubling in thirds and sixths was regularly practiced. In the late 19th century, Debussy and his followers made frequent use of "planing", the doubling of melody in parallel chords (figure 11.4).

Figure 11.4

Debussy: Prelude to "The Afternoon of a Faun", m. 48–52.

In 20th-century big-band jazz and similar styles, extensive use is made of planing and free parallel doubling of melodic material. In many instances, this melodic doubling provides the entire harmonic texture in the winds (figure 11.5).

Figure 11.5

Nestico: Hay Burner, m. 85–88.
1968 Banos Music. International Copyright Secured.
Reprinted by permission.

Transcription

Examples of Monophonic Scoring

As an example of the process of scoring monophonic textures, we will score the melody shown in figure 11.6 for junior high school wind players.

Figure 11.6

"Greensleeves" (traditional English song)

An examination of the melody shows a range from b to d² with low tessitura centered around the tonic note e¹. Since the key of E minor is not good for junior high school band, we will first transpose the line. The keys of G minor and D minor are available, and we will choose D minor for this illustration. Also, the dotted eighth-sixteenth-eighth rhythmic figure that occurs throughout is rather difficult for young musicians, so we will put the melody in $\frac{3}{4}$ time by dividing each measure into two measures and doubling the note values.

Figure 11.7

"Greensleeves" (traditional English song)

Consulting the range chart for junior high school (figure 11.1), we find that the melody could be played in its entirety by the B-flat clarinet, alto saxophone, and B-flat trumpet. The flute could play the melody an octave higher, and the baritone saxophone and trombone could play it one octave lower.

The clarinet would be playing in the lower middle register for the most part, where the tone is somewhat hazy. This might be an interesting sound for this melody, particularly since the higher notes in the melody would be in the brighter upper register, which might color the climax tones of the melody in an interesting way. The alto saxophone would be playing in the center of its range, where the tone will be penetrating and bright, and the B-flat trumpet would also be in a comfortable range except for the concert b and c1, which have intonation problems. The flute would be in an easy range, as would the baritone saxophone and trombone, except for the trombone's B, which is in seventh position and should be avoided with younger players.

We next consider the shape of the melody and the dynamics we would like to achieve. The melody clearly climaxes at the beginning of the second half of the melody, and that climax is repeated four measure later. We will choose the second climax point as the higher of the two in terms of dynamics. It is here that we will have the maximum density. We will begin the melody quite softly in the clarinets and build in the second phrase toward the climax point. Figure 11.8 (on the following page)shows one possible scoring that follows the plan above. Notice how the division of the third and fourth phrases are handled in the standard way (logical musical units in all instruments and shared tones at the point of division) and how, at the same time, most of the difficulties in the trumpet and trombone are avoided.

Figure 11.8

"Greensleeves" (traditional English song)

Now we will arrange the same melody for a high school orchestra that has pairs of instruments in the winds (flute, oboe, clarinet, bassoon, horn, trumpet, trombone) plus strings. We will transpose the melody to the key of G minor, which will accommodate both the strings and winds. (D minor would also be a good choice.) High school musicians should be able to play the dotted eighth-sixteenth-eighth rhythmic figure, so we will leave the original rhythms intact.

Figure 11.9

"Greensleeves" (traditional English song)

Consulting the high school range chart on page 199, we find that the melody could be played by the flutes, oboes, clarinets, trumpets, and violins at the original pitch and by the flutes and violins an octave higher. The clarinets, horns, trombones, violas, and 'cellos can play the melody an octave lower, and the bassoon and 'cello two octaves lower. The double bass is the only instrument in the ensemble that cannot play the entire melody, and it can play all but the lowest note (D) three octaves lower. A detailed study of the way the melody fits the registers of each of the instruments would follow, but we will omit the details of this study here.

This time we will treat the melody in a different way in terms of dynamic plan. The first phrase will be strong and the second phrase an echo. The third phrase will be the climax point of the piece and the final phrase an echo of this climax. We will concentrate on the string section in the first phrase and the woodwinds in the second. The brass will enter on the final measure of the second phrase to prepare for the major climax of the work in the third phrase. (This also has the advantage that the brass won't have to enter suddenly in the high register.) The final phrase will feature woodwind doubling of the strings. Also note the flourish that has been added to the strings on their entrance just before the third phrase. Such flourishes add greatly to the excitement of a crescendo.

Figure 11.10

"Greensleeves" (traditional English song)

Workbook: Assignments A–C, pp. 127–132.

Suggestions for Further Study

Orchestration books often deal with monophonic texture in sections that refer to scoring individual melodic lines, orchestral unison, or melody. Useful books include:

Burton, Stephen Douglas. *Orchestration.* Englewood Cliffs, N.J.: Prentice Hall, Inc., 1982 chapter 27, p. 338.

Piston, Walter. *Orchestration.* New York: W. W. Norton & Company, Inc., 1955, chapter 19, p. 355.

Rimsky-Korsakov, Nicolai. *Principles of Orchestration.* New York: Dover Publications, Inc., 1964, 1922, 1912, chapter 2, p. 36.

12   Scoring Homorhythmic Textures and Harmony

Homorhythmic textures include situations where all parts are in the same rhythm (figure 12.1a) and where there is some independence of rhythm in the parts (figure 12.1b). A typical homorhythmic texture is in four parts, with a chord for each melody tone, and standard voice leading in the parts. This texture is sometimes referred to as "hymn style" or "part writing."

Figure 12.1

a. "America"

b. Bach: *O Ewigkeit, du Donnerwort* (Oh Eternity, Thou Word of Thunder), BWV 20.

Scoring with No Doubling

Homorhythmic textures sound best when the parts are played by instruments that blend well and where there is a balance among the four parts. Any of the standard quartets described in chapter 10 will produce a good effect, if the parts lie well within the ranges of the instruments. Figure 12.2 shows the first phrase of America (figure 12.1a) scored for a pair of clarinets and a pair of bassoons (or a pair of trumpets and a pair of trombones).

Figure 12.2

A scoring for the saxophone quartet (two alto saxophones, one tenor, and baritone saxophone) is shown in figure 12.3.

Figure 12.3

Figure 12.4 shows the same work scored for strings.

Figure 12.4

"America"

A wider-spaced version of the texture can be obtained by moving the soprano part up one octave, assigning the alto voice (second violin) to the tenor part raised by an octave, and giving the original alto part to the tenor voice (viola), as shown in figure 12.5. This strategy for opening up a texture will generally produce good results when the lines are within the instrument's ranges.

Figure 12.5

"America"

**Doubling in
Homorhythmic
Textures**

Two basic principles for doubling homorhythmic textures are:

1. The original soprano and bass parts must remain the uppermost and lower-most parts in the doubled version. The bass supports the harmony and must remain the lowest part if the harmony is to sound correct. The original melody must be at the top if it is to be clearly heard.

2. Equal doubling should generally be applied to all parts. This is necessary for purposes of balance. You must consider the actual number of players, rather than the number instrumental parts in determining balance. Bear in mind that there are often several players on some of the parts in bands and orchestras.

The principles will always be satisfied when two or more well-scored units are combined, as shown in figure 12.6, which combines the scoring in figure 12.2 with that in figure 12.5. (The addition of the standard double bass doubling of the 'cellos does not upset the balance and provides desirable support of the bass part in full textures.) It is a good strategy to consider large mixed ensemble textures as being combinations of several units, each with a well-balanced scoring.

Figure 12.6
"America"

We will now score the first phrase of "America" for an orchestral woodwind section in pairs (flutes, oboes, clarinets, and bassoons). Not only must you double each of the four parts, but you must carefully consider the registers of the individual instruments in assigning the parts. For this reason, the scoring shown in figure 12.7 will be totally unsatisfactory. Even though there is equal doubling of each part, the fact that the oboes are in their strongest register while the flutes are in their weak lower register results in an imbalance that favors the alto part over the soprano.

Figure 12.7

"America" (unsatisfactory scoring)

Transcription

A much more satisfactory scoring is shown in figure 12.8. This version meets the general requirement for equal doubling, while placing the instruments in good registers where they can balance.

Figure 12.8

"America"

In scoring for the brass section, it is necessary to consider the dynamic level, since two horns are required to balance one of the other brass instruments at *mf* and above. We will score the first phrase of "America" at a *mp* dynamic level for an orchestral brass section consisting of four horns, three trumpets, three trombones and tuba. To accomodate the full ensemble at this dynamic level, we will transpose America to the key of B-flat major. This allows the soprano, alto, and tenor parts to be scored in a moderate register for the three trumpets. Since the number of instruments (eleven) will allow three instruments to double three of the parts, while only two double the fourth, we must choose which part is to be slighted. An inner part is generally chosen, since the outer framework is considered to be the more important. Notice that the melody is doubled an octave lower in this version. This is possible when it will not cross the bass part. Such "inner doubling" of the melody will thicken the texture by filling gaps in the harmony, as you can see in m. 3–5 of this scoring. However, care must be taken to see that inner doubling of the melody doesn't create undesirable dissonances with the tenor line. You should carefully consider whether additional thickening is desirable before employing inner doubling.

Figure 12.9

"America"

* The horns are written on four staves in this example only for purposes of illustration, to simplify labeling the voices to which they are assigned. The horns would be written on two staves, in the usual way, in an actual score.

Transcription

At a *f* dynamic level, the phrase can be scored in the original key (F major). The trumpets will play the soprano, alto, and tenor parts up one octave. At this level, the horns will be reduced to two separate parts by doubling the first and third and the second and fourth horns in unison. Now there are effectively nine separate instrumental parts to be distributed over the four lines in the texture. We will choose to place three of these parts on the melody and two on each of the remaining lines. The effect of this scoring will be massive and brilliant.

Figure 12.10

"America"

* The horns are written out of order (I-III and II-IV) in this example only for purposes of illustration, to simplify labeling the voices to which they are assigned. The horns would be written in the usual way in an actual score.

Using the general principle of combining two well-scored units, a satisfactory scoring for full woodwinds and strings can be made by combining figure 12.5 (with double basses added) and figure 12.8; for brass and strings by combining figure 12.5 (with double basses added) and figure 12.10; and for woodwinds and brass by combining figure 12.8 and figure 12.10. A full orchestral version could be created by combining all three results above. It should be noted, however, that the woodwinds would not make a significant contribution to the orchestral tutti, since they would be in their middle registers for the most part and combined with the brass playing in their upper register. A better distribution of the orchestral forces can be obtained by moving the upper woodwinds into their upper registers, where they can compete with the brass (figure 12.11). This scoring of the woodwind section would probably not stand on its own very well, due to the large gap in the middle of the texture, but it will be very effective in a tutti setting. Notice that only the soprano and alto are carried into the upper register, since close intervals tend to compete with each other in unsatisfactory ways at the high and low extremes of pitch. The first violins have been split into two parts in octaves to support the first flute line.

Figure 12.11
"America"

Figure 12.12 shows the phrase scored for a full band, using strategies similar to those in the examples already presented (complete units in the woodwind and brass sections). The key of B-flat has been chosen for this setting.

Examples from Literature

The Jubilee Overture by Carl Maria von Weber (figure 12.13 on the following page) closes with a grandiose statement of "God Save the King" ("America"). Here the basic homorhythmic texture in the winds is overlaid with florid passagework in the strings. While the part-writing differs in certain details from the version we have been using for our demonstrations, it is worth studying as an example of homorhythmic scoring. (CD 5, cut 31)

Figure 12.12

"America"

Figure 12.13

Weber: Jubilee Overture, m. 356–361.

Transcription

One of the most famous passages in homorhythmic texture is the theme to the final movement of Brahms's Fourth Symphony, as shown in figure 12.14.

Figure 12.14

Brahms: Symphony No. 4, in E Minor, op. 98, IV, m. 1–8.

Workbook: Assignments A–B, pp. 133–135

Suggestions for Further Study

A number of orchestration books deal specifically with homorhythmic texture, although they never refer to it by that name. It may be covered under the topic of scoring of chords, or chorale phrases. Books that have useful information include:

Burton, Stephen Douglas. *Orchestration*. Englewood Cliffs, N.J.: Prentice Hall, Inc., 1982, chapter 28, p. 348.

Kennan, Kent, and Donald Grantham. *The Technique of Orchestration*, 4th edition. Englewood Cliffs, N.J.: Prentice Hall, Inc., 1990, 1983, 1970, 1952, chapter 10, p. 173.

Piston, Walter. *Orchestration*. New York: W. W. Norton & Company, Inc., 1955, chapter 24, p. 396.

Rimsky-Korsakov, Nicolai. *Principles of Orchestration*. New York: Dover Publications, Inc., 1964, 1922, 1912, chapter 3, p. 63.

13 Scoring Polyphonic Textures

Relative Importance of Lines

Polyphonic textures are made up of melodic lines, which may be equal or unequal in importance. If the lines are of equal importance, you should consider them to be primary melodies (PM). If they are unequal, the more-important line is a primary melody, while the less-important line is a secondary melody (SM). You should decide the relative importance of each line before beginning to score in polyphonic texture. (At this point, you may wish to review the section on polyphonic texture in chapter 3, page 40 to clarify your thinking.)

Lines of Equal Importance (PM)

If all lines are primary melodies (PM), they must be able to be heard equally. This requires equal weight on each part. While the requirement for balance among primary melodies should be carefully observed in all polyphonic textures, there is no requirement that the instruments blend. In fact, sharply contrasting colors can enhance the clarity of polyphony, by giving each part a unique color to help the listener follow the line. Figure 13.1 is an example of two primary melodies that are scored with contrasting colors. (CD 3, cut 30)

Figure 13.1

Mendelssohn: Incidental music to A Midsummer Night's Dream, op. 61, V (Intermezzo) m. 37–50.

<table>
<tr><td>Lines of Unequal
Importance (PM
versus SM)</td><td>In textures with both a primary melody and a secondary melody, the primary melody is generally scored more heavily than the secondary melody, as shown in the following excerpt from Hindemith's Symphony in B-flat. (CD 2, cut 27) Again, there is no need to blend colors in such situations because contrasting colors are generally preferred. (Notice in figure 13.2 that the difference in scoring is also emphasized by a difference in dynamic level.)</td></tr>
</table>

Figure 13.2

Hindemith: Symphony in B-flat for Concert Band, III (Fugue), m. 10–14.

<table>
<tr><td>Doubling in
Polyphonic
Textures</td><td>Most doubling in polyphonic textures is at the unison (see figures 13.1 and 13.2). Octave doubling tends to reduce the clarity of the lines, particularly when such doubling results in lines being enclosed or crossed by other lines, as shown</td></tr>
</table>

Scoring Polyphonic Textures 229

in figure 13.3. (See chapter 10, pages 187–192 to review the discussion on masking and crossing of voices.)

Figure 13.3

Bach: Invention no. 6, BWV 777, m. 1–3.

Summary of doubling principles	1. Unison doubling is preferred over octave doubling.
	2. When octave doubling is used, avoid crossing or enclosing melodic lines.
	3. The original soprano and bass parts must remain the upper and lower parts in the doubled version.

Scoring an Example

We will now score an example to demonstrate a step-by-step approach to scoring polyphonic textures. (Refer to page 193 for the general plan for making an arrangement, which will be the basis for the following discussion.) The work is a section of a prelude by Wilhelm Friedemann Bach, one of the sons of J. S. Bach.

Figure 13.4

W. F. Bach: Prelude, m. 1–20.

The work is entirely polyphonic, with a three-part texture in measures 1–9, a two-part texture in measures 9–16, and three-part texture (a transposed and somewhat modified statement of the first four measures) in measures 17–20. The upper line is clearly the PM throughout, with the lower two parts being SM.

Identifying Melodic Motives and Phrases

Since polyphonic textures are made up of melodic lines, it is important that we find the logical ending points in all the lines, so we can give the various instruments melodic material that makes musical sense. The ending points may mark the end of melodic motives or of complete musical phrases. Since the lines in polyphonic textures are relatively independent and may have their own phrase structure, you should play each line alone and determine logical ending points. In figure 13.5, brackets have been used to indicate possible melodic groupings. Play the line and see if you agree with this analysis.

Figure 13.5

W. F. Bach: Prelude, m. 1–20.

The middle line forms one phrase from measure 1 through measure 9, and a second phrase from measure 17 through measure 20 (figure 13.6).

Figure 13.6

W. F. Bach: Prelude, m. 1–20.

The lower line is most difficult to break into phrases, since it consists entirely of continuous eighth-note motion. Figure 13.7 shows a possible phrasing using overlapping phrase endings. Play the line in figure 13.7 and see if you agree with this phrasing.

Figure 13.7

W. F. Bach: Prelude, m. 1–20.

Compare the phrasing of the individual lines and you will see that the lines seldom agree in phrasing. This is typical of polyphonic music.

Examining the Resources in the New Medium

We will score this excerpt for a small classical orchestra consisting of two flutes, two oboes, two bassoons, and strings. This approximates the orchestra that would have existed at the time of W. F. Bach. Following the conventional practice of the day, the transcription will be centered on the strings, with the winds providing doubling to fill out the texture. This will be the only attempt to observe the orchestration norms of the period—in other ways, the score will be modern in style. This ensemble should provide ample resources for scoring a two- and three-part texture.

An examination of the ranges of the lines in the prelude versus the ranges of the instruments in the orchestra reveals a few potential problems. The line beginning in measure 6 and closing in measure 10 (see figure 13.8) is quite extensive in range. The viola is only instrument in the orchestra capable of playing the entire line comfortably. Once this line is assigned to the viola the remaining lines in measures 6–10 must be assigned to other instruments. Fortunately, the tenor line falls just within the range of the violin and will be played by the second violins, leaving the lower line to the 'cellos (with possible bass doubling).

Figure 13.8

W. F. Bach: Prelude, m. 7–10.

A second problem may arise in situations where tutti ensemble is needed, and there are only two or three widely spaced lines from which to choose. The final four measures of the excerpt are an example of this potential problem. Octave doubling of a line may be necessary here, but the lines must be kept from crossing each other.

Making a Detailed Plan of the Transcription

In planning the transcription, first note that the opening and closing sections are in three-part texture, while the middle of the work is in two-part texture. This is a clear indication that the composer wanted the outer sections to be heavier than the middle section. This will be indicated in the scoring by using the winds only in the outer sections. Also note that the total range of the texture in the final section is greater by one octave than the range of the opening section. This is accomplished by transposing the bass line down by a fourth, while the upper two parts are transposed up by a fifth. (This creates the gap described above.) This is a clear indication that the final section is to be scored more heavily than the first section. A tutti texture for the final section will be used and a slightly smaller ensemble at the opening. Additional weight at the end could also be created by increasing the dynamic levels, or by employing octave doubling.

The section from measure 12 through measure 16 is characterized by shorter melodic motives than the other sections. This will be emphasized by changing the instrumentation for each of these motives to create an antiphonal effect. Figure 13.9 shows the original score marked up with these basic decisions about instrumentation. The final transcription will be worked out along the lines of this plan.

Figure 13.9
W. F. Bach: Prelude, m. 1–20.

Production of the Score

The next task will be the production of the score. In your transcriptions, this may be a pencil score, if you are working by hand, or a score that looks much like the following, if you are working on a computer. You will need to produce a set of parts and have the work read to check your decisions. Figure 13.10 shows the final score.

Figure 13.10

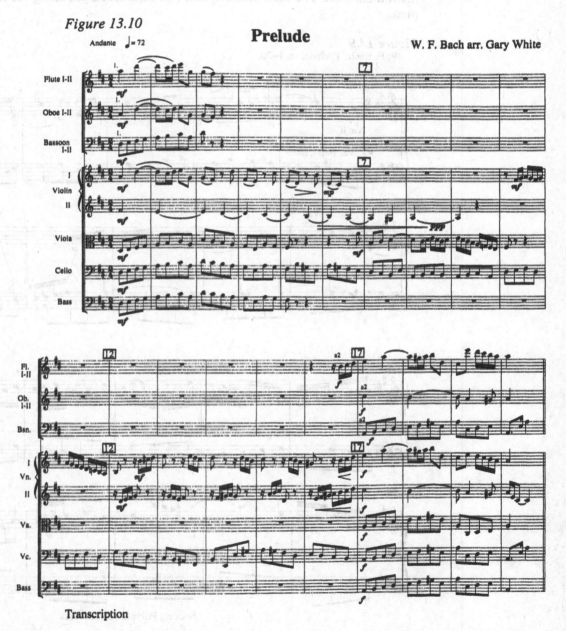

Prelude

W. F. Bach arr. Gary White

Transcription

In the first three measures, single woodwind instruments are used to double the strings. This saves the full wind section for the tutti texture at the end of the piece. This section is marked *mf* and the final section *f* to enhance the contrast. The middle section of the work is scored exactly as the plan in figure 13.9 indicated, but the last five measures need some discussion. The plan indicated in measure 16 that the texture should "build to full." This was accomplished by adding to the doubling at the end of the measure. This effect is underlined with a crescendo to *f* in measure 17. In the final four measures, the woodwinds double all three lines. Also in measures 17–18, the violas are added as an octave doubling of the bass line, which helps to fill the rather large gap in the original texture. However, the violas are in danger of crossing the middle line in measure 19, so they are moved back to unison doubling. Octave doubling returns in the final measure. Notice that in each case the shift in doubling occurs where there are fourths or fifths in the line. This makes the shift nearly invisible, because the line has a leap anyway. In the final measure, the oboes remain on A, since the fall to C-sharp would take the oboes into the extremes of their lower range. The violas and basses also remain on A to avoid overemphasizing the bass figure at the end.

Summary

This chapter has presented a step-by-step process for scoring compositions in polyphonic texture. Briefly, the process is:

1. Do a textural analysis of the work, concentrating on the relative importance of each line. Assign PM to all parts, if they are equal in importance, or PM and SM, if they are unequal in importance.

2. Look at each line separately and determine the phrasing and motific structure. This process divides each line into logical musical units. Don't overlook the possibility that there is an overlap (elision) of motives or phrases, where the last note of one group is also the first note of the next.

3. Examine the resources in the new medium to see if there are sufficient resources for the transcription. Try to anticipate problems in range or other technical difficulties you are likely to encounter.

4. Make a detailed plan of the transcription. This can be shown in pencil on the score itself. Specific instrument assignments are more important in lighter sections than in tutti sections, but it's good to have a general plan, even for the heavier sections of the score.

5. Produce the score. At this point it, becomes important to provide careful editing, showing all dynamic levels and articulations. Don't forget the heading material, instrumentation, and tempo markings. Add rehearsal numbers at logical points in the work, so the conductor will have convenient places to start while rehearsing the work.

6. Make a set of parts and have the work read. Make any final changes in the score and parts to correct deficiencies that were noticed in the reading.

Workbook: Assignments A–B, pp. 137–141.

Suggestions for Further Study

Most orchestration books deal with polyphonic texture, sometimes referring to it as contrapuntal texture. Books that have useful information include:

Adler, Samuel. *The Study of Orchestration*, 2nd edition. New York: W. W. Norton & Company, 1989, 1982, chapter 15, p. 459.

Kennan, Kent, and Donald Grantham. *The Technique of Orchestration*, 4th edition. Englewood Cliffs, N.J.: Prentice Hall, Inc., 1990, 1983, 1970, 1952, chapter 16, p. 291.

Piston, Walter. *Orchestration*. New York: W. W. Norton & Company, Inc., 1955, chapter 23, p. 388.

14 Scoring Homophonic Textures: *Melody and Accompaniment*

As you learned in chapter 3, homophonic texture consists of one or more melodies and an accompaniment that provides both harmonic and rhythmic support. Homophonic texture became the predominant texture in the classical period (1750–1825) and has remained the most common texture in later periods.

Balance and Blend in Homophonic Textures

Homophonic textures may involve all of the basic textural elements (PM, SM, PSM, SS, HS, RS, and HRS), and the requirements for balance and blend among these elements is quite complex. (Review chapter 3, if the textural elements are not clear to you.) General principles for balance and blend among the textural elements are:

1. Primary melodies (PM) are usually scored so they will stand out from the accompaniment elements, because they typically are scored more heavily and in contrasting colors. If the colors are similar, the contrast is often accomplished by indicating higher dynamics for the PM than the accompaniment elements. A general rule of thumb is that the dynamic level of PMs should be two levels higher than the accompaniment. (If the accompaniment is marked *p*, the melody should be at least *mf*.)

2. Secondary melodies (SM) are scored more lightly than PMs, but slightly more heavily than the other accompaniment elements. There is no preference for blend between PM and SM, and they may be in contrasting or similar colors.

3. Parallel supporting melodies (PSM) are usually scored to blend with the melody they support (either PM or SM). They generally balance with this melody.

4. Static support (SS) is a background element and should be kept considerably below the level of the PM and SM. SS is typically an element of the accompaniment and should blend and balance with other accompaniment elements.

5. Harmonic support (HS) is a part of the accompaniment and should be kept below the level of melodic materials. If there are several instruments playing the HS role, they should balance and blend with each other.

6. Rhythmic support (RS) is a part of the accompaniment and should be kept below the level of melodic materials. There is no preference for blend between RS elements and other elements of the texture, and various RS elements need not blend with each other.

7. Harmonic and rhythmic support (HRS) is a combination of the above two elements in the same instrument or textural element. HRS elements should be kept below the level of melodic materials but should balance and blend with each other. HRS elements are often separated into HS and RS elements, when piano accompaniments are transcribed for instrumental ensembles.

This brief summary of the balance and blend requirements for various textural elements will serve as a reference as you begin scoring homophonic textures. You will see these principles at work in the examples that follow.

An Example of Homophonic Texture

The first example is the opening phrase of Mendelssohn's Songs Without Words, op. 19, no. 2 (figure 14.1), which will be transcribed for a small orchestra.

Figure 14.1

Mendelssohn: Songs Without Words, op. 19, no. 2, m. 1–5.

<table>
<tr><td>Separating the
Textural
Elements</td><td>The first step in rewriting homophonic textures is an analytical process that separates the various textural elements. To illustrate this process, we will dissect the Mendelssohn example in a step-by-step manner and then score it. Once you are more familiar with rewriting accompaniment patterns, it will not be necessary to write out all of the steps of the process, but at first it may prove helpful to do so.</td></tr>
<tr><td>Primary Melody</td><td>The first step of the process is to separate the primary melody from the rest of the texture (figure 14.2).</td></tr>
</table>

Figure 14.2

Mendelssohn: Songs Without Words, op. 19, no. 2, m. 1–5.

<table>
<tr><td>Secondary Melody
and Parallel
Supporting Melody</td><td>Identify and separate any secondary melodic material (SM or PSM) from the texture. In this example, a PSM is embedded within the accompaniment texture (figure 14.3).</td></tr>
</table>

Figure 14.3

Mendelssohn: Songs Without Words, op. 19, no. 2, m. 1–5.

Static Support   Identify and separate any static supporting parts (SS). In this example, the bass is clearly a static supporting part, with some notes in the inner part of the accompaniment providing octave doubling (figure 14.4).

Figure 14.4

Mendelssohn: Songs Without Words, op. 19, no. 2, m. 1–5.

Harmonic Support   Identify and separate any harmonic supporting parts (HS) from the texture. In this phrase, a HS part appears in the lower treble clef. The implied chords in the accompaniment have been added in figure 14.5.

Figure 14.5

Mendelssohn: Songs Without Words, op. 19, no. 2, m. 1–5.

Rhythmic Support All that remains is the rhythmic support (RS), which is a continuous sixteenth-note figure. It is important that you take note of the general contour of the material supplying the rhythmic support. Common patterns are rising figures, descending figures, and oscillating figures. In this case, the RS part is an oscillating figure (figure 14.6).

Figure 14.6

Notice that the HRS elements of the original texture have been separated into harmonic and rhythmic elements in this analysis. The separation of these elements is a very important step in the process of creating instrumental accompaniment textures from piano accompaniments, since they will often be assigned to different instruments in the transcription.

Examining the Resources in the New Medium

This phrase will be transcribed for a small orchestra with the following instrumentation: two flutes, two oboes, two clarinets, two bassoons, and strings. This medium should be ample for this example, and an examination of the various textural elements reveal no serious problems that need to be addressed at this time.

Creating a Detailed Plan of Instrument Assignments

The PM and PSM should blend with each other and contrast with the accompaniment. Two clarinets have been chosen for this purpose (figure 14.7).

Figure 14.7

Harmonic Support, Static Support, and Rhythmic Support

The supporting parts will need to be fairly light so as not to overbalance the clarinets. The strings will be chosen for this supporting role, since they will provide both the color contrast and delicacy needed for this accompaniment. The general character of the original HRS needs to be preserved. The sixteenth-note figures in measures 1 and 2 may be preserved intact, but the wider range of the figures in measures 3 through 5 will need to be adjusted to keep them from becoming too prominent in the texture. (The listener's attention will tend to be drawn to instruments playing material with lots of wide leaps.) The modified version of the sixteenth-note figure shown in figure 14.8 is more compact, yet preserves the character of the original. This is a good example of the kind of rewriting that is often necessary in transcribing homophonic textures.

Figure 14.8

The SS element will form a steady bass line, while the remaining HS element (the lower line in the treble clef of the original) will be the upper line in the accompaniment. The sixteenth-note figure shown in figure 14.8, along with the elements just described, will be sufficient accompaniment for the clarinets. Figure 14.9 shows the completed score. Notice that the dynamics assigned to the string parts are two degrees below those of the melodic materials, reflecting the desired balance between these elements. Also notice that articulations and bowings have been carefully considered for all instruments. While they maintain the general spirit of the orignal, they are not precisely the same. The original slurs and ties were general indications of phrasing while the articulations and bowings in the transcription are a much more detailed indication of the articulation of each instrument.

Figure 14.9

Mendelssohn: Songs Without Words, op. 19, no. 2, m. 1–5.

Transcribing Piano Accompaniment Patterns

Piano accompaniment textures frequently require fairly extensive rewriting when transcribed for band and orchestra instruments. The piano creates considerable resonance through the sympathetic vibration of many strings when a single string is sounded. This effect is considerably enhanced when the damper pedal is depressed, and composers take advantage of this resonance in writing accompaniment textures. As many people have observed, the band and orchestra "have no pedal." The sustaining effect of the piano's resonance must be created in other ways. Also, many figures that are idiomatic to the piano are very difficult or impossible for other instruments (which may have their own idiomatic figures that are difficult or impossible on the piano). To gain an understanding of the changes necessary when transcribing piano accompaniment textures, we will examine a number of examples from works that were written first for piano and later transcribed by the composer for orchestra. These examples have been chosen from Bizet's *Jeux d'Enfants* and Ravel's *Pavane pour une infante défunte.* Figure 14.10 shows the opening passage from the Galop from *Jeux d'Enfants*. (CD 1, cut 26) The original four-hand version is shown below the orchestral score.

Figure 14.10

Bizet: *Jeux d'Enfants,* op. 22, V (Galop), m. 1–4.

While the PM and bass line (SM) have been reproduced exactly, the after-beat figures in the center of the texture have been altered to continuous eighth notes in the orchestral version. This change fills out the harmonic background and is much easier for the middle strings than a series of after-beats. The resonance of the piano is simulated by the continuous chords. An idiomatic pattern for piano that would be difficult for the strings is altered to be more idiomatic for strings. (Also note that these string figures would be nearly impossible on the piano.)

Later in the same work, the passage shown in figure 14.11 occurs. (CD 1, cut 29)

Figure 14.11

Bizet: *Jeux d'Enfants*, op. 22, V (Galop), m. 73–78.

In this passage, the PM in the bass is reproduced exactly, while the broken octave figures in the accompaniment are scored as repeated-note figures in the violins. Notice that both octaves are represented in the transcription (first violins on upper octave, second violins on lower octave). In addition, the winds are added on sustained notes to simulate the resonance that will build up in the piano. In measure 75, a SM is reproduced exactly in the violas and bassoons.

A more elaborate example of rewriting accompaniment textures is the opening measures from Ravel's *Pavane pour une infante défunte*, shown in figure 14.12. (CD 4, cut 16)

Here again, the PM is reproduced exactly in the first horn, while the rather spare accompaniment in the original is considerably fleshed out in the rest of the orchestra. The SM in the bass is divided between 'cellos and basses but is reproduced exactly. The inner eighth-note figures have been rewritten as parallel thirds in the second violins and violas. The staccato character of these elements is reproduced by asking the strings to play pizzicato. To create the effect of the ongoing resonance of the piano, Ravel has created a three-part harmonic progression out of the pitches in the accompaniment and placed it in the bassoons and second horn. This is an excellent example of the separation of HS and RS elements in a texture that was originally HRS. The creation of sustained HS from HRS elements is an important part of the technique of transcription of accompaniment textures.

Later in the same work, the accompaniment becomes much more active with broken chord patterns, arpeggiated chords, and a clear indication of pedaling to sustain the lower elements of the texture and build additional resonance (figure 14.13 on page 250). (CD 4, cut 19)

Figure 14.12

Ravel: *Pavane pour une infante défunte,* m. 1–6.

Figure 14.13

Ravel: *Pavane pour une infante défunte,* m. 60–61.

Transcription

Here Ravel uses the harp to provide the ongoing sixteenth-note motion. Notice that the harp patterns are similar to, but not exactly the same as, the piano patterns. Ravel has rewritten the part to be more idiomatic for the harp and to pick up the bass line and some of the chords on the second and fourth beats. The left-hand chords in the piano version become a pizzicato figure in the 'cellos, and the effect of the pedal is expressed in a separate HS part in the bassoons, horns, violas, and basses.

A final example from the Ravel is a passage very near the end of the work (figure 14.14). Ravel has completely changed the effect of the end of the work in the orchestral version—substituting a decrescendo for the fortissimo close of the piano version. (CD 4, cut 20)

Figure 14.14
Ravel: *Pavane pour une infante défunte*, m. 66–72.

Notice that the arpeggio in the piano version becomes a glissando in the harp in the orchestration, and the broken-octave thirds in the inner parts of measure 67 become a new rhythmic figure in the flutes and clarinets in the orchestral version. Again we see sustained harmony in bassoons to provide support for the bass line in measures 67 and 68. The arpeggiated figures on the third beat of measure 70 and the first beat of measure 71 become harp chords in the orchestral version. Finally, a touch of orchestral color substitutes for the chord in the last measure (harmonics in harp, first violin, and viola).

The foregoing examples demonstrate the careful rewriting techniques you will need to learn to transcribe keyboard music for instrumental ensembles. Notice in each case that while the composer has changed the external appearance of the accompaniment significantly, he has made every effort to maintain the character of the original accompaniment. You will need to develop your creative imagination to accomplish this task.

Other Common Piano Figurations

The following examples do not exhaust the possible accompaniment patterns, but they will assist you in arriving at good transcriptions of piano textures. You can find the pattern that most nearly approximates the texture you are transcribing and make necessary adjustments. Instrumentation has not been specified in these examples, and you may need to make adjustments to create idiomatic figures for the instruments involved.

Broken Octaves (or Other Intervals)

Broken-interval figurations are usually transcribed as repeated notes (figure 14.15).

Figure 14.15

becomes

The continuous sixteenth-note motion has been moved into the higher octave and divided between two instruments. This will avoid excessive fatigue for any one player and gives each a sensible melodic/rhythmic motive to play. The lower octave becomes quarter notes to express the continuing resonance of the piano.

Arpeggiated Chords

Arpeggiated chords often draw attention away from melodies and provide no sustained harmony when played by orchestral or band instruments (figure 14.16).

Figure 14.16

The range of the continuous sixteenth-note motion has been limited, and a sustained harmonic background (HS) has been provided.

If the Alberti bass lies low in the piano range, it will become necessary to lift the moving parts into the middle register and provide sustained harmony in the original register (figure 14.17).

Figure 14.17

Rolling arpeggios are particularly challenging to transcribe successfully. It is important to move most of the motion into the middle register, while maintaining a sense of the repeating arpeggios (figure 14.18).

Figure 14.18

Widely spaced arpeggios must be confined to smaller ranges with widely spaced sustained harmony to express the resonance developed by these figures (figure 14.19).

Figure 14.19

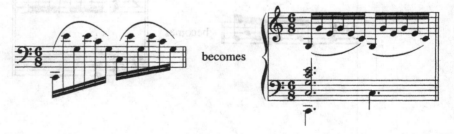

Alternating Bass and Chords

Another common pattern is alternating bass notes with chords. This pattern is adopted in keyboard music to create a separation of the bass from the inner harmony, while freeing the right hand to play the melody. The bass voice is a SM and must be treated as such, and the inner harmony parts must be made into figures that make musical sense. The common "waltz bass" is shown in figure 14.20.

Figure 14.20

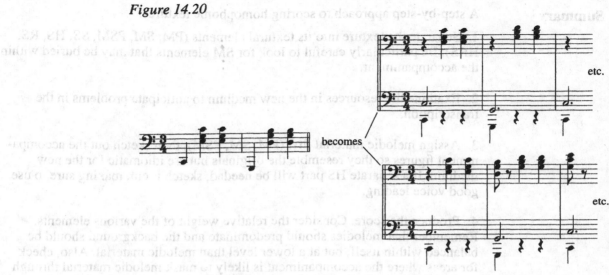

The short notes in the lower register reproduce the original effect of the pattern, and a sustained bass an octave above expresses the resonance of the piano. The after-beat figures have been turned into three-note motives in the lower example. These are more grateful to play than pure after-beats. These added chords also have the advantage of providing continuous HS, which may be needed in such accompaniments.

Rapid alternation of bass with chords creates nearly impossible chordal backgrounds if transcribed directly. It is important in such cases to make the inner repeated-note figures more continuous (figure 14.21).

Figure 14.21

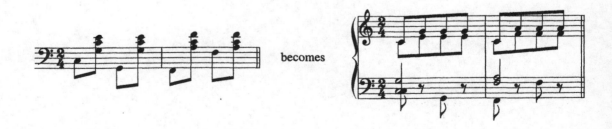

Summary

A step-by-step approach to scoring homophonic textures:

1. Separate the texture into its textural elements (PM, SM, PSM, SS, HS, RS, HRS). Be particularly careful to look for SM elements that may be buried within the accompaniment.

2. Examine the resources in the new medium to anticipate problems in the transcription.

3. Assign melodic material first (PM, SM, PSM), then sketch out the accompaniment figures so they resemble the originals but are idiomatic for the new medium. If a separate HS part will be needed, sketch it out, making sure to use good voice leading.

4. Produce the score. Consider the relative weight of the various elements. Remember that melodies should predominate and the background should be balanced within itself, but at a lower level than melodic material. Also, check for areas where the accompaniment is likely to mask melodic material through crossing or overlap. Rewrite as needed.

5. Consider the overall effect of the score. Is there a good balance between thick and thin textures? Are all instruments used effectively, and are any instruments slighted? Rewrite as needed.

6. Edit the score to include dynamics and articulations for each instrumental line.

7. Produce parts and have the work read. Make final adjustments based on what you hear in the reading.

Workbook: Assignments A–B, pp. 142–150.

Suggestions for Further Study

Most orchestration books deal with homophonic texture, sometimes referring to it as melody and accompaniment. Books that have useful information include:

Adler, Samuel. *The Study of Orchestration*, 2nd ed. New York: W. W. Norton & Company, 1989, 1982, chapter 15, p. 459.

Burton, Stephen Douglas. *Orchestration*. Englewood Cliffs, N.J.: Prentice Hall, Inc., 1982, chapter 28, p. 348.

Kennan, Kent, and Donald Grantham. *The Technique of Orchestration*, 4th edition. Englewood Cliffs, N.J.: Prentice Hall, Inc., 1990, 1983, 1970, 1952. chapter 16, p. 291.

Piston, Walter. *Orchestration*. New York: W. W. Norton & Company, Inc., 1955, chapter 20, p. 364.

Rimsky-Korsakov, Nicolai. *Principles of Orchestration*. New York: Dover Publications, Inc., 1964, 1922, 1912, chapter 2, p. 36 (melody only).

D Arranging

As stated in the introduction to part C, this book makes a distinction between transcription and arranging. In transcription the goal is to preserve, as nearly as possible, the original musical effect. Arranging involves the composition of certain elements, such as introductions, transitions, and codas, as well as planning the overall form of a piece. You may ask what might motivate an arranger to interject his or her own musical personality into music that another has created. If arrangers are simply trying to place their personal stamp on a piece of music (perhaps at the expense of the original musical material), then arranging is a disreputable art and deserves the contempt some musicians feel for it. There are, however, a number of good reasons for making an arrangement, including:

1. Making a shorter version of a longer work for a particular musical purpose.

2. Simplifying a work so it can be performed by younger or less-experienced musicians.

3. Making a complete work out of fragmentary or incomplete musical materials.

4. Combining elements of several different works into a unified single composition.

In such situations, arranging can be a valid technique and worthy of your serious consideration.

This part will deal with several specific arranging skills, including:

1. Creating accompaniment textures (chapter 15). This skill is often needed if the original material includes no accompaniment, or if the accompaniment is too complex for less-experienced musicians.

2. Writing introductions, transitions, and codas (chapter 16). Arrangers must often construct these "framing" and connecting sections to link up diverse musical materials and create a unified composition.

3. Creating a tonal plan of an arrangement (chapter 17). A well-conceived tonal plan gives an arrangement coherence and direction.

Matters of Musical Style

Since arranging is a form of composing, the arranger inevitably leaves a personal stylistic mark on the final product. Most texts on arranging are highly personal documents that detail the author's stylistic preferences and favorite "tricks" and devices. This book will attempt to present a more general approach—leaving matters of style to be developed by you as you become more skilled as an arranger. Chapters 15 through 17 use a tonal and harmonic idiom that is relatively free from personal taste. This idiom is the major-minor tonal system, employing diatonic triads, seventh chords, simple modulation to nearly related keys, secondary dominants, and standard "common practice" voice leading. In short, the tonal material will be that of the first year of undergraduate music theory. After you have become skilled in the techniques presented here, you are encouraged to extend the principles to more-advanced harmonic systems, scales other than major and minor, and later styles of voice leading. Chapter 18 will present one of the author's own published arrangements. This example will, of course, be in a more personal style. In chapters 19 and 20, which deal with jazz and marching band, the style of the musical examples will be appropriate to the jazz and commercial music idioms that these ensembles normally employ.

A Final Word

If you doubt that you have the creative ability to be an arranger, you may be surprised to find that the following chapters are rather straightforward—not requiring creative genius to complete. If, on the other hand, you feel your own creative juices flowing, you shouldn't find the materials overly restrictive. In either case, you will be able to improve your arranging skills and feel the satisfaction of having a product of your own creative imagination come to life in performance.

15 Creating Accompaniment Textures

The Musical Functions of an Accompaniment

The primary function of accompaniment textures is to provide harmonic and rhythmic support for a melody. An accompaniment must perform its work unobtrusively for the most part. Because the melody should be the center of the listener's attention, the accompaniment should not call attention to itself as a general rule. On the other hand, if the accompaniment is bland and boring, it decreases the musical interest of the entire texture. Learning to provide an accompaniment with sufficient musical interest, while not overshadowing the melody, will be the principal goal in this chapter.

A Polish folk song will be set in homophonic texture to illustrate the process of creating an accompaniment (figure 15.1).

Figure 15.1

Polish Folk Song

The technique of harmonizing a melody is beyond the scope of this book. If you need help with harmonization and voice leading, consult any book on the subject. (The author's *The Harmonic Dimension* or Benward and White, *Music in Theory and Practice*, both published by Wm. C. Brown, are two examples). Here is a summary of important considerations:

1. Clear cadences at phrase endings. It is best to identify phrase endings and establish the cadence type of each cadence before proceeding with harmonization.

2. Strong harmonic progressions that give a feeling of forward motion toward the cadences. Circle progressions (chord progressions with root motion in falling fifths) are generally the strongest progressions in tonal music and should predominate.

3. A consistent harmonic rhythm. Once established, a consistent pattern (every quarter note, one chord per measure, or another pattern) gives a feeling of predictability to the harmonization, which allows it to fall into the background of the listener's attention. The rhythm of harmonic change generally underlines the meter, which means that chords often change at the bar lines.

4. A good bass line. Remember that inverting a chord will often produce a better bass line, but constant inversions tend to weaken the harmonization.

Now we return to the Polish folk song (figure 15.1). This melody is in four-bar phrases, a total of four phrases in all. The first and third phrases conclude with half cadences, while the second and fourth phrases imply authentic cadences. The harmonic rhythm of one chord per measure seems appropriate, since the melody often outlines chords within the measure. The harmonic implications of the melody are quite clear, and it could be harmonized with nothing but the tonic and dominant seventh chords (figure 15.2).

Figure 15.2

Polish Folk Song

This harmonization, while quite simple, would provide the necessary harmonic support for the melody. It has a consistent harmonic rhythm, which underlines the meter and strong circle progressions throughout. To avoid the risk of monotony in a two-chord harmonization you might choose to substitute the subdominant seventh chord for the tonic in two locations (figure 15.3). The accompaniment texture will be developed using this harmonization.

Figure 15.3

Polish Folk Song

Rhythmic Support

The rhythmic support function in homophonic texture nearly always requires a rhythm that differs from that of the melody. The basic idea of rhythmic independence or *rhythmic counterpoint* is that the rhythm of the accompaniment should move when the melody is holding a note. You should first establish the basic rate of flow for the rhythm of the accompaniment. This could be the quarter note, as shown in figure 15.4, which could establish the standard waltz bass style of accompaniment.

Figure 15.4

To give the accompaniment a more distinctive rhythmic support you could choose an eighth-note rate of flow for this texture. The first step in creating a unique rhythmic motive for the accompaniment is to fill in the missing eighth notes in the melody to create a continuous eighth-note flow (figure 15.5).

Figure 15.5
Polish Folk Song

The goal is to establish a rhythmic motive that can be repeated in most measures and will fill out the missing eighth notes in the melody. Observing figure 15.5 you can see that activity is never needed on the first beat of the measure and seldom needed on the final eighth note. This suggests that the rhythmic motive in figure 15.6 can be used in most measures to create an eighth-note flow. This motive will form a good rhythmic counterpoint with the rhythms of the melody in most measures and can easily be modified to provide some variety and to fill out the final eighth notes in measures 4, 8, 12, and 16.

Figure 15.6

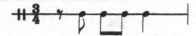

If the arrangement was for inexperienced musicians, you might choose to use this motive in most measures of the accompaniment. The motive is easily played and makes good musical sense. For more experienced musicians, you might want to give the motive a more distinctive character. One way of doing this, which would also give the accompaniment a sense of unity with the melody, is to incorporate some of the rhythms of the melody into the motive. Observe that the dotted eighth and sixteenth pattern is used in measure 10, and dotted quarter and eighth figures occur in most measures. Using these cues, you might modify the motive as shown in figure 15.7.

Figure 15.7

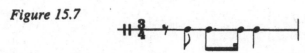

This motive will prepare the listener for the rhythm in measure 10 and give the musicians playing the accompaniment a more interesting figure to perform. This motive will be used as the basis for an accompaniment (figure 15.8). Remember that the inner parts of the accompaniment texture must never cross the melody, so consider the total range of the melody in choosing a position for the inner harmony.

Figure 15.8

Polish Folk Song

As stated at the beginning of the chapter, the bass is often a SM. The bass part of the previous accompaniment (figure 15.8) consists only of the roots of the chords and has only minimal melodic interest. By adding nonharmonic tones and using two inversions you could create a bass that is a true SM (figure 15.9). Notice that a few changes have been made in the inner parts and a tonic chord in first inversion is substituted for the subdominant seventh chord in measure 11 to accommodate the new bass part.

Figure 15.9

Polish Folk Song

**Rhythmic
Density of
Accompaniment
Textures**

Accompaniments in homophonic textures vary in rhythmic activity, from rather sparse, discontinuous textures, as shown in figure 15.10 (CD 4, cut 23), to continuous rhythmic activity, as shown in figure 15.11 on page 268. (CD 3, cut 11) The accompaniment in figure 15.9 was of average density. Variations in accompaniment style can be used to underline important formal divisions in an arrangement, if you maintain consistent activity within sections. Consider variation in rhythmic density as one way you can create variety and interest in your accompaniments.

Figure 15.10

Tchaikovsky: *Capriccio Italien,* op. 45, m. 19–23.

Figure 15.11

Holst: First Suite in E-flat for Military Band, op. 28, no. 1, II (Intermezzo), m. 123–127.

Arranging

Summary

This chapter has presented a step-by-step process for creating an accompaniment. You could go through the same logical process and arrive at a totally different texture that would satisfy the purposes of accompaniment—to provide both harmonic and rhythmic support in a musically satisfying setting. Briefly, the steps for creating accompaniments are:

1. Harmonize the melody if no harmonization exists. Consider phrase endings, cadences, harmonic rhythm, strong chord progressions, and bass line in creating a harmonization.

2. Establish a basic rate of flow for the texture and fill in gaps in the melody to create continuous motion.

3. Examine the patterns formed in step 2 with the goal of establishing a rhythmic motive that will fill most of the gaps in the melody.

4. Consider giving the rhythmic motive in step 3 a more distinctive character by using rhythmic patterns found in the melody itself.

5. Sketch in an accompaniment using the motive in step 4 and the chords in step 1. Remember to keep the inner harmony below the melody.

6. Consider opportunities for secondary melody. SM most often occurs in the bass, but other voices might be involved. Phrase endings are often good times for SMs, since the melody may stop momentarily at these points.

7. Modify the accompaniment to accommodate any SM you create.

Workbook: Assignments A–B, pp. 151–152

Suggestions for Further Study

Some orchestration books deal with creating accompaniment textures, often in a section on arranging piano accompaniments for orchestra. Books that have useful information include:

Adler, Samuel. *The Study of Orchestration*, 2nd edition. New York: W. W. Norton & Company, 1989, 1982, chapter 16, p. 510; chapter 17, p. 569.

Burton, Stephen Douglas. *Orchestration*. Englewood Cliffs, N.J.: Prentice Hall, Inc., 1982, chapter 28, p. 348.

Kennan, Kent, and Donald Grantham. *The Technique of Orchestration*, 4th edition. Englewood Cliffs, N.J.: Prentice Hall, Inc., 1990, 1983, 1970, 1952, chapter 11, p. 188.

Piston, Walter. *Orchestration*. New York: W. W. Norton & Company, Inc., 1955, chapter 20, p. 364.

Rogers, Bernard. *The Art of Orchestration*. Greenwood Press, 1970, reprint of 1951 edition, chapter 13, p. 126.

Wagner, Joseph. *Band Scoring*. New York: McGraw-Hill Book Company, Inc., 1960, chapter 26, p. 275.

16   Writing Introductions, Transitions, and Codas

Arrangers often write introductions, transitions, and codas to frame and link up the thematic materials in an arrangement. In this chapter, you will learn how to compose these connecting sections. Here, for the first time, you will encounter situations where there are no preexisting materials to guide your musical decisions. This freedom can be both exciting and anxiety-provoking. While it gives you the opportunity to be a composer, it brings with it a paradox: if anything is possible and all things are equally good, how can you choose what to do? Or, if all the choices are not equally good, but no objective criteria exist to distinguish the good from the bad, how can you be sure of making good choices? While it is not possible to state absolute criteria for judging your compositional decisions, we will examine some standard patterns that other composers have used to create these sections. If these patterns are followed, they will likely produce satisfactory results. In the end, you must rely on your own musical judgment, or the judgment of others, as a guide.

We will begin by examining the introduction to Tchaikovsky's Waltz of the Flowers from the Nutcracker Suite. (CD 5, cut 6) A condensed score (with a harmonic analysis) of the introduction and the opening of the A theme is shown in figure 16.1. Listen to the work and follow the score until you are familiar with the work and understand the harmonic analysis. The symbols used in the analysis may differ slightly from those to which you are accustomed and may require explanation from your instructor.

Figure 16.1

Tchaikovsky: Nutcracker Suite, op.71a, III *(Valse des Fleurs)*, m. 1–49.

Harmonic Pattern of an Introduction

The introduction of the Waltz of the Flowers is built entirely on dominant harmony. There are no tonic chords at all and the effect is like an extended half cadence. Many introductions have this characteristic. For another example, listen to the third movement of Bizet's *Jeux d'Enfants* (CD 1, cut 21).

A more extended introduction, which is actually a separate section in contrasting tempo, can be seen in the first movement of Haydn's London Symphony shown in figure 16.2. (CD 2, cut 20) Here the introduction is in the parallel minor key and contains several modulations and secondary dominants that leave the key unsettled. Notice that this introduction also ends with a half cadence.

It appears that the harmonic material of introductions should point forward to the theme and emphasize dominant harmony. In particular, it is important to close the introduction on the dominant chord (half cadence).

Figure 16.2

Haydn: Symphony no. 104 in D Major (London), Hob. I: 104, I (Adagio-Allegro).

Arranging

(modulation)

(closing passage sustaining the dominant)

AM: I^6 V^6 vii^{o6} I ii^6 V^7/ii ii^6 vii^{o7}/ii ii^6 IV^6/V V

A Theme in Dominant

I V^6_5 I

IV^6 iii^6 ii^6 I^6 vii^{o6} I V I V^7/ii V^7/V V^7

Writing Introductions, Transitions, and Codas

(linear progression)

vi V_5^6 I

(I) V^7

Codetta

vi ii^6 V^7 I vii^{o7}

In the exposition section of Haydn's London Symphony, there are two statements of the primary theme: one in the key of D major, beginning in measure 1, and one in the key of A major (the dominant key) beginning in measure 49. Between these two statements, there is a transition section that contains the modulation and a passage that prepares for the theme in measure 49. This passage begins in measure 34 and continues through measure 48. As you can see from the analysis, the modulation begins in measure 36, where the dominant of A major appears, and continues through several secondary dominants that ultimately arrive on the dominant chord in measure 41. The remainder of the

Harmonic Pattern of a Transition

passage (m. 41–48) is clearly centered on the dominant chord. This passage is typical of transition sections, which often have the following characteristics:

1. A modulation and/or a passage with considerable chromatic harmony at the beginning of the transition. The function of this material is to weaken the previous key center and prepare for the following section, which may be in a new key.

2. A closing passage that sustains the dominant. This extended dominant creates anticipation for the following thematic section. It functions in much the same way as the end of an introduction.

As you can see, the harmonic pattern of a transition section is similar to that of an introduction in that it closes on the dominant. The idea that the dominant harmony is the harmony of preparation for following material is fundamental to the system of tonal harmony.

Harmonic Pattern of a Coda

The exposition section of the London Symphony (figure 16.2) contains a closing section with the harmonic pattern of a coda (m.83–107). (This section in a sonata form is often called a *codetta* or "little coda," because it closes the exposition section rather than the entire work.) It begins with a strong perfect authentic cadence in the key of A major (mm. 82–83) and is marked by frequent strong cadences (m.95–96, 99–100, 103–104). The final four measures are built on a tonic pedal in the key of A major. This pattern is typical of coda sections, which often have the following characteristics:

1. Frequent strong cadences on the tonic. The reiteration of cadence signals the listener that the end of a section is approaching and prepares the listener for a major punctuation in the form.

2. A final section based entirely on the tonic chord or containing a tonic pedal. This closes the section and provides the sense of finality.

Listen to the coda at the end of the first movement of the London Symphony. (CD 2, cue 20 is the beginning of the movement) You will hear its similarity to the codetta in the exposition section. The coda at the end of this movement requires more time to create a sense of balance. Consequently, it is much longer.

Melodic Characteristics of Introductions, Transitions, and Codas

The introduction to Tchaikovsky's Waltz of the Flowers (figure 16.1) is based on the opening melodic motive of the A theme. This motive appears in m. 1–3, m. 5–7, and again in m. 9–10, where it is followed by four statements of the second measure of the motive.

The melodic materials in transition and codetta sections of Haydn's London Symphony (figure 16.2) are strongly related to the theme itself, as a motific analysis will show. Figure 16.3 is the melody of the primary theme of the movement with melodic motives marked.

Figure 16.3

Haydn: Symphony no. 104 in D Major (London), Hob. I: 104, I (Adagio-Allegro) (Exposition) m. 1–8.

Figure 16.4 shows the primary melodic material from the transition section (measures 34–48) marked with possible motivic relationships to the main theme (figure 16.3). You may or may not agree with all the motific relationships shown in figure 16.4, but the central point is that the melodic material in the transition section is based extensively on the main theme.

Figure 16.4

Haydn: Symphony no. 104 in D Major (London), Hob. I:104, I (Adagio-Allegro) m. 34–38.

* I= inversion, R=retrograde, RI=retrograde inversion

Figure 16.5 shows the primary melodic material in the codetta section of the exposition (measures 83–102) with the motives marked as before. Again, you see that material from the main theme is used in the closing section.

Figure 16.5

Haydn: Symphony no. 104 in D Major (London), Hob. I: 104, I (Adagio-Allegro) m. 83–102.

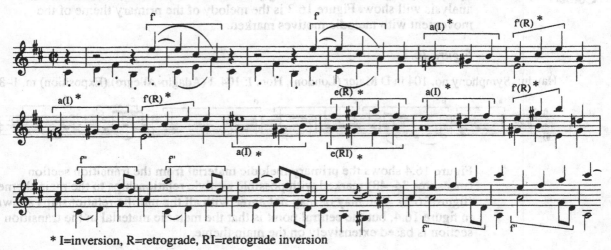

* I=inversion, R=retrograde, RI=retrograde inversion

In conclusion, effective introductions, transitions, and codas can be created by using the melodic materials of the themes and certain harmonic formulas centering on the tonic and dominant harmonies.

Creating a Transition Section

As an example, we will compose a transition section which leads from the Polish folk song in chapter 15 (figure 15.9 on page 266) to a second Polish folk song shown in figure 16.6.

Figure 16.6

Polish Folk Song

This transition will connect two contrasting themes. The folk song in figure 15.9 (theme I) is in a minor key, a moderate tempo, and 3/4 meter, while the melody in figure 16.6 (theme II) is in a major key, a faster tempo, and 2/4 meter. To make the tempo and meter shift, you could close the transition section with a pause. A break in tempo is usually an effective way to connect sections with both tempo and meter change.

Finding the Duration of the Section	To get some idea of the duration of the transition section, begin by conducting through theme I in your mind. Try to imagine, as clearly as possible, what theme I will sound like in full orchestration. When you come to the end of theme I, continue into an imaginary transition leading to theme II. At this point, you will have no clear idea of the musical content of the transition, but you will have some idea of its duration. After several attempts you might conclude that the transition section should be approximately one four-bar phrase in length. (You might come to a different conclusion that would be equally valid.) You may also begin to hear some music that might work for this transition, but it may not be clear enough to play or notate. The process of imagining a transition sets your creative imagination to work at filling the "empty time" with music. If this sounds difficult (or even silly) to you, please give it a serious try. You may be pleasantly surprised with the results.

Establishing a Harmonic Basis for the Section	Next you would create the harmonic pattern for the section. Since theme I has a prevailing harmonic rhythm of one chord per measure, the same harmonic rhythm can continue through the transition. First, make a modulation from G minor to E-flat major followed by a half cadence in E-flat. We really need only four chords, the last of which will be the dominant in E-flat. At the beginning of the transition, you might decide to avoid the authentic cadence at the end of theme I, substituting a deceptive cadence (figure 16.7).

Figure 16.7

You are now on what will become the new tonic chord, and you need to tonicize it with a strong harmonic progression leading to the dominant. The strongest harmonic progression in tonal music is the circle progression, so you might sketch the progression shown in figure 16.8, which is a circle progression leading to the dominant chord.

Figure 16.8

E♭M: I   vi   ii   V⁷

This progression will be the basis of the transition.

Melodic Material   Notice that the melodic motive on the last measure of theme I is similar to the motive in measure 11 (figure 16.9).

Figure 16.9

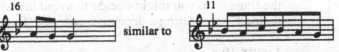

similar to

You can substitute this motive, which seems to make the melody want to move forward, rather than stop (figure 16.10).

Figure 16.10

Another version of the same motive, followed by two motives derived from measure 15, will complete the transition (figure 16.11).

Figure 16.11

gm: i   V⁷ VI   iv   V⁷
                        E♭M: ⌊VI   ii⁶

Notice that the accompaniment figures of theme I have been continued through the transition to maintain unity with the previous section. An inversion of the supertonic chord has been used to create a better SM in the bass.

Extracting Melodic Motives From a Theme

As you can see, an important aspect of composing connecting and framing sections is the use of melodic motives extracted from themes. The ideal melodic motive is a sequence of two to five pitches that is easily identified as a part of the theme. The opening motive of the melody may be used, but internal motives are equally useful and have the advantage of not having been used several times in the melody already. As an example, a number of melodic motives will be derived from the Polish folk song. Figure 16.12 is the melody with twenty-one possible melodic motives marked.

Figure 16.12

Polish Folk Song

The twenty-one motives shown in figure 16.12 probably do not exhaust all of the possibilities. There is a wealth of melodic material to choose from in any melody. When motives are used in connecting and framing sections, they will often need to be altered slightly to fit the harmony. You can see how the motives in measures 3–5 (figure 16.11) are altered through expansion of intervals to fit the prevailing harmony. These alterations also have the advantage of providing variety in the melodic material, while maintaining continuity with the theme.

It is often useful to create melodic sequences from the motives in themes that can be used in connecting and framing sections. This process separates the motive from the melody itself and allows you to concentrate your attention on it in isolation. Figure 16.13 shows sequences built on several motives from the Polish folk song.

Figure 16.13

Arranging

Summary

The following is a step-by-step approach to creating an introduction, transition, or coda. You need not follow this process rigidly. Experiment with variations on this outline to see what works best for you. Composing is a highly individual activity, no single procedure works for everyone.

1. Examine the theme or themes with which the section will connect. Note the key, tempo, and character of each theme to gain a general impression of the style of music you will likely need.

2. Find an approximate duration for the section. Conduct your way through an imaginary section several times, starting and/or ending with a thematic section. For an introduction, imagine introductory music leading up to the first theme. For a transition, begin with the last phrase of the previous theme and continue until the next theme begins. For a coda, start with the last phrase of the final theme and continue until a feeling of conclusion emerges. You need not have any clear idea of the musical content of the section to imagine some kind of appropriate music filling the time. After several attempts, you can determine an approximate number of measures for the section.

3. Develop a harmonic plan for the section. The harmonic plans developed from the exposition of the London Symphony will give you general schemes. You should follow the schemes fairly closely at the beginning but can deviate from them later, when you have more confidence. A general process for establishing the harmonic plan is as follows:

    a. Decide on the harmonic rhythm. The harmonic rhythm of adjacent sections is your best clue here. For example, a transition should probably start with a harmonic rhythm that is not too different from the previous thematic section. Conduct through the imaginary section again and imagine the chord changes happening regularly in the rhythm you choose. Does this harmonic rhythm feel comfortable? Should it be faster? Slower?

    b. Sketch in the basic harmonic pattern for the section. You may use popular music chord symbols, roman numerals, or the notes themselves to indicate the harmony. These sketches are for your own use, so include only enough detail to be able to remember your ideas when you return to them on another day. The harmonic progressions in the surrounding themes are good clues to the progressions you might include in the section. Sometimes one of the phrases of a theme can be modified to work in a transition, introduction, or coda. Try various possibilities, and be alert for any feeling that a progression "wants" to lead in a particular direction. You will use both your intellect and your intuition in this process. You have, no doubt, written chord progressions in previous music theory classes. These progressions give you material with which to work. However, the best, and most creative, ideas come from your own intuition. Your sense of proportion may be altered when the tonal materials begin to take shape. Check your progression by connecting it to the surrounding thematic material and make any adjustments you feel are necessary.

4. Work out the primary melodic material (PM) of the section. If you have not already done so in step 1, make a survey of possible melodic motives. You will find many more motives than you will likely need, but spend some time with each one. A helpful exercise is to take a motive and create a melodic sequence from it. This frees the motive from its place in the melody and concentrates your attention on it. Work out the melodic material for the connecting section, using some of the motives. Remember that the motives may need to be reshaped to fit the harmonic progression. Play the melodic line by itself to determine if it makes good musical sense. Make any necessary adjustments.

5. Work out the secondary melodic material (SM) of the section—in particular, the bass line. Play the PM and SM together to see if a good counterpoint is formed. Make any necessary adjustments.

6. Work out details of accompaniment texture. It is a good practice to make accompaniment textures match surrounding thematic materials, but this is not always a requirement.

7. Play through the section, connecting it with the surrounding thematic material to see if the connection is smooth and logical.

As you can see, the process of composing connecting sections is a cyclic process, in which your first rough ideas are gradually refined as new materials are added. You can expect some false starts in this process, and you may have to scrap some of your original ideas and begin again. In arranging, you should consider no decision final until the entire composition is finished.

Workbook: Assignments A–F, pp. 153–154.

Suggestions for Further Study

Orchestration books generally do not deal with the compositional aspects of arranging. For this topic, you may consult books dealing specifically with arranging. Most of these books present highly personal techniques, but good information can be gleaned from such books as:

Bennett, Robert Russell. *Instrumentally Speaking.* Melville, N.Y.: Belwin-Mills Publishing Corp., 1975.

Cacavas, John. *Music Arranging and Orchestration.* Melville, N.Y.: Belwin-Mills Publishing Corp., 1975.

Erickson, Frank. *Arranging for the Concert Band.* Miami, Fla.: CPP/Belwin, Inc., 1983.

17 Planning the Form: *Tonal Plan of an Arrangement*

The previous chapters have dealt with some of the elements of form: themes, introductions, transitions, and codas. This chapter will consider the structure of an arrangement as a whole—the overall shape and plan of a composition.

Unity versus Variety

One of the primary concerns in planning the form of an arrangement is clarity of design. A listener should feel comfortable with the musical events as they unfold. This feeling of comfort comes from a sense that the music is progressing in a natural way. While an audience (unless they are professional musicians) will not be able to verbalize about the sources of this comfortable feeling, we know that it comes, in part, from subtle cues in the music that can be used to predict future events, and the satisfaction that comes when these future events actually take place. Psychologists call this phenomenon expectation. A concrete example of expectation at work is the extended dominant harmony at the end of an introduction or transition. The pause on, or reiteration of, the dominant chord is a cue that an important musical event (a theme) is to follow. When a theme does follow, the listener feels comfortable that the music is progressing in a natural way. A second comfort factor is repetition. When a musical idea is stated, we expect to hear that idea again. When it recurs, we accept it as a natural occurrence As an arranger, you must be aware of the expectations your musical materials create in the listener and take care that these expectations are satisfied. A composition that satisfies the listener's expectations is said to have unity.

However, if all our musical expectations are immediately satisfied, there is little need to listen carefully to the music, and our attention begins to wander. If, on the other hand, we feel that we can generally predict the musical future, but sometimes find that these predictions are not borne out, we are more likely to keep our attention on the music. The factors that make the musical future unpredictable will be called variety. In general, variety in music comes about through changes in melodic, rhythmic, harmonic, or textural elements. For example, a change in the accompaniment texture creates variety, because it can't be anticipated. A modulation creates variety, because we don't know where the music is going until the new key is confirmed. A new melody creates variety, because it can't be predicted. Variety is the second major concern in planning an arrangement.

Unity and variety are opposing forces in a musical composition. Taken to the extreme, variety can result in chaos, while unity can result in boredom. A good composition contains both forces in a satisfying proportion. While there are no definitive rules to guide your musical choices in this regard, there are many fine examples throughout the literature of music to serve as examples. Indeed, the standard formal outlines (sonata form, rondo form, theme and variations, etc.) exist because they are models of a satisfactory balance between unity and variety. A study of the standard forms in music is beyond the scope of this book. If you need help in understanding these forms please consult Benward-White *Music in Theory and Practice*, vols. I–II, or any textbook on musical form.

An Example of Formal Planning

The following section is a description of the process of planning an arrangement for junior high school concert band. In this discussion, you should concentrate more on the strategy than the individual decisions being made. This arrangement will use the two Polish folk melodies introduced in the previous chapters. A third Polish folk tune will be added to complete the thematic material for this arrangement. The three melodies are shown in figure 17.1

Figure 17.1

Theme I

Theme II

Theme III

The form of this work will not necessarily follow any of the classical forms. It will be in a genre often called fantasy or tone poem that is common for such single movement works for school groups. Factors of unity and variety have been considered in choosing the three melodies. There will be a good variety of tempo. Theme I seems moderate to slow in tempo, theme II might be moderately fast, and theme III can be played very quickly. The three themes have good potential for contrast in mode, with theme I in minor and themes II and III in major. The common Polish heritage gives the three melodies a unity that goes far beyond the surface and will also be an advantage when it comes to giving the work a title. In addition, there is a similarity between the opening motive of theme I and theme III that might be exploited in the work somewhere (figure 17.2).

Figure 17.2

Since the work is intended for junior high school musicians, you must concern yourself with any potential difficulties the themes are likely to present for the students. The meters are quite easy for junior high school students, as are the rhythmic patterns. (See chapter 9 for a discussion of the relative difficulty of various meters and rhythms.) The keys will be chosen as the formal plan develops, but you should note immediately that the key of theme III must be changed to fit the junior high school level.

The Order of the Themes

Choosing the order of the themes is largely a subjective process, but the factors influencing the decision are:

1. At least one of the themes should be repeated during the course of the work to provide a sense of unity in the form. The strongest and most interesting melody should be chosen for this repetition.

2. Successive themes should provide contrast.

Based on these considerations, you might choose theme I as the strongest theme. Note that it will also provide good contrast with both of the other themes, which are similar in tempo.

At this point, you might decide to open and close the work with theme I. That will assure a strong opening and closing section. The motive in measure 9 might be developed into coda material.

Since theme I contrasts with both theme II and theme III, it might also be placed between them. This suggests a rondo-like pattern: A B A C A. You can begin to experiment with different ordering of the themes by playing them on the piano. Try various keys until you find combinations you like. Remember to keep the keys within the bounds of those appropriate for junior high level. You must also concern yourself with which instruments are going to be able to play the themes in the various keys. To give the work tonal closure, the first and last statements of theme I might be stated in the same key. The pattern of keys would need to allow for this return of the original tonic. After considerable experimentation, you might choose the following tentative pattern of themes and keys:

Figure 17.3

Theme I gm:	Theme II B♭M:	Theme II FM:	Theme I dm:	Theme III FM:	Theme I gm:

The alternation of slow and fast material is maintained, and theme II, which is rather short, is repeated in a new key, which will add the interest necessary to allow the repetition of this melody. The key relationships are in similar interval relationships, as shown in figure 17.4. (Key relationships will be considered in more detail later in this chapter.)

Figure 17.4

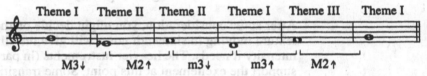

These decisions are subjective but not arbitrary. You may see sequences of themes and keys that appeal to you more and might be just as satisfying.

Introduction, Transitions, and Coda

The arrangement must have some coda to bring it to a conclusion. Whether there will be an introduction and transitions remains to be decided. After considerable thought, you might conclude that theme I will sound best if it follows a short introduction. If the work has no transitions, it might seem like little more than a medley of tunes, but if transitions were placed between each of the themes, it could seem too predictable. This, again, is a subjective choice, but after some experimentation, you might tentatively decide on the following pattern:

Figure 17.5

Introduction	Theme I	Transition	Theme II	Theme II	Transition?

Theme I	Theme III	Theme I	Coda

Planning for the Climax

It is important that the arrangement have a single climax point, and you need to plan in advance how to achieve it. After trying out various patterns in your mind, you might decide that the final statement of theme I is the best climax point. Since theme I is at a slower tempo than the preceding theme, it will require careful planning to bring the climax about at that point. Several possibilities present themselves as possible solutions to this problem:

1. Theme I could be taken at, or near, the tempo of theme III to avoid the relaxation of tension that often accompanies a decrease in tempo.

2. The highest dynamics and heaviest textures could be reserved for the final statement of theme I. In particular, heavy percussion might give the additional weight needed to secure the climax.

3. The background textures could speed up so they continue at approximately the same rate as theme III, while theme I goes on in its original tempo. This will create the climax through complexity of texture.

After some consideration, you might decide on the third choice. A background texture moving in sixteenth notes will give the climax the excitement and intensity it needs. The heavier instruments (in particular, the percussion) could support the excitement at this point. Some transition will likely be necessary between theme III and theme I to prepare for the climax. This material will probably need to build in dynamics and density toward the climax point.

Planning the Tension Curve of the Arrangement

Having decided on the climax point, you should turn your attention to the opposite extreme—the point of greatest relaxation. The climax will only seem climactic when compared to the anticlimax—the point of minimum tension. You might choose the center statement of theme I for the anticlimax. This seems to be an excellent anticlimax point, since it involves the same theme as the climax of the work. With the high and low point of the work determined, you can draw a general tension curve of the entire work. This little graph will guide you in the choice of dynamics and density of texture in each section.

Figure 17.6

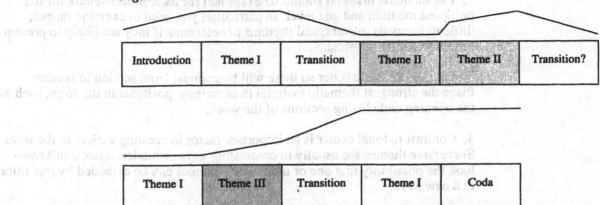

Introduction	Theme I	Transition	Theme II	Theme II	Transition?

Theme I	Theme III	Transition	Theme I	Coda

Writing the Arrangement

With this tentative formal plan in mind, you could set to work on the arrangement itself. None of the decisions made to this point are final, and the plan may be altered several times before the arrangement is completed. The actual musical material "takes on a life of its own" and influences the final product in ways that are impossible to predict in the planning stage. However, with this plan as a starting point, you could work out the details of the arrangement section by section, creating the necessary accompaniment textures and connecting sections (as described in chapters 15 and 16), and modifying the plan as needed in the process. We will leave this arrangement unfinished at this point. In the next chapter, you will see a completed arrangement by the author (using different thematic material), which will give you the opportunity to study the process of completing an arrangment in greater detail.

Summary

The preceding brief example illustrates the process of planning an arrangement. The specific details of the particular themes and the decisions made here are of little importance. It is the process that you should concentrate on. The process of planning an arrangement is a cyclic one, like the process of creating a connecting section (see chapter 16). There are many factors to be considered, and each has an effect on the resulting composition. As your attention is drawn to each of the factors, the plan gradually emerges, but the decisions made earlier in the process may well be modified by later decisions. There is no clear, step-by-step process to follow; but the following list will remind you of important issues you need to address:

1. The thematic material must offer both unity and variety and be of sufficient interest to bear some repetition. In particular, consider: tempo, meter, mode, range, and melodic contour for each of the themes. It is important that the themes offer some sense of unity as well as variety.

2. The thematic material should be examined for its appropriateness for the proposed medium and age level. In particular, you need to examine ranges, difficult intervals, meters, and rhythms to determine if they are likely to present problems for the musicians.

3. Plan the thematic order so there will be contrast from section to section. Place the strongest thematic material in prominent positions in the form, such as the opening and closing sections of the work.

4. Contrast in tonal center is an important factor in creating variety in the form. Successive themes are usually in contrasting keys or modes. Also, don't over-look the possibility that one or more of the themes can be extended by repetition in a new key.

5. An important unifying factor is the pattern of key relationships within the work. Consider the pattern formed by the successive keys to see if they form a coherent pattern. Return of the original key gives a feeling of unity, as do consistent interval relationships between keys. (Details on various key relation-ships are in the following section.)

6. Some sort of coda will likely be necessary to bring the work to a conclusion. What is the best thematic material for this section? The coda is often, but not always, built on motives from the last thematic section of the work.

7. Consider whether an introduction is appropriate or needed. Some themes can be launched without introduction, while others require at least a few measures of preparation.

8. Consider whether or not transitions are needed between each of the thematic sections. If two themes are strongly contrasting in tempo, meter, or key, they often need a transition to keep the composition from seeming disconnected and abrupt. On the other hand, constant transition can become commonplace and boring. It is often best to move from one theme to another in a direct way, by simply taking up the next theme without pause. (Specific details regarding key relationships in relation to transitions are in the following section.)

9. Consider the possibility of small internal codas (codettas) at the end of themes. Codettas can often substitute for transitions or even merge with them.

10. Determine the climax point of the arrangement, and plan the dynamics, density and complexity of texture to build toward this climax point and move away from it.

11. Determine the anticlimax point (the point of lowest tension) and plan how to move toward it and away from it.

12. Plan a tentative tension curve for the entire work, based on the chosen climax and anticlimax points.

Key Relationships Between Themes

An important factor in choosing the key structure of an arrangement is the relationship between successive themes. Some key changes seem quite natural and pass by nearly unnoticed by the listener, while others are more distant and create considerable tension until the new key is firmly established. It is important that you accurately judge the emotional effect of the key relationships you choose in an arrangement. For the most part, the key changes should be of the more natural type, but a distant relationship can create considerable surprise on occasion.

Closely Related Keys

The key relationships that seem the most natural involve the *closely related keys*, which are the keys whose key signatures differ from each other by no more than one accidental. The chart in figure 17.7 summarizes the closely related keys. The six keys that can be enclosed by a box like the one shown on the chart are closely related to each other. You can easily find the closely related keys to any key by placing that key in the center position of box. (The box in the illustration shows the closely related keys of F major and D minor.)

Figure 17.7

Major keys: C♯ F♯ B E A D G │C F B♭│ E♭ A♭ D♭ G♭ C♭

Minor keys: a♯ d♯ g♯ c♯ f♯ b e │a d g│ c f b♭ e♭ a♭

You can easily shift to a closely related key, even without a transition, and the listener will scarcely notice that a change has taken place. Most key relationships in arrangements fall into this catagory.

Rising Second Relationships

In this century, listeners have become accustomed to key shifts in rising major or minor seconds through popular music, which uses this relationship routinely to create a sense of climax near the end of a song. While these key relationships are so common that they seem quite natural to listeners, they do create slightly more tension than moves to closely related keys. Rising second key relationships are excellent choices when you wish to generate an increase in tension without shocking the listener.

Falling Second Relationships

Falling major and minor second relationships, while less common than rising seconds, can be used effectively. They seem somewhat less natural to the listener and tend to have the effect of decreasing tension because of the darker effect of a lower key.

Distant Relationships

All other key relationships should be considered distant. If they are approached with a transition that leads the listener smoothly to the new key, they can be made to seem quite natural; but if they are approached without such preparation, the listener will feel considerable tension until the new key is firmly established.

An Example of Key Relationships at Work

The arrangement that was planned earlier in this chapter will provide an example of key relationships. The keys are summarized in figure 17.3. The first key change is from G minor to E-flat major. As you can see in figure 17.8, this is a move to a closely related key and seems quite natural.

Figure 17.8

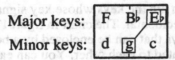

The second key change involves a rising major second (from E-flat major to F major), which was used to generate an increase in tension in the second statement of theme II. The third and fourth key changes involve closely related keys: D minor and F major.

Figure 17.9

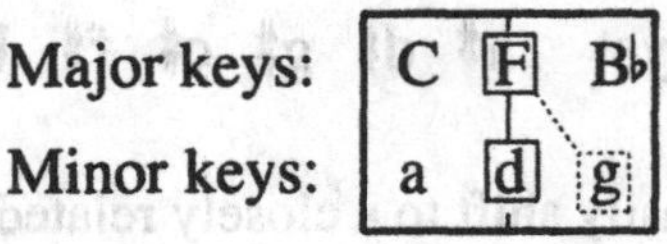

Major keys: C F B♭
Minor keys: a d g

The final key change is another rising major second relationship (from F major to G minor), but this is also a closely related key, as you can see from the chart in figure 17.9. There are no distant key relationships in the arrangement, so the pattern of keys will seem quite natural to a listener.

As an arranger, you must always be aware of the effect your key changes will have on the listener and plan to achieve the effect you want. While the closely related keys and keys in second relationship should predominate, there is certainly a place for the surprise and tension of a more distant relationship when a strong effect is intended.

Workbook: Assignment, p. 155

18 A Finished Arrangement for Concert Band

Chapter 17 introduced the process of planning an arrangement, starting with the thematic materials and evolving a plan that included the order of themes, key relationships, introduction, transitions, coda, and a tension curve for the arrangement. This chapter will analyze a finished arrangement, showing how such a plan was worked out in a completed arrangement. The harmonic material in this work goes beyond the common practice style and represents a more-contemporary approach to tonal relationships.

Afton Water

Afton Water is an arrangement for concert band (grade 3 level). It is a fantasy on three Scottish airs and ballads that appear in *The New Scottish Orpheus*, the authoritative collection of such tunes. The three themes are a melody for the ballad Barbara Allen (theme I); a melody sung to Robert Burns' O Gin My Love Were Yon Red Rose (theme II); and the title tune, which is a melody sung to Burns's poem that begins "Flow gently, sweet Afton, among thy green braes" (theme III) (figure 18.1).

Figure 18.1

Theme I - "Barbara Allen"

Theme II - "O Gin My Love Were Yon Red Rose"

Theme III - "Afton Water"

A condensed score for the arrangement is shown in figure 18.2. Listen to the work on the accompanying compact disk until you are familiar with it and have studied the analysis. (CD 5, cut 34)

Figure 18.2

White: Afton Water

Analysis

The three themes are presented in order (theme I, theme II, theme III) and are followed by a return to theme I to close the work. The title theme gets the most development of the three themes and provides much of the ascent to the climax of the work at the end.

Key scheme

The key scheme of the work centers around C minor (theme I) and its relative major, E-flat major (theme III). Theme II is stated in A natural minor (a distant key from C minor) and B-flat natural minor (a rising second relationship from A minor). The second statement of theme II in B-flat minor is followed by theme III in E-flat major (another distant key). At the end of the work, the coda is in C major, an extended Picardy third.

Figure 18.3

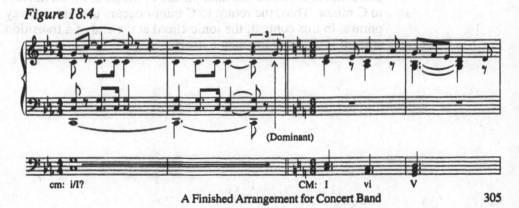

Theme I	Theme II	Theme II	Theme III	Theme I	Coda
cm	am	b♭m	E♭M	cm	CM

As you can see in figure 18.3, the central tonic C is complemented by keys a minor third below and above (A minor and E-flat major), so there is consistency in the key scheme, even though two key relationships are distant.

Connecting Sections

The connecting sections, while quite brief for the most part, are crucial to making the key scheme seem natural. They will be examined in some detail.

In measures 16–17, there is a very brief codetta that consists of nothing more than a restatement of the cadence chord (figure 18.4). At first, it appears that there is nothing done to smooth the connection with theme II in A minor, but closer inspection reveals two factors that make the connection seamless:

1. The tonic chords in measures 16 and 17 contain no third, leaving the mode ambiguous at this point. Given the common practice of a Picardy third as a final cadence, it is not unreasonable for the listener to hear a major third in this chord. In fact, in the coda (measures 100–106), the cadence chord of this theme is C major. C major and A minor are closely related keys, requiring no modulation to seem quite natural.

2. Theme II is harmonized in C major at the beginning. It is only with the cadence in measures 25–26 that the A minor tonic emerges.

Since theme II contains the modulation from C major to A minor, the connection between the themes needs only to establish the parallel major (C major).

Figure 18.4

cm: i/I?

(Dominant)

CM: I   vi   V

The transition between theme II and theme III (measures 41–55) is the only extended transition in the work. Here a distant key relationship must be worked out, along with a drastic change in tempo and meter. The transition opens with a passage that evades the cadence of the final phrase of theme II by repeating a motive several times (figure 18.5).

Figure 18.5

Theme II—final cadence

Transition—m. 41–46

The repeated motive leads to the dominant in m. 45–48, and in m. 49–52 the final phrase of theme II is stated in augmentation (in $\frac{3}{4}$), thus establishing the meter for the following section. The tonic chord in measure 52 contains a picardy third, which closes the section on a B-flat major sonority. B-flat is reiterated in m. 53–55, and this leads smoothly to the key of E-flat major, since theme III begins on B-flat. Here the previous tonic note is the dominant of the new key, and a change of mode (B-flat minor to B-flat major) accomplishes the key shift.

The return to theme I in measure 92 requires a change in tempo, meter, and key (figure 18.6). The first part of this transition (m. 84–86) takes care of the rhythmic relationships. There is a slowing of the tempo in the final phrase of theme III, so the eighth notes are nearly the speed of the quarter notes of theme I. There is no need for a modulation at this point, since the second part of the transition is based on the final phrase of theme I, which moves from E-flat major to C minor. Thus, the return to C minor occurs in a natural way at the end of the phrase. In this context, the tonic chord at the end of a transition is quite logical, since it is a part of the theme itself.

Figure 18.6

Transition—m. 84–91

Slower ♪ = 120

EᵇM:

to cm:

rit. . . .

stays in EᵇM:

♪ = 108–120

The coda (m. 100–106) is prepared in m. 98–99 by an augmentation of the final phrase of theme I. This leads to two statements (in m. 100–101) of a motive that is a combination of the motive at the end of each phrase of theme I and the rhythmic motive that has been in the accompaniment at each cadence (figure 18.7).

Figure 18.7

Cadence—Theme I

cadence motive

new coda motive:

rhythmic motive

This is followed by a reiteration of the tonic and dominant in the bass in m. 102–103, and finally a repeated tonic note in m. 104–106.

The connecting sections in Afton Water are constructed out of melodic and harmonic elements of the themes in every case, ensuring the unity of the work. Distant key relationships are brought closer through change of mode in two cases, and modulations that occur within the themes themselves are also exploited.

Tension Curve for Afton Water

Figure 18.9 is a summary of the previous analysis, along with a tension curve for Afton Water. This tension curve was drawn in the process of writing this chapter and contains much detail that was not known in the planning stages. An initial tension curve might have looked something like figure 18.8.

Figure 18.8

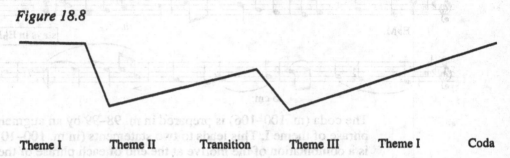

Theme I   Theme II   Transition   Theme III   Theme I   Coda

The idea of a climax near the end of the work was a part of the earliest planning, as was the need for a strong beginning and a light second theme. Theme III was conceived early on as the area of the work that would begin at the anticlimax point and build to the climax. A secondary climax was placed before theme III to provide maximum contrast at the anticlimax point. The many dips and turns of tension within the final work were generated by the materials themselves, as they began to "have a life of their own."

This chapter has taken you inside the author's thought processes and given you some insight into his composing process. The materials and devices used in creating Afton Water were arrived at by close examination of the themes themselves and are unique to this piece. Once you establish a good working method, you will invent and discover your own devices that will be unique to the thematic material with which you are working.

Figure 18.9

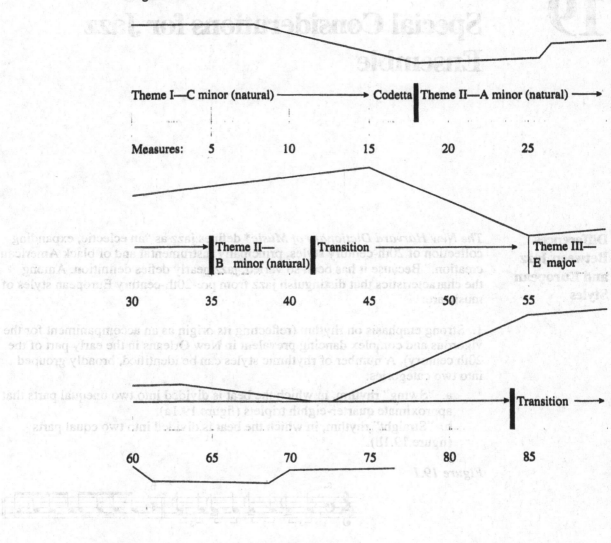

Theme I—C minor (natural) ⟶ Codetta ▌Theme II—A minor (natural) ⟶

Measures:　　5　　　　　　10　　　　　　15　　　　　　20　　　　　25

▌Theme II—　　　　　Transition　　　　　　　　　　Theme III—
　B minor (natural)　　　　　　　　　　　　　　　　E major

　　　30　　　　　35　　　　　40　　　　　45　　　　　50　　　　　55

　　　　　　　　　　　　　　　　　　　　　　　　　　▌Transition ⟶

　　　60　　　　　65　　　　　70　　　　　75　　　　　80　　　　　85

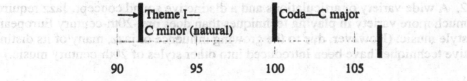

▌Theme I—　　　　　▌Coda—C major
　C minor (natural)

　　　90　　　　　95　　　　　100　　　　　105

Workbook: Assignment, p. 156

19 Special Considerations for Jazz Ensemble

Differences Between Jazz and European Styles

The New Harvard Dictionary of Music* defines jazz as "an eclectic, expanding collection of 20th-century styles, principally instrumental and of black American creation." Because it has been so varied, jazz nearly defies definition. Among the characteristics that distinguish jazz from pre-20th-century European styles of music are:

1. Strong emphasis on rhythm (reflecting its origin as an accompaniment for the vigorous and complex dancing prevalent in New Orleans in the early part of the 20th century). A number of rhythmic styles can be identified, broadly grouped into two categories:

    a. "Swing" rhythm, in which the beat is divided into two unequal parts that approximate quarter-eighth triplets (figure 19.1a).
    b. "Straight" rhythm, in which the beat is divided into two equal parts (figure 19.1b).

Figure 19.1

2. A wide variety of articulations and a distinctive sound concept. Jazz requires much more variety in playing techniques than does pre–20th-century European-style music. (However, due to the growing influence of jazz, many of its distinctive techniques have been introduced into other styles of 20th-century music.)

3. A flexible approach to pitch, with many "bent" or "blue" notes and glissandi between pitches.

4. Considerable emphasis on group and solo improvisation. Having roots as it does in an extemporaneous oral tradition, jazz is singularly difficult to notate accurately. Even if precise notation were possible, it would violate the spontaneous character of the style.

Jazz Instrumentation

The instrumentation of jazz is quite varied, ranging from unaccompanied solo instruments to large ensembles that rival the symphony orchestra in size and composition. Most jazz writing is done for three kinds of groups:

1. Combos, consisting of a rhythm section (some combination of keyboards, guitar, bass, and drums) and one or more wind instruments (usually of contrasting color and range).

2. Small bands, consisting of a rhythm section and at least one section of like wind instruments.

3. The standard jazz ensemble or "big band," consisting of saxophones, trumpets, trombones, bass, guitar, keyboard, and drums. The saxophones sometimes double on flute and various clarinets, and the trumpets on flugelhorn. F horns are sometimes added to the ensemble. Strings and other orchestral instruments may be added to form a jazz orchestra. (See figure 2.4 on page 26 for an example of a standard jazz ensemble score.)

This chapter will focus on scoring for the standard jazz ensemble or big band. It developed out of the big bands of the 1930s and 1940s and exists today in the form of stage band and jazz ensemble in schools and colleges, as well as jazz arts groups (concert jazz bands) in many larger cities. You should not, however, overlook the unique and satisfying opportunities to be found in writing for combos, which are often associated with jazz ensemble programs in the schools.

The jazz ensemble contains four main sections: the saxophone section, the trumpet section, the trombone section, and the rhythm section.

The Saxophone Section

The standard big band saxophone section consists of two alto saxophones, two tenor saxophones, and one baritone saxophone. Experienced players (on the college or professional level) usually double on one or more of the following instruments: flute, alto flute, clarinet, bass clarinet, oboe, English horn, and bassoon. The double-reed doubles are less common than the clarinet and flute doubles. The saxophones blend very well with the two brass sections and may be used in any combination or alone as a solo section. Saxophone sections are often amplified in concert settings to create a better balance with the brass.

The Trumpet Section	The trumpet section consists of four or five trumpets, one or more of whom may double on flugelhorn. The trumpet section provides the primary strength in the upper register of the ensemble. While not quite as agile as saxophones, they are capable of considerable virtuosity, particularly in the middle register. The trumpet section requires more rest than the other sections of the ensemble, particularly if asked to play in the upper register (where the trumpets are often written in jazz arrangments). The "lead" part is sometimes shifted temporarily to another member of the trumpet section to even out the playing load, but this does not diminish the need for frequent rests. When the trumpet section rests, the saxophones become the primary treble instruments.
The Trombone Section	The trombone section consists of three to five trombones, with the lowest part often played on bass trombone. Doubling is not common in the trombone section. The trombone section provides a thick, rich sound in the middle and bass registers. They are the least agile of the wind instruments and generally do not participate in rapid passage work. If the lowest member of the section is a bass trombone, it should not be written in unison with the other trombones in passages that lie above the bass staff.
The Rhythm Section	The rhythm section is the core of the jazz ensemble. Its basic function is to provide harmonic and rhythmic support (HRS) for the ensemble and various soloists. In addition, members of the rhythm section may play solos from time to time.
	The standard rhythm section consists of piano, guitar, bass, and drums. The pianist may double on various electronic keyboards, including electric piano, synthesizer, and organ. A second guitar player may be added to the rhythm section of large jazz ensembles.
	Figure 19.2 shows the rhythm section parts for a passage from a typical jazz ensemble score. Details of how to write parts for rhythm section instruments are contained in the notation section later in this chapter.

Figure 19.2

Nestico: Hay Burner
1968 Banes Music, International Copyright Secured.
Reprinted by permission.

Easy Swing (♩ = 132)

The piano and guitar players improvise a harmonic accompaniment texture to support the ensemble. This technique, called "comping," is a highly developed skill. Experienced piano and guitar players can be relied on to create an appropriate accompaniment from a part consisting of chord symbols and an indication of general style. If specific rhythms or melodies are required, write them into the part. If the piano or guitar comping is not desired, write "tacet" or "no fills" over the applicable measures.

The bass is a very important member of the jazz ensemble. Not only is it responsible for providing a strong sense of the rhythmic character of the music, but it also provides the true harmonic bass of the ensemble, which is often missing from the wind sections of the score. The bass part varies from little more than rhythmically decorated chord roots (HRS), typical of commercial and pop music, to a "walking bass" (SM) in swing jazz. Rock and Latin jazz styles typically have a bass with repetitive melodic motives (SS). Experienced bass players can provide an appropriate bass line from a part that consists of chord changes and a description of the style. A bass line should be written for less-experienced players or in situations where a specific line is required, but in such cases the chord changes should also be provided.

The drums are nearly equal in importance to the bass. The drummer provides steady rhythmic support (RS) throughout most textures. It also complements the wind instruments with "kicks" that reinforce their rhythmic figures and with "fills" that provide rhythmic counterpoint between the end of one phrase and the beginning of the next, (figure 19.3).

Figure 19.3

In most situations, the drum part is improvised from general descriptions of style, a technique called "playing time." It is actually somewhat of a misnomer to refer to this person as a "drummer," since the standard "trap set" (figure 19.4) ("drum set" or "kit") is an integrated collection of drums and cymbals, which typically includes:

1. A snare drum mounted on a stand.

2. A bass drum played with a foot pedal.

3. A high-hat ("foot," "top hat," "sock") cymbal mounted on a stand with a foot pedal.

4. A floor tom-tom mounted on a stand.

5. One or two tom-toms mounted on the bass drum.

6. Two suspended cymbals mounted on stands: a "ride" cymbal ("right hand," "top") on the player's right and "crash" cymbal ("left hand," "fast") on the player's left.

Figure 19.4

Drummers often own a number of small percussion instruments that may be called for from time to time. These include: cowbell, triangle, wood block, tambourine, bell tree, and various Latin American instruments. Jazz ensembles sometimes include separate percussionists who play vibraphone and other keyboard percussion instruments or who specialize in Latin American instruments.

Jazz Notation   In addition to conveying your other intentions, it is very important for jazz notation to allow for the improvisational character of the music and to suggest with appropriate symbols the wide variety of jazz articulations. A standard practice for notating jazz is not yet established, but the following recommendations will get you started.

Notation of Harmony

Jazz chords are usually notated with a capital letter for the root of the chord followed by various symbols to describe the quality. Figure 19.5 shows the root-position voicings of the chords most often used in jazz (all spelled on a C bass). This chart follows the recommendations of Brandt and Roemer's *Standardized Chord Symbol Notation*.

Figure 19.5

Chord inversions are shown by the addition of a diagonal line to the right of the basic chord symbol, followed by the letter denoting the bass note for the inversion (figure 19.6a). The diagonal line can also be used to indicate a bass note that is dissonant with the chord above it, as shown in figure 19.6b.

Figure 19.6

Figure 19.6

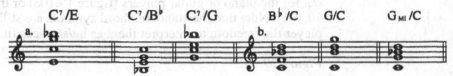

The basic method of notating chord "changes" (harmonic progressions) is to write the chord symbols above a set of *hash marks* or vergules, which indicate how many beats each chord is to be played (figure 19.7). The details of voicing the chords are left to the guitar or piano player, the actual bass line to the bass player, and the actual melodic improvisation to the soloist. This system is effective in conveying the essential harmonic structure of the music, while allowing for the spontaneity characteristic of jazz music.

Figure 19.7

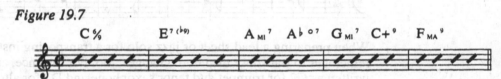

Jazz musicians often play from "lead sheets," which contain a melody line with chord symbols above, as shown in figure 19.8. A compilation of such lead sheets is referred to as a "fake book."

Figure 19.8

Even when a jazz solo is written out, chord symbols should always be provided above the notes. If the solo is a recognized classic, having the chord symbols will allow the player to embellish the solo or to replace it with his/her own improvisation. If the arrangement is for inexperienced jazz musicians who might not be able to create an effective improvised solo, it will help them in learning the connection between chord symbols and melodic improvisation (figure 19.9).

Figure 19.9

In similar fashion, specific chord voicings and bass lines are sometimes written out for the piano or guitar players (figure 19.10a) or the bass player (figure 19.10b). Note that the standard chord symbols are still provided, allowing the player the freedom to interpret them as he/she sees fit.

Figure 19.10

When preparing a lead sheet or jazz solo for a transposing instrument, be sure to remember to transpose the chord changes, too. For instance, an F7 chord will be written as G7 for trumpet and tenor saxophone and D7 for alto saxophone.

Notation of Rhythm and Phrasing

Jazz rhythms are broadly divided into "swing" and "straight" styles. In recent times, the straight styles have become associated with Latin American and rock music and are often designated, for instance, "samba" or "bossa nova" style or "rock" style. Jazz is usually notated in simple meter ($\frac{4}{4}$ or $\frac{3}{4}$ or $\frac{2}{2}$) and the general style of rhythm indicated with a label placed above the music, as shown in figure 19.11.

Figure 19.11

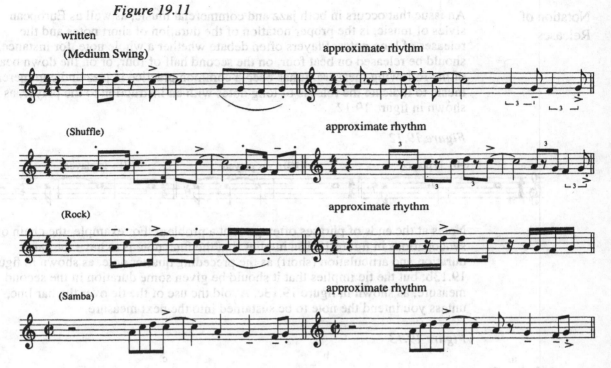

Musicians appreciate having parts copied out for them that reflect the music's phrases, which are usually four or eight measures in length. This is especially important for rhythm section parts, which do not usually indicate the melodic phrasing of the winds. Since it is standard practice to write four or eight measures per system, deviations from this (such as for three-measure or six-measure phrases) can be made at the discretion of the copyist or may be suggested to the copyist by the arranger.

<table>
<tr><td>Notation of
Releases</td><td>An issue that occurs in both jazz and commercial music, as well as European styles of music, is the proper notation of the duration of short notes and the releases of long notes. Players often debate whether a whole note, for instance, should be released on beat four, on the second half of four, or on the down beat of the following measure. It has been a common practice in jazz and commercial music to indicate the release of long notes with an instruction to the player, as shown in figure 19.12.</td></tr>
</table>

Figure 19.12

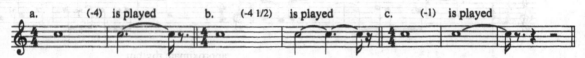

Notes at the ends of phrases often present a problem. For example, the chain of syncopations in figure 19.13a implies that the final note is to have the same duration and articulation (short) as the preceding quarter note, as shown in figure 19.13b; but the tie implies that it should be given some duration in the second measure, as shown in figure 19.13c. Avoid the use of the tie over the bar line, unless you intend the note to be sustained into the next measure.

Figure 19.13

Notation of
Special
Articulations

The notation of pitch bending and pitch distortion requires additional notational symbols. Although there is no standard notation for some of these effects, a few of the more common one are shown in figure 19.14, along with the names often associated with each effect.

Figure 19.14

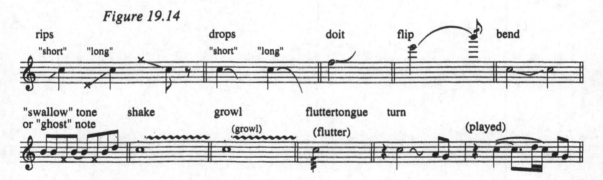

Notation of Special Timbres

Tone color is exploited in jazz through the use of doubling and muting. The most frequent doublings are: trumpet/flugelhorn, sax/flute, sax/alto flute, sax/clarinet, and sax/bass clarinet. Such changes of instrument are notated in the parts with an instruction to the player to change ("take" or "to") to the new instrument, as shown in figure 19.15.

Figure 19.15

In addition to the straight mute, cup mute, and harmon mute mentioned in chapter 5, brass players often use a rubber plunger. This produces a wah-wah effect similar to the harmon mute, but "tubby" in sound. Sometimes when a muffled, blended tone color is called for, the hat or the bucket mute is used. A similar effect is produced when players direct their bells into the stand ("in stand") or cover their bells with their left hands ("hand over bell"). Since mutes have a tendency to distort the pitch and tone in the upper and lower registers, it is best to keep muted passages in the middle register as much as possible.

In all writing involving timbral change, make sure you allow sufficient time for the player to switch instruments or to remove or add a mute. Allow about five seconds (a measure or two in ballad tempo and up to ten measures in fast tempo) for such changes.

Notation of Rhythm Section Parts

As John Cacavas points out in *Music Arranging and Orchestration*, "the drive and push that a rhythm section must generate is extremely difficult to translate into written notation" (p. 123). The complexity that would result defeats the freedom that is inherent in jazz styles. It is much better to indicate the general style and keep rhythmic notation fairly simple.

The simplest possible part is a chord chart (as in figure 19.7), along with a style indication such as "medium swing," "brisk samba," etc. This sometimes suffices for the entire rhythm section, especially if its members are experienced and the arrangement contains no complications.

Usually, however, there is at least a separate drum part, and often a separate bass part. Specific chord voicings and bass lines are notated as in figure 19.10a and 19.10b. Specific rhythms are shown for piano, guitar, or bass, as in figure 19.16. If specific pitches are desired, write them in too.

Figure 19.16

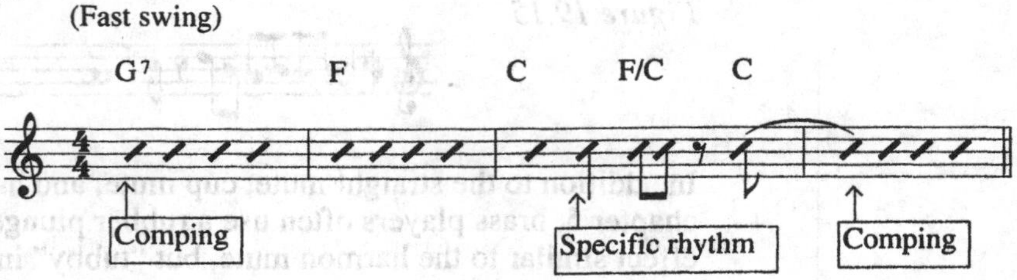

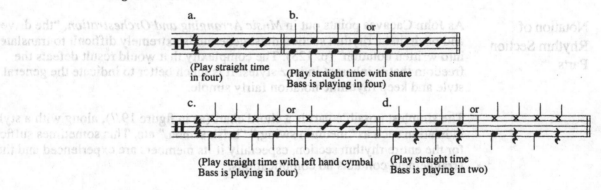

A good drummer can improvise a better drum part than any detailed part you can write. In many cases, they can find most of the stylistic and rhythmic information they need in the lead trumpet part. Bearing this in mind, you should provide the drummer with a basic "road map" that will indicate:

1. The basic beat and rhythm pattern, along with an indication of what the bass player is doing, as shown in figure 19.17.

Figure 19.17

2. The style and dynamics you want, including whether the rhythm should flow smoothly or punch and whether it should be more simple and relaxed or more complex and busy.

3. The rhythmic figures being played by the brass and woodwinds, if you want the drummer to coordinate with those rhythms (figure 19.18a), and suggestions as to how they should be supported (figure 19.18b). This is especially important in the "shout" chorus or other tutti passages.

Figure 19.18

4. The mallets, sticks, or brushes you intend for the drummer to use.

As is the case for the other rhythm instruments, when specific rhythms are desired for the drummer, they should be written out, as in figure 19.19.

Figure 19.19

Drum parts are often quite repetitious, especially during improvised solos. You may use various short cuts to avoid excessive notation, such as the ones shown in figure 19.20.

Figure 19.20

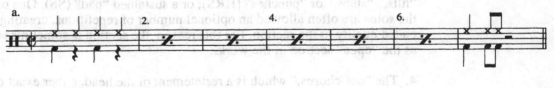

Similarly, in piano and guitar parts, repetitions of a chord voicing or melodic motive may be expressed in more abbreviated form, as in figure 19.21.

Figure 19.21

Form of an Arrangement

The simplest form for a jazz arrangement is as follows:

1. Introduction (usually 4–8 measures).

2. The "head," which is a statement (usually by the full ensemble) of the primary thematic material (typically a 12-bar blues pattern or a 32-measure song). The head is frequently truncated by one or two measures to allow for a solo "break" (an unaccompanied, cadenzalike "fill") by the first soloist. Occasionally, the head may extend into the first solo, either with a decrescendo through a measure or two of sustained harmony or exploding with a written-out tutti break, a drum kick, and a powerful tutti fall-off, out of which the solo emerges.

3. One or more solo "choruses" (based on the formal structure of the head) accompanied by the rhythm section providing harmonic and rhythmic support (HRS and RS) and occasional entrances of the winds playing some sort of background material, such as "lines" or "riffs" (SM); "comping patterns," "fills," "stabs," or "punches" (HRS); or a sustained "pad" (SS). One or more of the solos are often allowed an optional number of repetitions, creating an open-ended quality to the section. For this reason, the section is sometimes referred to as the "open" section of the work.

4. The "out-chorus," which is a restatement of the head, either exact or with variation.

5. Coda (usually brief).

This basic form can be expanded to include transitions between the elements (which may include modulations to new keys) and written-out "shout" or soli choruses inserted between the improvised choruses. Shout choruses display the power and vitality of the ensemble as a whole, while soli choruses feature the agility and virtuosity of a section of the ensemble.

Texture in Jazz Arranging

Big band jazz is normally thought of in terms of *section scoring*, which means that all instruments in a section (saxophones, trumpets, or trombones) are playing and that each is assigned a different part. Most commonly, the melody is at the top of the texture, and the remaining instruments play parallel supporting melodies (PSM) that fill out the chords in three, four, or five parts (figure 19.22).

Figure 19.22

Garland: "In the Mood," m. 9–10.

IN THE MOOD by Joe Garland. © 1939, 1960 Shapiro, Bernstein & Co., Inc.
Copyright Renewed. Used by permission.

This extensive planing can involve one section of the band or any combination of sections. If the full ensemble is involved, the trumpet and trombone parts often duplicate each other in octaves. The saxophone section is often written with an open spacing, in some cases overlapping both the trumpet and trombone sections. The alto saxophones are sometimes written in unison with the upper trumpets, if the parts lie within their range. Figure 19.23 shows typical voicings for full winds.

Figure 19.23

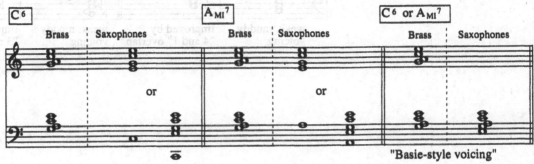

In addition to the skill of writing such basic close-position voicings, there are various techniques that allow you to compensate for problems with extreme registers or to open up a close spacing for a more-spacious effect. Not only must you learn these additional techniques, some of which are presented below, but you must also become proficient at shifting among them as the situation demands.

Overlapping the Trumpet and Trombone Sections

In lower-register voicings, the trumpets and trombones may be treated as a single section, with one or both of the upper two trombones allowed to double one or both of the lower two trumpets. This overlapping overcomes the inherently less powerful sound of the low-register trumpet parts, thus creating a better general balance. It also raises the trombones out of the less-resonant lower register, thus helping to keep the texture from getting too muddy (figure 19.24). Since raising the trombone voicing one inversion creates an overlap with the fourth trumpet, it will be called a "4 and 1" overlap. Raising the trombone voicing two inversions, so that the first trombone doubles the third trumpet, will be called a "3 and 1" overlap.

Figure 19.24

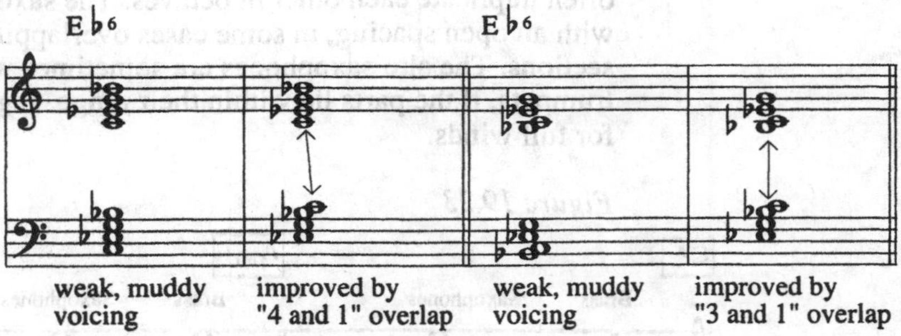

weak, muddy voicing   improved by "4 and 1" overlap   weak, muddy voicing   improved by "3 and 1" overlap

Opening the Texture in the Saxophone Section

A simple method for creating effective open textures in the saxophones is the use of so-called "drop 2" and "drop 2 and 4" spacings. A progression in close spacing (figure 19.25a) can be opened somewhat by dropping the second line from the top one octave (figure 19.25b). A further opening can be accomplished by dropping both the second and fourth lines by an octave (figure 19.25c). "Drop 2" spacing can also be used for trombones. Be careful that the dropped voice is not so low as to muddy the texture.

Figure 19.25

drop 2

drop 2 and 4

Full-ensemble Scoring

Figure 19.26 shows a typical full-wind scoring. If the winds played this passage without the rhythm section (as sometimes occurs in "shout" sections), they would be in monophonic texture with planing. With the addition of harmonic and rhythmic support (HRS) in the rhythm section, however, the overall texture would be homophonic.

Figure 19.26

Bissell: "I Think I'm Falling in Love With You," m. 87–89.

Background parts often contain contrapuntal elements called "fills" (HRS or SM), "stabs" (HRS), "pads" (SS), or "riffs" (SM). These may be unison figures; more often, they are scored in full chords, similar to the scoring of the PM (figure 19.27).

Figure 19.27

Garland: "In the Mood," m. 9–10.

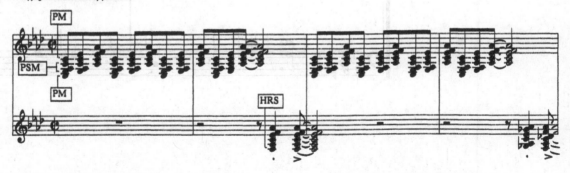

The background material sometimes assumes the role of a more or less continuous melodic line, and the texture becomes truly polyphonic (figure 19.28). (This illustration is over-simplified due to the omission of the rhythm section. The accompaniment it adds to the PM and SM creates a composite texture which is homophonic.)

Figure 19.28

Miller: "Moonlight Serenade," m. 1–4.

MOONLIGHT SERENADE by Miller. Copyright © CPP Belwin, Inc., Miami, FL.

Notice in figure 19.28 that the PM is in both the top and bottom parts of the woodwind texture. When the parallel harmony is in five parts, this doubling of the melody in octaves is quite common.

Solos (written out or improvised) are usually accompanied only with the rhythm section, although the winds may enter periodically to provide fills, pads, stabs, or riffs (figure 19.29).

Figure 19.29

Bissell: "Sunday on the Bayou," m. 64–70.

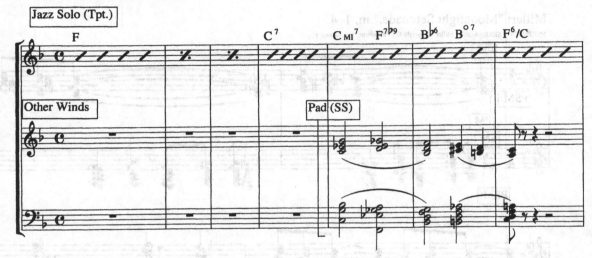

Bissell: "Sunday on the Bayou," m. 79–84.

Of course, jazz ensemble arranging is more varied than these typical examples show, and nearly any kind of texture or harmonic voicing may be used. However, the further you venture away from the standard textures and voicings described above, the more difficult it becomes to preserve the stereotypical big-band sound.

Workbook: Assignments A–F, pp. 157–168.

Suggestions for Further Study

Books that deal with arranging for the big band include:

Cacavas, John. *Music Arranging and Orchestration.* Melville, N.Y.: Belwin-Mills Publishing Corp., 1975.

Garcia, Russell. *The Professional Arranger-Composer.* New York: Criterion Music Corp., 1954.

Grove, Dick. *Arranging Concepts. A Guide to Writing Arrangement for Stage Band Ensemble.* Studio City, Calif.: First Place Music Publications, Inc., 1972.

Mancini, Henry. *Sounds and Scores: A Practical Guide to Professional Orchestration.* Northridge, Calif.: Northridge Music, Inc., 1973.

Riddle, Nelson. *Arranging by Nelson Riddle.* Secaucus, N.J.: Warner Brothers Publications, Inc., 1985.

Russo, William. *Jazz Composition and Orchestration.* Chicago: University of Chicago Press, 1968.

Sebesky, Don. *The Contemporary Arranger.* Melville, NY: Alfred Publishing Co., Inc., 1975.

Wright, Rayburn. *Inside the Score: A Detailed Analysis of Eight Classic Jazz Ensemble Charts.* Delevan, N.Y.: Kendor Music, Inc., 1982.

Books that deal in particular with notation of jazz include:

Brandt, Carl and Clinton Roemer. *Standardized Chord Symbol Notation. A Uniform System for the Music Profession.* Sherman Oaks, Calif.: Roerick Music Co., 1976.

Roemer, Clinton. *The Art of Music Copying.* Sherman Oaks, Calif.: Roerick Music Co., 1973.

Books that deal with popular music or give lead sheets for standard and jazz tunes include:

Ewen, David. *All the Years of American Popular Music: A Comprehensive History.* Englewood Cliffs, N.J.: Prentice-Hall, Inc., 1977.

Sher, Chuck, and Bob Bauer, eds. *The Real Book.* Petaluma, Calif.: Sher Music Co., 1988.

The Best Fake Book Ever [1,000+ songs], Winona, Minn.: Hal Leonard Publishing Corporation, 1990.

The Ultimate Broadway Fake Book [610 songs], Winona, Minn.: Hal Leonard Publishing Corporation, 1984.

This is the Ultimate Fake Book—It Contains Over 1,200 Songs, Winona, Minn.: Hall Leonard Publishing Corp., 1988. (Standard tunes)

Wilder, Alec. *American Popular Song, The Great Innovators, 1900–1950*. New York: Oxford University Press, 1972.

Wong, Dr. Herb, (ed.). *The Ultimate Jazz Fake Book*. Winona, Minn.: Hal Leonard Publishing Corp., 1988.

Books that supplement fake books by showing how to use variations of a song's original chords include:

Collins, Ann. *How to Use a Fake Book*. Winona, Minn: Hal Leonard Publishing Corporation, 1985.

Levine, Mark. *The Jazz Piano Book*. Petaluma, Calif.: Sher Music Co., 1989.

Mantooth, Frank. *Voicings for Jazz Keyboard*. Winona, Minn.: Hal Leonard Publishing Corporation, 1986.

Mantooth, Frank. *The Best Chord Changes for the World's Greatest Standards*. Winona, Minn.: Hal Leonard Publishing Corporation, 1990.

Mantooth, Frank. *The Best Chord Changes for the Most Requested Standards*. Winona, Minn.: Hal Leonard Publishing Corporation, 1990.

Books that deal with the history of jazz and jazz arranging include:

Schuller, Gunther. *Early Jazz: Its Roots and Musical Development*. New York: Oxford University Press, 1968.

Schuller, Gunther. *The Swing Era: The Development of Jazz, 1930–1945*. New York: Oxford University Press, 1989.

20 Special Considerations for Marching Band

General Considerations

Most marching bands perform outdoors, an environment that presents unique challenges for the arranger. Many details are lost due to competing noises or absorption by the air. The true test of the effectiveness of a marching band arrangement is not the way it sounds in the rehearsal room, nor on a recording made in a studio setting by a music publisher, nor even outdoors when the band is in a static position, but rather when it is performed in such active outdoor settings as parade marching or drill maneuvers. It is your responsibility as an arranger to score for the marching band so it will be effective with the band moving in an outdoor environment.

Textural Elements

An examination of the fundamental textural elements as they are used in marching band music will illustrate its differences from concert music.

Primary Melody

The most important element in a marching band arrangement is the primary melody (PM). No other element should be allowed to mask it. Masking can occur when the strongest instruments are not assigned to the melody or when it is not sufficiently doubled. Figure 20.1 illustrates the use of primary melody in an introduction. Note that the melodic fragment is scored in the trombones, which in outdoor performance will project through the other textural elements.

Figure 20.1

An arranger may choose to use no primary melody for a brief moment. This often happens in introductions and transitions or when sound effects, such as tone clusters or "chime sounds" (stacked fourths), are desired.

Secondary Melody

A secondary melody (SM) should complement the primary melody by:

1. Becoming more active when the primary melody is inactive and moving more slowly when the PM is active.

2. Supporting the harmonic structure.

3. Using contrary motion to the primary melody whenever possible.

4. Using imitation if appropriate.

A secondary melody is an important element in an arrangement. Because it contributes to the linear interest or flow of the arrangement, a SM can be more important to an arrangement than a harmony part. Secondary melodies can appear in any register, but the tenor-range instruments (trombones, baritone horn, and tenor saxophones) are the most commonly used. If the secondary melody is scored in the bass register, the results may tend to be too heavy. Figure 20.2 illustrates a SM in the tenor register of the band, as well as a SM in the bass/baritone register.

Figure 20.2

Becket: "Columbia, the Gem of the Ocean," m. 1–2.

Occasionally, the upper woodwinds will play a SM that is simply *figuration*, consisting of rapid scales, trills, and grace notes. This technique, once common in marching band arrangements, has lost its appeal due to difficulties in projecting the part and excessive playing demands on performers who are marching. Figure 20.4 illustrates a typical woodwind figuration.

Figure 20.3

"Blow the Man Down" (American Chantey), m. 1–4.

Parallel supporting melodies (PSM) serve both a harmonic and melodic function. The style of the music determines if PSMs are identical in rhythm to the PM or less active. The parallel supporting melodies in figure 20.3 are identical in rhythm to the primary melody.

Figure 20.4

Lambert: "When Johnny Comes Marching Home"

Because some parallel supporting melodies can reach into the low range of instruments, you may choose to reduce the activity of the parts to avoid a muddy effect. Figure 20.5 shows the same melody as in figure 20.4 with two harmony parts that are not rhythmically identical to it. Note that both parts still follow the melodic contour of the primary melody.

Figure 20.5

Lambert: "When Johnny Comes Marching Home"

It is important to note that using more than three different PSMs tends to clutter a marching band arrangement. In most cases, two PSMs provide sufficient support to the PM.

Static Support

Static support (SS) has only limited use in marching band arranging. Ostinati generally do not carry well and are ineffective. Pedal points, on the other hand, are effective, especially if scored in the bass and heavily reinforced. Figure 20.6 shows a pedal point which has been used to dramatize the ending of an arrangement.

Figure 20.6

Trills played by higher-pitched instruments also provide SS and can be quite effective in outdoor settings. Note that the trill scored for piccolos, flutes, and clarinets in figure 20.7 is in the upper ranges of these instruments to ensure maximum projection.

Figure 20.7

Harmonic and Rhythmic Support

Harmonic and rhythmic support (HRS) is usually present in a marching band arrangement. The most important HRS is that provided by the bass. Bass supporting parts not only underline the harmonic structure, they can add increased rhythmic activity to the arrangement. Common bass effects are:

1. Walking bass (figure 20.8a).

2. Tonic/dominant patterns (figure 20.8b).

3. Rhythmic repetitions (figure 20.8c).

4. Added activity with nonharmonic tones (figure 20.8d).

Figure 20.8

Be careful that the bass line does not become overly active, since this tends to diminish the effectiveness of the part.

HRS is used in the inner parts in many styles of music. This is particularly effective when chord changes occur regularly in every bar or in two-bar groups, as in much popular music. There are many rhythmic patterns that may be used as HRS, and they generally have stylistic implications. For example, the HRS used in rock styles tends to place considerable emphasis on the beat, as illustrated in figure 20.9.

Figure 20.9

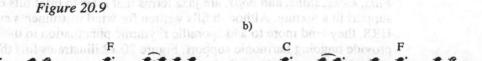

HRS in jazz styles tend to have syncopation and rests between chords. Even when used in rock and other styles, such patterns are typically referred to by the jazz terminology *comping rhythms*. Figure 20.10 is an example of comping rhythms.

Figure 20.10

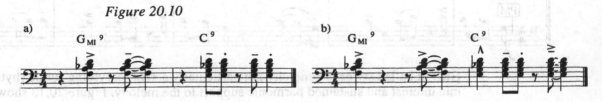

Figure 20.11 shows a rock-style comping rhythm as the only textural element in an introduction. Note the absence of rests between chords. The entrance of a primary melody after the double bar will be more noticeable because of the absence of primary melody in the introduction.

Figure 20.11

Fills, *kicks*, *stabs*, and *bops*, are jazz terms that refer to brief bits of rhythmic support in a texture. Although fills written for wind instruments are labeled as HRS, they tend more to add sporadic rhythmic punctuation to the melody than to provide ongoing harmonic support. Figure 20.12 illustrates fills that are scored against a tenor-register melody.

Figure 20.12

"Good Night Ladies" (College Song), m. 1–4.

HRS in ballad styles is generally not particularly active, providing subtle rhythmic interest and sustained harmonic support to the melody. Figure 20.13 shows two appropriate uses of HRS for a ballad style.

Figure 20.13

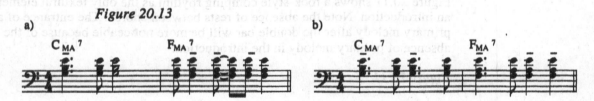

Latin rhythms are a source of many HRS patterns. Several common Latin rhythms are shown in figure 20.14.

Figure 20.14

Rhythmic Support

Marching band percussion sections have changed rapidly over the past twenty years. It is now possible to achieve "tonal" effects with various sizes of bass drums and multiple tom-toms. However, the primary function of the percussion section is still to provide rhythmic support (RS) (figure 20.15a). Notice in figure 20.15b that the percussion section in a contemporary arrangement still supports the music rhythmically, while also including more variety of timbre and providing more interest to the players and listeners.

Figure 20.15

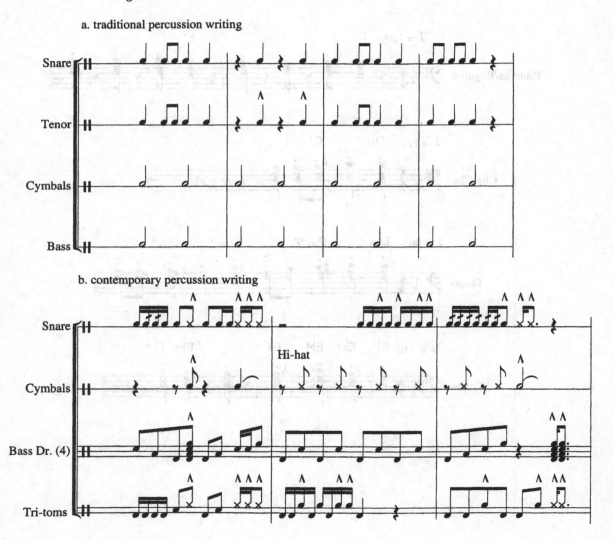

a. traditional percussion writing

b. contemporary percussion writing

In contemporary percussion scoring, it is common to see a great deal of rhythmic activity provided by the percussion section, which adds energy and drive to the arrangement. Care must be taken, though, to create patterns that are playable by the average marching band percussionist.

Figure 20.16

a. good writing

b. too complex

With the addition of tonal bass drums (each tuned to a different pitch), different sizes of cymbals, and multiple toms, it is possible and common in contemporary percussion writing to approximate the effects that a drum-set player can achieve. This is of particular importance, since the majority of pieces that marching bands play are in popular and jazz styles. Figure 20.17a shows a four-bar pattern in a popular style that might be played by a drum-set player. Figure 20.17b shows the same phrase scored for a marching band percussion section.

Figure 20.17

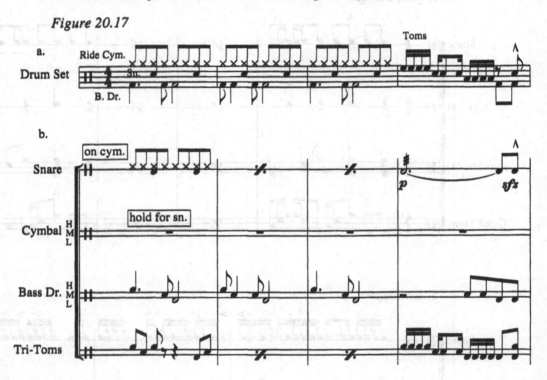

Assignments for Each Instrument in the Marching Band

The instrumentation of the marching band is more restricted than that of a concert band. The outdoor setting, with the performers moving about the field, places new limitations on the effective range and technical demands placed upon the players. Given these restrictions, one challenge you will face in scoring for this ensemble is to get sufficient variety in sound to make an interesting arrangement. It is important to examine each instrument's primary and secondary musical functions in the ensemble (Figure 20.18).

Figure 20.18

Instrument	Most common assignments	Secondary assignments
Piccolo	PM (15va)	HRS, SS
Flute	PM (8va)	HRS, SS
Clarinet	PSM (8va)	PM, HRS, SS
Alto Saxophone	PSM	PM, SM, HRS
Tenor Saxophone	SM	PM, HRS, SS
Baritone Saxophone	HRS	PM, SM, SS
Trumpet (Cornet)	PM, PSM	HRS
F Horn (Mellophone)	PSM	PM, SM, HRS
Trombone	SM, HRS	PM, PSM, SS
Baritone Horn	SM, HR	SPM, PSM, SS
Basses (Sousaphones)	HR	SPM, SS
Mallet Percussion	PM (alone or with PSM), HRS	PSM, SS
Snare Drum	RS	
Bass Drum	RS	
Cymbals	RS	
Multiple Toms	RS	

Ranges

In outdoor performance, the instruments are restricted to their strongest registers to ensure that they will be heard. Three other factors affect the practical ranges of the instruments:

1. The musicians are usually playing and marching at the same time. It is not practical for brass players to play in the upper register for any length of time while marching.

2. Temperature extremes often cause significant intonation problems, particularly in the upper registers of the woodwinds.

3. Players have little opportunity to rest, since most marching band arrangements are scored tutti throughout.

Figure 20.19 shows the practical ranges of the wind instruments commonly used in marching band scoring.

Figure 20.19

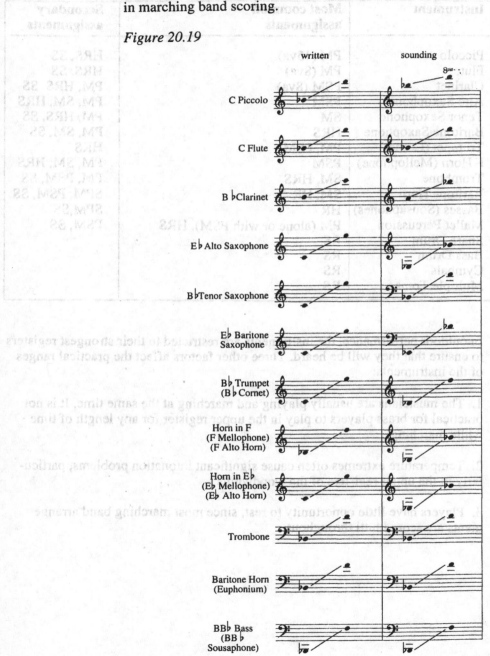

Woodwinds

The woodwinds have much less carrying power than the brass in an outdoor environment. They are used primarily to double lines in the brass, with the exception of occasional figurations. The woodwinds can be used to reinforce any line in the texture that is in their range.

Piccolo and Flute

The piccolo and flute are usually written as one part, designated "Flute & Piccolo." Since the piccolo transposes up an octave, the result is an octave doubling of the flute line. The flute and piccolo can be most effectively used in doubling the PM an octave higher than the trumpets, as shown in figure 20.20.

Figure 20.20

It is also possible to have the flute and piccolos play a supporting role if they are doubled by other treble instruments. Figure 20.21 shows a HRS part scored for treble instruments, including piccolos and flutes.

Figure 20.21

Figurations are appropriate for flute and piccolo. The more active line can usually be heard over the primary melody if the stronger registers of the instruments are used (figure 20.3).

Clarinet

Most modern marching band arrangements contain only one part for the clarinets. The earlier practice of writing three clarinet parts has been abandoned due to the lack of carrying power of the instruments. The clarinets often double a PSM (the second or third trumpet parts) at the octave. This puts the clarinets in their best register and supports the inner voices in the trumpets. Figure 20.22 shows this common and effective technique.

Figure 20.22

Cichy: "Cyclone Cheer."

A part can also be written that combines elements of the first, second, and third trumpet parts transposed up an octave (figure 20.23). This is commonly referred to as a *repiano* part.

Figure 20.23

Sanderson: "Hail to the Chief."

If the primary melody is scored in the alto or tenor voice of the band, the clarinets can still double a trumpet part at the octave (figure 20.24).

Figure 20.24

Becket: "Columbia, the Gem of the Ocean," m. 1–4.

If a figuration is used, the clarinets should be scored with the flute and piccolos for maximum sound projection (figure 20.3).

Alto Saxophone

Most modern arrangements have only one alto saxophone part. Two parts may be written if the alto saxophone section is large. The alto saxophones will normally double either the second or third trumpets parts. (Both trumpet parts could be doubled if two parts are written.) It is also possible to combine the alto saxophones and horns on a parallel supporting melody below the third trumpets (figure 20.25), but the alto saxophones should not be allowed to stand alone on a part unless it is a reinforcement of the PM written down one octave.

Figure 20.25

The alto saxophone may be used to double the trombones and baritone horn. In a top-heavy band, it is advantageous to score the alto saxophones lower in the texture (figure 20.26).

Figure 20.26

Tenor Saxophone	Tenor saxophone parts often also serve as treble clef baritone horn parts: "tenor saxophone/baritone T.C." The tenor saxophones normally double either the baritone horn or the trombones. Many times the tenor saxophones, baritone horns, and trombones are scored together on secondary melodic material (figure 20.27).

Figure 20.27

Foster: "Oh, Susanna."

Baritone Saxophone	Not all marching bands will have a baritone saxophone, but this instrument can be quite effective in supporting a weak tuba section. The part for baritone saxophone will nearly always double the tuba line.
Brass	The brass section is the dominant force in the marching band. Standard arrangements include three trumpet parts, one horn part, two trombone parts, one baritone horn part, and one tuba part. Two horn parts and three trombone parts are sometimes provided, but the third trombone will normally double the baritone horn in such cases. If you are scoring for a particular band, you can adjust the number of brass parts to match the strength of each section.
Trumpets (Cornets)	The trumpet section, having the highest range of the brass, tends to dominate the marching band. Most marching band arrangements are scored with three separate parts, with the first trumpets on the PM, the second trumpets on the first PSM, and the third trumpets on the second PSM. When the PM is in the lower register, the second and third trumpet parts may double each other to keep the third trumpet out of the lowest register, or both the second and third trumpet

parts may double the first trumpet. This is particularly true if the line requires rapid articulation. Figure 20.28 is an example of overlapping parts in the trumpet section.

Figure 20.28

Smith: "The Star-Spangled Banner."

If the band is young or inexperienced, the trumpets are divided into two parts, with the first trumpets on the PM and the second trumpets on PSM. When the PM is transferred to a lower voice in the band, the trumpet section may provide an accompaniment or be allowed to rest.

Horns (Alto Horns/ Mellophones)

The horn section (like the alto saxophones) has considerable freedom in its assignments within an arrangement. The horn section is usually not strong enough to carry an independent part and is often doubled with the alto saxophones (figure 20.25). The horns can also double one of the trombone parts (figure 20.26) or double the PM an octave lower, particularly if the band is top-heavy (figure 20.29).

Figure 20.29

Foster: "Oh! Susanna."

Trombones

If the trombone section is strong, it is desirable to score more than one part. However, a weak trombone section will be swallowed up if split into several parts. It is advantageous when scoring for a young band to write only one trombone part, but in an average-size marching band of older players, two parts are generally written. You should avoid writing so low for the trombones that it produces a muddy bass register. Figure 20.30 demonstrates two voicings of a C major chord.

Figure 20.30

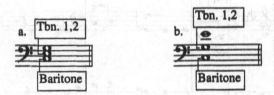

The first voicing (figure 20.30a) will produce a muddy sound because of close spacing in the lower register. The second voicing (figure 20.30b) will produce a clear and strong-sounding chord. In an texture with a SM in the tenor range, it is important to assign enough instruments to the SM to allow maximum clarity and projection. Normally, the trombones, baritone horn, and tenor saxophones will be doubled on any important secondary melodic material.

Baritone Horns (Euphoniums)

While the baritone horns can add substance to the low register of the band, most marching bands do not have large baritone horn sections. Since the baritone horn does not have the penetrating power of the trumpets and trombones, the arranger must be careful in assigning the baritone horn a place in the texture. The baritone horn often doubles the lowest trombone part in an accompaniment texture. When a SM appears in the tenor range, the baritone horn should double the trombone and tenor saxophone part (figure 20.27). The baritone horn, trombones, tenor saxophones, and possibly the horns and alto saxophones should be scored in unison when the PM is in the tenor register (figure 20.31).

Figure 20.31

Becket: "Columbia, the Gem of the Ocean", m. 1–4.

If the bass section of the band is weak or needs to be brought out, the baritone horn can play the tuba part an octave higher (figure 20.2).

In a ballad or chorale style, the baritone horn can double the primary melody in the trumpets an octave lower. This technique is particularly effective on lyrical lines, due to the warm and resonant quality of the baritone horn (figure 20.32).

Figure 20.32

Ward: "America, the Beautiful", m. 1–4.

**Basses
(Sousaphones)**

The basses are the principal bass instruments in the marching band. With the current trends in popular music for an active bass line, the bass part in marching band arrangements can be both interesting and musically satisfying to the players. Occasionally, when the primary melody is transferred to the tenor voice of the band, it is possible to double the basses on the melody in unison or octaves, if a particularly strong effect in desired (figure 20.33).

Figure 20.33

College Song: "Good Night, Ladies", m. 1–6.

Percussion

The percussion section in a modern marching band includes snare drums (tuned to a high pitch), multiple toms, tonal bass drums (each tuned to a different pitch), and cymbals. Some bands have incorporated a percussion "pit" section that positions itself in front of the band. Instruments that may be included in this pit include: timpani, gongs, full-size mallet percussion instruments, drum sets, and a variety of other percussion instruments. Scoring for a pit section will not be considered in this book.

Mallet Percussion   The use of mallet percussion (sometimes referred to as melodic percussion) is relatively new to marching band arranging. Since earlier days when the glockenspiel played the PM with one mallet, instrument manufacturers have created a line of small-range mallet instruments including vibraphone, xylophone, marimba, and orchestra bells especially designed for marching band. Because of each instrument's particular tone quality, separate parts are sometimes written for each mallet percussion instrument. In most cases, the mallet percussion embellish the PM, but they can be used as a part of the accompaniment texture. Active melodies and rapid passages are no longer a problem, since most mallet percussion instruments are placed in tabletop fashion and played with more than one mallet. Figure 20.34 shows a typical mallet percussion part.

Figure 20.34

College Song: "Good Night, Ladies", m. 1–6.

Snare Drum

The snare drum is the primary rhythmic support (RS) element in the marching band. Modern snare drum carriers have stabilized the snare drum, allowing the player to play much more active parts than before. Through the rhythmic support of the snare drum, an arrangement can gain forward momentum and direction, as shown in figure 20.35. Snare drum parts are never divided unless an antiphonal effect warrants the division.

Figure 20.35

Bass Drum

Bass drum parts tend to be less active than other drum parts, due to the relatively long decay time of the instrument. Typical bass drum parts include playing on the beat and elaborating metric patterns. The recent introduction of tonal bass drums has added a new dimension to the bass percussion. By incorporating several bass drums at different pitches, an arranger can simulate some of the effects of a drum set. These techniques can provide greater variety and add strength to the bass line. In writing tonal bass drum parts, the arranger includes all "pitches" on the neutral clef, although the players only play their particular pitch. as shown in figure 20.36.

Figure 20.36

Tonal bass drums can also fulfill another important function by reinforcing the bass (tuba) line. This is done by imitating the contour of the bass line, as shown in figure 20.37.

Figure 20.37

Some arrangers, not understanding the concepts of tonal bass drum writing, tend to write ascending and descending patterns that fit the PM. In most cases, this does not create strong rhythmic support. You should avoid writing a pattern such as the one in figure 20.38 unless it matches the contour of a walking bass pattern.

Figure 20.38

Single-note bass drum lines as seen in figure 20.38 will be swallowed up by a large marching band and will provide no metric foundation. Doubling tones among the bass drums will provide a stronger metric support for a large band (figure 20.39).

Figure 20.39

Cymbals

Cymbals provide highlights on accents and climaxes. They can also be used for ongoing rhythmic support. Cymbals create a wide variety of sounds through different playing techniques. Considerable interest can be generated by using a variety of cymbal sounds in an arrangement. A common technique is for the snare drum or multiple tom players to play on the cymbals with their sticks. This simulates the "ride cymbal" effect that is prominent in popular music. The simulation of the "hi-hat" effect can be accomplished by having the snare drum or multiple tom players play on closed cymbals. Figure 20.40 illustrates common scoring techniques for snare drum and cymbals. Note the instruction for the cymbal players.

Figure 20.40

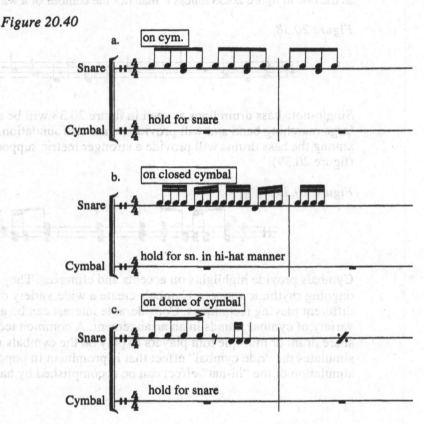

Thought must be given when designing drills and formations, so that percussionists will be able to "couple-up" for these special effects.

Some marching band arrangements call for various sizes of cymbals, but they are mostly a visual effect. The differences in sound are subtle.

Multiple Toms

Multiple toms are a relatively new addition to the standard instrumentation of the marching band, but they are now widely used. Multiple toms may come in clusters as small as two (duos) or as large as five (quints). (Larger clusters may be available.) The role of multiple toms is to integrate elements of the snare drum and bass drum parts into a cohesive whole. The actual order of the multiple toms must be considered when scoring, since some patterns will be much easier to play than others. Multiple toms usually are not set-up in ascending or descending order, because they would be heavier on the low side and difficult to carry. Figure 20.41 represents common set-ups for tom-tom clusters.

Figure 20.41

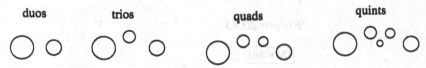

As with the bass drums, the multiple toms can achieve many tonal effects utilized by drum-set players. Several typical patterns are shown in figure 20.42.

Figure 20.42

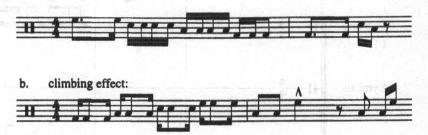

A Step-by-step Approach to Scoring for the Marching Band

The central issue in scoring for the marching band is the outdoor performance environment, which obscures all subtle effects. The number of independent lines in marching band arrangements is smaller than in concert arrangements, and all textural elements are doubled extensively to allow them to project. The overall size, instrumentation, and playing ability of a particular marching band should influence your choice of textural elements and number of independent lines. The following step-by-step method is an organized way of creating a marching band score.

Scoring Essential Textural Elements

The most important elements in a marching band arrangement are the primary melody (PM), harmonic and rhythmic support (HRS) and bass (HRS or SM), and secondary melody (SM). You should first score these elements (PM, HRS, and SM) in the brass. Additional textural elements, including parallel supporting melodies (PSM) and static support (SS), will add substance, but are not a prerequisite for effective scoring. When scoring music in pop style, more emphasis is usually placed on highly active harmonic and rhythmic support (HRS); a secondary melody will not be an essential element.

In some cases, when the percussion is prominent, you may need to write these parts at the same time as the wind parts. Figure 20.43 illustrates a rhythmic figure that is passed down from treble to bass clef instruments and then to the percussion. The percussion figure would likely be written early in the arranging process.

Figure 20.43

Figure 20.44 represents a climactic point in an arrangement. The percussion could be added at this point to support the crescendo and mark the climax.

Figure 20.44

Adding Additional Elements

Once the essential textural elements are scored, you should consider other elements that will support the particular style of the arrangment. These elements are then scored for the remaining brass. In most styles of music, parallel supporting melodies (PSM) provide strong harmonic support to the primary melody and reinforce its rhythmic pattern. Scoring two parallel supporting melodies is normal (figure 20.4); however, music written in some jazz styles tend to use three PSM to include additional tones found in the harmony (figure 20.25).

Pop and jazz styles of music tend to rely on HRS to provide an appropriate accompaniment to the primary melody. In these styles, it is common to see three, and in some cases, four separate HRS parts and no PSM (figures 20.12 and 20.26). When scoring for less-experienced bands, use only two lines of harmonic and rhythmic support (figure 20.45).

Figure 20.45

Static support, which is primarily limited to pedal points and trills, must be strongly reinforced to create the desired dramatic effects (figures 20.6 and 20.7).

Adding Woodwind Reinforcement

Once the brass parts are complete, you can add woodwind doublings for reinforcement. Assign each woodwind instrument to one of its common or secondary assignments (figure 20.18). Figure 20.46 shows how the woodwinds have been used to reinforce the PM and PSM.

Figure 20.46

Cichy. "There is a Place I-o-wa,"

Adding Rhythmic Support in the Percussion

The percussion is usually scored last. That does not mean that the percussion is just an afterthought and not essential to the arrangement. Scoring the percussion after the other parts gives you the opportunity to view the arrangement as a whole and write percussion figures to underline and clarify the wind parts.

Workbook: Assignments A–F, pp. 169–186.

Suggestions for Further Study

Several recommended books specializing in marching band arranging include:

Heine, R. W., and C. L. Spohn. *The Marching Band: Comparative Techniques in Movement and Music*. Boston: Allyn & Bacon, 1969.

Vinson, J. *Arranging for the Marching Band*. Lebanon, Ind.: Studio 224, 1981.

General treatises addressing marching band arranging include:

Cichy, R. D. *Procedures for Editing Marching Band Arrangements to Achieve Maximum Sound for Outdoor Performance*. Master's Thesis, The Ohio State University, 1985.

Heine, R.W. *A Method of Simplified Scoring for the Marching Band*. Master's Thesis, The Ohio State University, 1950.

(These works are available through inter-library loan from The Ohio State University.)

Other books specializing in scoring for bands associated with outdoor performance include:

Hind, H. C. *The Brass Band*. London: Hawks & Son, 1934.

Hoby, V. *Military Band Instrumentation*. London: Oxford, 1936.

White, W. C. *Military Band Arranging*. New York: Carl Fischer, 1924.

A Appendix: *Ranges of Band and Orchestral Instruments*

The following charts are a summary of the range information presented through-out the book. It is brought together here for your convenience.

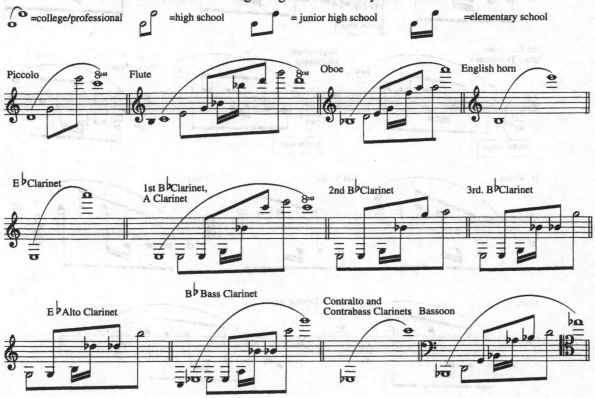

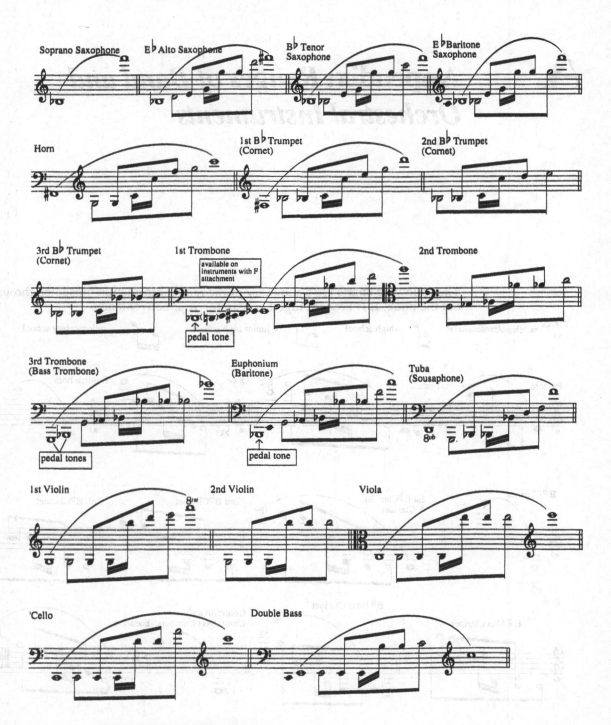

Ranges of Band and Orchestral Instruments

B Appendix: *The Human Voice: Chorus*

The human voice is the most common musical instrument and certainly the model that most mechanical musical instruments originally emulated. Since we all have a voice, it might seem that there would be general understanding of the nature and capabilities of the instrument, but that is far from the truth. The voice is difficult to understand because the mechanism is inside the body and not entirely under our conscious control. It is a complex musical instrument that remains somewhat mysterious, in spite of extensive scientific investigation. In this brief appendix we will deal only with the voice as it is used in choral ensembles.

Voices (Choral)	French	German	Italian
	soprano	Sopran	soprano
	alto	Alt	alto
	ténor	Tenor	tenore
	basse	Baß	basso

Ranges

Figure B.1

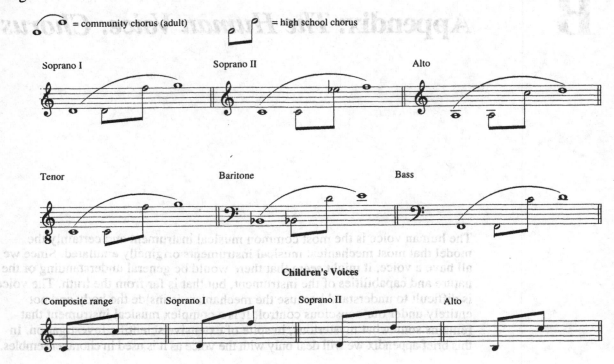

Children's Voices

Composite range   Soprano I   Soprano II   Alto

Changing Male Voices (Cambiata Voice)

1st Change   2nd Change   Baritone (Junior High School)

Transposition

The voices are written at actual pitch, except for the tenor, which is usually written in the treble clef and transposed by an octave (figure B.2).

Figure B. 2

tenor voice

written   sounding

| **Tessitura and Stamina** | Tessitura is a very important consideration in writing for the voice. In general, the tessitura should be near the middle of each singer's range. However, continuous singing in any register will result in fatigue, and vocal parts should allow the singers to move about over most of their range. Frequent short rests are essential, particularly for younger singers. |

Part Writing

In writing vocal music, you must be especially careful to use good voice leading in all parts, since singers have more difficulty than instrumentalists in finding their pitches. The principles you learned in earlier theory training were designed specifically to ensure parts that were easily sung, and you will never go wrong by observing these principles in writing for voices. Modern styles, of course, have moved much more toward parallel writing (planing) in all parts, but the basic voice leading principles that prohibit awkward intervals such as augmented seconds and tritones and avoid too many leaps in parts are good principles in all musical styles.

In accompanied vocal music, it is always easier if the accompaniment provides the pitch before important entrances, and you are inviting disaster if you write an accompaniment that only confirms the pitch after the chorus has already entered (perhaps on a slightly different pitch).

Text Setting

A unique aspect of writing for the voice is that the music must express a text. An arrangement usually begins with a preexisting text and melodic line. However, you must be careful to reflect the text clearly and accurately in the parts you write for the accompanying voices. Several general principles should guide your work:

1. All voices should have sensible texts to sing. Read the text that each part will be singing and ask yourself if the text makes sense. It is not necessary for all parts to have the complete text, and it is common for parts to repeat segments of the text when needed, but the resulting text for each part should make sense when read by itself.

2. Text generates a rhythm when spoken, and the rhythms of the parts must accurately reflect the general rhythm of the text. This does not mean that all unstressed syllables should be given a single note value (an eighth note, for example) and all stressed syllables a single note value (a quarter note, for example), which would result in a boring and repetitive rhythm in the arrangement. It does mean that relatively stressed syllables should, in general, be given longer note values and the unstressed syllables shorter note values if the text is to be clearly understood by the listener.

3. Phrases of text are spoken with a rising and falling inflection, and the lines should, in general, reflect these natural "spoken melodies." It is, of course, nearly impossible in part writing to have all parts express this natural melodic contour, but intelligibility is enhanced when prominent lines do so.

Intelligibility and Register

Words are most intelligible when sung in the middle and lower registers of the voice. In the upper register, there is a tendency for vowels to sound more and more alike and this has a negative impact on intelligibility. The effect is more pronounced in the soprano voice and less so with the lower voices. A good strategy in text setting is to have the singers state the text in the middle register and repeat it in the upper register for emphasis. There is little problem with losing the meaning of the text in this way.

Notation

The special notation rules for voice all arise from the presence of text. The text is laid under the staff, with each syllable separated by one or more dashes (figure B.3). Each syllable should be directly below the note on which it is to be sung. Dynamic indications of all kinds are placed above the staff to keep them out of the way of the text. The traditional practice is for beaming to be used only when a group of notes is to be sung on a single syllable; otherwise, notes are flagged separately. Modern practice has tended toward beaming all note groups, regardless of syllabication, but the examples in this book follow the traditional practice. Groups of notes to be sung with a single syllable are slurred together. If more than one note is to be sung on the final syllable of a word, an extension line is drawn after the word, extending to the last note to be sung under that syllable. If the word is followed by punctuation, the extension line begins one space after the punctuation mark.

Figure B.3

Brahms: *Ach, wende diesen Blick*   op. 57, no. 4, m. 16–21.

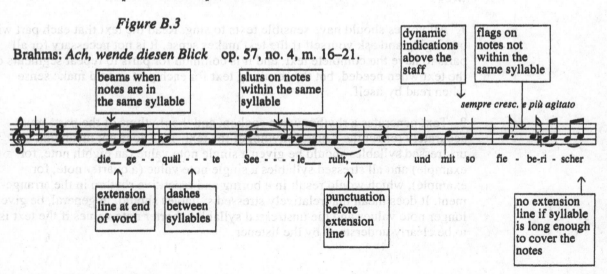

Standard Choral Ensembles

Choruses vary in size and makeup from small unison choirs to large eight-part choirs. They may be either unaccompanied (*a cappella*) or accompanied by piano, other instruments (organ, harp, etc.), or ensembles (orchestra, wind ensemble, etc.). The addition of solo instruments or solo voices to the chorus is quite common. There are, however, a number of "standard" choral ensembles that occur often enough to merit discussion.

Two-part Children's Chorus (SA)

Music for two-part children's chorus is usually accompanied by the piano, which fills out harmonies and provides a bass line (figure B.4).

Figure B.4

White: "I Am Waiting," m.35–43.
Copyright © Gary White. Reprint by permission.

Be very careful to provide strong pitch cues in the accompaniment and use unison writing quite often to give young singers confidence. Devices such as antiphonal (question and answer) passages and passages that begin in unison and split into two parts near a cadence are also quite effective and inspire confidence in young singers. Parallel thirds are effective and usually can be taught quite easily. Truly independent two-part writing is relatively rare for this ensemble.

Three-part Chorus (SAB)

This chorus is the standard vocal ensemble in the junior high or middle school. The ensemble is usually accompanied by the piano to provide security and fill out the harmony (figure B.5). The male voices are combined together into a single "baritone" part that observes the rather restricted range of the male voice which has only recently changed, and may not yet be settled. The parts can be fairly independent, but care should be taken to make the entrances of the baritones very clear and obvious, since the young men, not yet accustomed to finding pitches in the bass register, are easily confused.

Figure B.5

Traditional (arr. Roy Ringwald): "The Holly and the Ivy".

Four-part Chorus (SATB)

The four-part mixed chorus is the standard adult choral ensemble. It may be either accompanied or unaccompanied (*a cappella*). If there is no accompaniment, the usual practice is to include a piano reduction marked "for rehearsal only" to simplify the task of the conductor (figure B.6). The chorus is written in open score, with the tenor parts transposed into the treble clef. The reduction shows all four parts on two staves, with the tenor parts written at pitch.

Figure B.6

White: Time Echoes II (Dark Swimming), m. 9–15.

Women's Chorus or Glee Club (SSA or SSAA)

The standard female chorus is a three-part chorus (SSA) with piano accompaniment. The usual disposition of parts is a closely spaced texture, resembling the soprano, alto, and tenor parts of an SATB arrangement with the bass provided by the piano, which either doubles the vocal parts as well or provides an independent accompaniment texture (figure B.7).

Figure B.7

Loewe (arr. C. Warnick): "How to Handle a Woman."

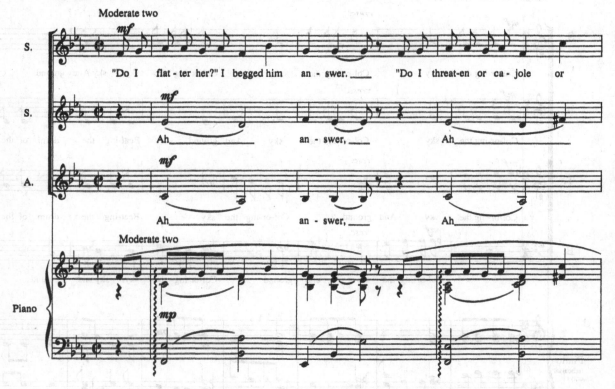

The four-part (SSAA) chorus is relatively rare, except for the "Harmony International" style, which is dealt with in the section on barbershop styles.

Men's Chorus or Glee Club (TTBB)

The standard male chorus is a four-part (TTBB) ensemble, either accompanied or *a cappella*. The two tenor parts are written in the treble clef in transposition, and if there is no accompaniment, a piano reduction is provided with the tenor parts written at pitch, using either the treble or bass clefs as needed (figure B.8).

Figure B.8

Mendelssohn: *Der Jäger Abschied.*

Barbershop Styles

A particular style of singing, promoted by the Society for the Preservation and Encouragement of Barber Shop Quartet Singing in America, is an unaccompanied four-part male quartet or chorus (TTBB) with the primary melody in the second tenor (called "lead"), a harmony part that remains above the lead in the first tenor (called "tenor"), closely spaced harmony in the baritone part (which often crosses the lead), and a bass part that provides a true harmonic bass.

Female choruses called "Harmony International" (formerly "Sweet Adelines") are four part unaccompanied quartets or choruses with parts that duplicate the functions described above at the octave. The four parts are written as if they were for male chorus (singers are instructed to transpose the bass clef parts up one octave) and are designated as lead, tenor, baritone, and bass. This unusual practice allows the groups to perform the literature written for the male groups without modification. Harmony International, Inc., is an umbrella organization that publishes barbershop music and promotes local choruses in the United States and abroad.

Space does not permit a complete description of this musical style, and you may wish to consult the books dealing with arranging for barbershop chorus listed at the end of this section or examine published music from the societies. For further information, contact the societies themselves.

Special Techniques

The use of isolated vowel sounds instead of words is well established as a choral accompaniment device. This effect has been overused in the past and has become somewhat of a cliché, but it remains a standard device. Humming can produce subdued and subtle backgrounds for individual and section melodies. Combinations of consonants with isolated vowels and humming can be used to imitate the sounds of various instruments, giving the chorus the character of an instrumental ensemble. *Scat singing* is a vocal technique similar to instrumental imitation, that developed as a part of vocal jazz, and is now a standard part of the choral jazz style.

Several textural patterns occur often enough in choral writing to be given names such as: *choral fan*, *pyramid*, *choral pedal point*, and *choral cadenza*. These patterns are discussed in detail in the books on choral arranging listed below.

The use of the vocal mechanism in nontraditional ways, such as percussive sounds, hissing, etc., have been explored in much contemporary choral music.

Suggestions for Further Study

Two important texts for choral arranging are:

Ades, Hawley. *Choral Arranging, Expanded Edition*. Delaware Water Gap, Pa.: Shawnee Press, Inc., 1983.

Ostrander, Arthur E., and Dana Wilson. *Contemporary Choral Arranging*. Englewood Cliffs, N.J.: Prentice-Hall, Inc., 1986.

An older book, now out of print, but available in many libraries is:

Davison, Archibald T. *The Technique of Choral Composition*. Cambridge, Mass: Harvard University Press, 1966.

Orchestration books that include sections on accompanying the voice are:

Rimsky-Korsakov, Nicolai. *Principles of Orchestration*. New York: Dover Publications, Inc., 1964.

Rogers, Bernard. *The Art of Orchestration*. New York: Appleton-Century-Crofts, Inc., 1951.

An instrumentation book that includes the human voice:

Stiller, Andrew. *Handbook of Instrumentation*. Berkeley, Calif.: University of California Press, 1985.

Contemporary techniques are discussed in:

Anhalt, Istvan. *Alternative Voices: Essays on Contemporary Vocal and Choral Composition*. Toronto: University of Toronto Press, 1984.

Arranging for barbershop chorus is discussed in:

Barbershop Arranging Manual, available from the Society for the Preservation and Encouragement of Barber Shop Singing in America, 6315 Third Avenue, Kenosha, WI 53140–5199.

C Appendix: *Glossary of English, Italian, German, and French names and terms*

à (F.) To, at, in.

a (It.) To, from, by. The phrases a2, a3 (etc.) indicate the number of parts to be played by two, three (etc.) players.

à peine (F.) Scarcely, hardly.

a piacere (It.) The execution of the passage is left to the performer's discretion.

a tempo (It.) At the original tempo.

abdämpfen (G.) To mute.

aber (G.) But.

abgestossen (G.) alternate up bows and down bows.

Abstrich (G.) Down bow.

accelerando (accel.) (It.) Becoming faster.

accélérant (F.) Becoming faster.

accent (F.) Expression.

accentué (F.) Accented, marked, stressed.

accompagnando (It.) Accompanying.

accompagnant, en (F.) Accompanying.

accord (F.) Chord.

accordato, accordé (It., F.) Tune the instrument as specified.

accordo (It.) Chord.

Achtelnote, Achtelpause (G.) Eighth note, eighth rest.

adagio (It.) Slow, leisurely.

affettuoso (It.) Tenderly, with feeling.

affrettare (affrett.) (It.) Hastening a little.

agitato, agitando, agitare, con agitazione (It.) Agitated, excited.

agité (F.) Excited, restless.

air, à l' (F.) In the air, up.

Akkord (G.) Chord.

al (It.) To the.

alcuna (It.) Some.

al fine (It.) "The end," an indication to return to the start of a piece and to repeat it only to the point marked "fine."

aleggiare (It.) Fluttering, quivering.

alla breve (It.) Indicates two beats to a measure, at a rather quick tempo.

alla, alle, allo (It.) To the.

allargando (allarg.) (It.) Slowing down, becoming broader and sometimes also louder.

alle, alles (G.) All, every, each.

allegramente (It.) Cheerfully, gaily.

allegretto (It.) A moderately quick tempo, slower than allegro but faster than andante.

allegro (It.) A fast, lively tempo, faster than allegretto but slower than presto.

allègre (F.) Lively, sprightly, gay.

allein (G.) Alone, solo.

allentando (It.) Slowing down, slackening the tempo.

allmählich (G.) Gradually.

alma, con (It.) With spirit, soulfully.

als (G.) As.

alta, alto, altus (A.) (It.) The deeper of the two main divisions of women's (or boys') voices.

Altflöte[n] (G.) Alto Flute.

Altklarinette[n] (G.) Alto clarinet.

alto (E.) *Contralto* (It., F.), *Alt, Altistin* (G.).

alto[s] (A.) (F.) Viola.

alto clarinet (E.) *Clarinetto contralto* (It.), *Altklarinette* (G.), *clarinette alto* (F.).

alto flute (E.) *Flauto contralto* (It.), *Altflöte* (G.), *flûte en sol* (F.).

am (G.) By the, on the.

am Steg (G.) On the bridge.

amabile (It.) Sweet, loving.

ambedue bacchette (It.) With both sticks.

ancora (It.) Again.

andante (It.) A moderately slow tempo, faster than adagio but slower than allegretto.

andantino (It.) Usually, a tempo slightly faster than andante.

anfang (G.) Beginning, initial.

anima (It.) Spirit, animation.

animando (It.) With increasing animation.

animato (It.) Lively, animated, spirited.

animé (F.) Lively, animated.

anreissen (anreißen) (G.) In string playing, a forceful attack.

Antiken Zimbeln (G.) Antique cymbals.

antique cymbals (E.) *Crotali, piatti antichi* (It.), *Antiken Zimbeln* (G.), *cymbales antiques* (F.).

aperto (It.) Indicates open notes on the horn, open strings, and undamped piano notes.

appassionato (It.) Passionate, ardent.

appena (It.) Scarcely, hardly.

apprensivo (It.) Apprehensive.

après (F.) After.

arcata (It.) Bowing.

arcata in giù (It.) Down bow.

arcata in su (It.) Up bow.

archet (F.) Bow.

archetto (It.) Bow.

arco, archi (It.) The bow, or use the bow.

arditamente, ardito (It.) Boldly.

arioso (It.) Melodic, singing.

armonico (It.) Harmonic.

arpa[arpe] (A., *Arp.*) (It.) Harp.

arpège (F.) A broken chord.

arpeggiando, arpeggiato (It.) Playing broken chords.

arpeggieren (G.) Playing broken chords.

arpeggio (It.) A broken chord.

arraché (F.) Forceful pizzicato.

assai (It.) Much, very.

assez (F.) Quite, enough, fairly.

attacca (It.) Continue without a pause.

au, aux (F.) At the, to the.

auf (G.) Open up.

auf dem (G.) On the.

Aufstrich (G.) Up bow.

Ausdruck, mit (G.) With expression.

ausdrucksvoll (G.) Expressively.

Aussenseiten, an den (Außenseiten) (G.) On the outside (shell of a drum).

äusserst (G.) Extreme, utmost.

avant (F.) Before, in front of.

avec (F.) With.

bachetta, bachetti (It.) Drumsticks.

baguettes (F.) Drumsticks.

baigné de pedales (F.) Pedal throughout.

ballo (It.) Dance, ballet.

barcollante (It.) Tottering, staggering.

bariolage (F.) Bowing broken chords across the strings.

Baß [Bäße] (G.) Bass.

bass (E.) *Basso [bassi]* (It.), *Bass [Bässe] (Baß)* (G.), *basse[s]* (F.). The lowest male voice; the lowest member of the string family (see **double bass**).

bass clarinet (B. Cl.) (E.) *Clarinetto [clarinetti] basso* (It.), *Bass Klarinette[n] (Baßklarinette)* (G.), *clarinette basse[s]* (F.).

bass drum (B. drum) (E.) *Gran cassa* (It.), *grosse (große) Trommel* (G.), *grosse caisse* (F.).

basse (F.) Bass.

Bass Klarinette[n] (Bkl.) (Baßklarinette) (G.) Bass clarinet.

basso bassi (It.) Bass.

basso continuo (It.) The baroque practice of filling out the bass part with chords.

basson[s] (Bssn.) (F.) Bassoon.

bassoon (Bsn., Bssn.) (E.) *Fagotto [fagotti]* (It.), *Fagott[e]* (G.), *Basson[s]* (F.).

Bassflöte[n] (Baßflöte) (G.) Bass flute.

Basstuba{Basstuben} (G.) Tuba.

battere (It.) To beat.

batterie (Batt.) (F.) Percussion.

battuta (It.) Measure.

beaucoup (F.) Very, quite, much.

Becken (Beck.) (G.) Cymbals.

Becken am Rieman hängend (G.) Suspended cymbal.

bedächtig (G.) Unhurried, deliberate.

bedeutend (G.) Considerably, definitely.

beide (G.) Both.

beiden Fellen, auf (G.) On both drumheads.

beider Hände (G.) With both hands.

bel canto (It.) A florid style of singing.

bells (chimes) (E.) *Campane* (It.), *Glöcken* (G.), *cloches* (F.).

bémol (F.) Flat.

bemolle (It.) Flat.

ben, bene (It.) Well, quite.

bewegt (G.) Agitated.

bianca (It.) Half note.

bien (F.) Well, thoroughly.

bis (G.) Up to, until.

bis zum schluss dieser szene (G.) To the end of this scene.

bisbigliando (bis.) (It.) Whispering.

bischen, ein (G.) A little.

biscroma (It.) Thirty-second note.

blanche (F.) Half note.

blasen (G.) To blow, play, or sound.

Blasinstrument (G.) Wind instrument.

Blech (G.) Brass instruments.

blocs chinois (F.) Wood blocks.

blousée, blousez (F.) At the edge or rim.

bocca aperta (It.) Mouth open.

bocca chiusa (It.) Mouth closed.

Bogen (Bog.) (G.) Bow.

Bogenführung (G.) Bowing.

bois (F.) Woodwind.

bord, au (F.) At the edge (of a cymbal or drumhead).

bordo, sul (It.) On the rim or edge.

bouché (F.) Stopped note (in horns, etc.).

bowing (E.) *Arcata* (It.), *Bogenführung* (G.), *coup d'archet* (F.).

brass instruments (E.) *Ottoni* (It.), *Blech* (G.), *cuivres* (F.).

Bratsche[n] (Br.) (G.) Viola.

bref, brève (F.) Concise, brief.

breit (G.) Broadly.

breiter (G.) More broadly.

breve (It.) Concise, brief.

breve, alla (It.) Indicates two beats to a measure, at a rather quick tempo.

brillant (F.) Brilliant, showy, sparkling.

brillante (It.) Sparkling, spirited.

brindisi (It.) Drinking song.

brio, con (It.) Vigorously, with fire.

brisé (F.) Short detatched bow strokes.

buffa, buffo (It.) Comic, clownish.

cadenza (It.) A cadenza, florid passage, cadence, close.

cadre, sur le (F.) On the rim or body (of a drum).

caisse claire (C.cl.) (F.) Snare drum.

caisse roulante (F.) Tenor drum.

calando (cal.) (It.) Becoming softer and slower.

calme (F.) Tranquil, still, quiet.

campana, alla (It.) On the dome (of a cymbal).

campanaccio (It.) Cowbell.

campane (Cmp.) (It.) Bells (chimes).

campanelli (Cmp.) (It.) Glockenspiel.

cantabile (It.) In a singing style, lyrical, melodious, flowing.

cantilena (It.) Lullaby, melodious.

canto (It.) Song, voice.

capo (It.) Beginning.

capriccioso, capricciosamente (It.) Fanciful, playful.

capricieux, capricieusement (F.) Fanciful, playful.

carillon (F.) Glockenspiel.

cassa, sulla (It.) On the rim or body (of a drum).

celesta (Cel.) (E., It.) *Celesta* (G.), *célesta* (F.).

'cello (E.) See **violoncello**.

cembalo (It., G.) Harpsichord.

cencerros See **cowbell**.

centre, au (F.) At the center (of a cymbal or drumhead).

changez (F.) Take another instrument.

chant (F.) Song.

chevalet, près du (F.) At or near the bridge.

chinesisches Becken (G.) Crash or Chinese cymbals.

chitarra (It.) Guitar.

chiuso (It.) Closed, stopped.

chord (E.) *Accordo* (It.), *Akkord* (G.), *accord* (F.).

chromatisch (G.) Chromatic.

circa (ca.) (It.) About, approximately.

clarinet (C., Cl., Clt., Clar.) (E.) *Clarinetto [clarinetti]* (It.), *Klarinette[n]* (G.), *clarinette[s]* (F.).

clarinette[s] (Cl.) (F.) Clarinet.

clarinette[s] contrebasse (F.) Contrabass clarinet.

clarinette[s] basse (Cl. bs.) (F.) Bass clarinet.

clarinetto [clarinetti] (Cl., Clar.) (It.) Clarinet.

clarinetto [clarinetti] basso (Cl. basso, Clar. basso) (It.) Bass clarinet.

clarinetto [clarinetti] contrabasso (It.) Contrabass clarinet.

clarinetto [clarinetti] piccolo (Clar. picc.) (It.) Sopranino clarinet.

clavecin (F.) Harpsichord.

cloche de vache (F.) Cowbell.

cloches (F.) Bells (chimes).

coda (It.) End, concluding passage.

col, colla, colle (It.) With the.

colore (It.) Colored.

come (It.) How, like, as.

come prima, come sopra (It.) As at first, as previously.

comme (F.) Like, as, as if.

comodo (It.) Comfortable, easy.

con (It.) With.

continuo (It.) Continuous bass accompaniment.

contralto (A.) (It.) The deeper of the two main divisions of women's voices.

contrabass clarinet (E.) *Clarinetto [clarinetti] contrabasso* (It.), *Kontrabassklarinette[n] (Kontrabaßklarinette)* (G.), *clarinette[s] contrebasse* (F.).

contrabasso [contrabassi] (Cb., C. B.) (It.) Double bass, pl. contabassi or bassi (C. Bassi, Bi.).

contrabassoon (C. Bsn.) (E.) *Contrafagotto [contrafagotti]* (It.), *Kontrafagott[e]* (G.), *contrebasson[s]* (F.).

contrafagotto[contrafagotti] (Cfg., C. Fag., Cont. F.) (It.) Contrabassoon.

contrebasse[s] (C. B.) (F.) Double bass.

contrebasson[s] (C. bssn.) (F.) Contrabassoon.

coperto (It.) Covered, muted.

cor anglais (F.) English horn.

cor[s]; cor[s] à pistons (F.) Horn.

corda (It.) String.

corde, con (It.) With snares.

cornet (E.) *Cornetta (a pistoni)* (It.), *Kornett* (G.), *cornet à pistons* (F.).

cornet à pistons (*C. à p.*, *Pist.*) (F.) Cornet.

cornetta (It.) Cornet.

corno[corni] (*Cor.*, *C.*) (It.) Horn.

corno inglese (*C.* or *Cor. ingl.*) (It.) English horn.

corto (It.) Short, brief.

coup d'archet (F.) Bowing.

courante (F.) Running, rapid, flowing.

cowbells (E.) *Campanaccio* (It.), *Herdengeläut*, *Kuhglocke* (G.), *cloche de vache* (F.).

crash cymbal (E.) *Piatto cinese* (It.), *chinesisches Becken* (G.), *cymbales chinoise* (F.).

croche (F.) Eighth note.

croma (It.) Eighth note.

crotali (It.) Antique cymbals.

cuivré (F.) Played with a brassy tone.

cuivres (F.) Brass instruments.

cupola, sulla (It.) On the dome (of a cymbal).

cymbales (*Cym.*) (F.) Cymbals.

cymbales antiques (F.) Antique cymbals.

cymbales chinoise (F.) Crash or chinese cymbals.

cymbales suspendues par une courroie (F.) Suspended cymbals.

cymbals (**Cym.**, **Cymb.**) (E.) *Piatti* (It.), *Becken* (G.), *cymbales* (F.).

d' (It., F.) Of.

Daumen, mit den (G.) With the thumbs.

d'exécution (F.) Performance.

D.C. (It.) Short for da capo.

D.S. (It.) Short for dal segno.

da capo (**D.C.**) (It.) Repeat from the beginning.

da, dal, dalla, dalle, dall' (It.) Of the, from.

dal segno (**D.S.**) (It.) Repeat from the sign.

Dämpfer (*Dpf.*) (G.) Mute.

dans (F.) In.

dansant (F.) Dancing.

das (G.) The.

de (F.) Of, from.

de plus en plus (F.) More and more.

début (F.) Beginning.

deciso (It.) Determined, resolute.

decrescendo (It.) Becoming softer.

dehors (F.) Outside.

deliberamente (It.) Deliberately, ponderously.

dem (G.) The.

demi-pause (F.) Half rest.

demi-soupir (F.) Eighth rest.

den (G.) The.

der (G.) The.

détaché (F.) Alternate up bows and down bows.

deutlich (G.) Distinctly.

di (It.) Of.

die (G.) The.

dièse (F.) Sharp.

diesis (It.) Sharp.

diminuant, en (F.) Becoming softer.

diminuendo (It.) Becoming softer.

disperazione, disperto, disperatamente (It.) Wildly, despairingly, despondently.

distinto (It.) Distinctly.

dita, con la (It.) With the finger.

divisi (It.) Indicating separate parts where there normally is only one.

dolce, dolcemente (It.) Sweet, smooth, gentle.

dolcissimo (It.) As sweet and gentle as possible.

doppelgriff (G.) Double stop.

double bass (**D.Bs.**) (E.) *Contrabasso [contrabassi]*(It.), *Kontrabass [Kontrabässe]* (*Kontrabaß*) (G.), *contrebasse[s]* (F.).

double-croche (F.) Sixteenth note.

down bow (E.) *Arcata in giù* (It.), *Abstrich* (G.), *tiré* (F.).

drängend (G.) Pressing on.

dreifach (G.) Triple.

dreitaktig (G.) Three beats to a measure.

du (F.) From the, of the.

duetto (It.) Duet.

Dur (G.) Major.

durée (F.) Duration.

e, et (It.) And, is.

eco (It.) Echo.

écho (F.) Echo, echo tone.

Echoton (G.) Echo tone.

ed (It.) And.

effetto, con (It.) Dramatically, forcefully.

eighth note (E.) *Croma* (It.), *Achtelnote* (G.), *croche* (F.).

eighth rest (E.) *Pausa di croma* (It.), *Achtelpause* (G.), *demi*-sopir (F.).

eilen (G.) To hurrry.

ein wenig (G.) A little.

ein, eine, eins (G.) One, a, an.

elegante (It.) Graceful, polished.

elegiaco (It.) Mournful, lamenting.

Empfindung, mit (G.) With feeling, sensitively, tenderly.

empressé (F.) Hurrying, rapid.

en (F.) In.

encore (F.) Again, once more, still.

energico (It.) With vigor, powerfully.

énergique (F.) Vigorous, forceful.

energisch (G.) Vigorous, forceful.

Englischhorn (E. H.) (G.) English horn.

English horn (E. H.) (E.) *Corno inglese* (It.), *Englischhorn* (G.), *cor anglais* (F.).

ensemble (F.) Together.

enveloppé (F.) Muffled.

ernst (G.) Serious, earnest.

eroico (It.) Heroic, dramatic, melodramatic.

espansione, espansivo (It.) Expansion, broadening.

espressivo (espr., espress.), espressione, con (It.) With expression, with feeling.

estremità, all' (It.) At the edge (of a cymbal or drumhead).

et (F.) And.

étouffer, étouffés (F.) Dry; damped.

etwas (G.) Somewhat, rather.

expressif (F.) Expressively.

facile (F., It.) Free, easy flowing.

Fagott[e](**Fag., Fg.**) (G.) Bassoon.

fagotto[fagotti] (**Fag., Fg.**) (It.) Bassoon.

fantaisie, avec (F.) Freely, capriciously, whimsically.

fantasia, con (It.) Freely, with imagination.

fermata (It.) A pause, usually indicated by the sign ⌒

fermé (F.) Closed.

fervent (F.) Enthusiastic, devoted.

fervore, con (It.) With vehemence, ardently.

festivamente (It.) Joyfully, cheerfully.

feu, avec (F.) With fire, passionately.

fin (F.) End.

fine (It.) End.

Fingern, mit den (G.) With the fingers.

Flageolett-Töne (G.) Harmonic.

flat (E.) *Bemolle* (It.), *B* (G.), *bèmol* (F.).

Flatterzunge (G.) Fluttertongue.

flauto[flauti] (Fl.) or *flauto[flauti] grande (Fl. gr.)* (It.) Flute.

flauto[flauti] contralto (Fl. c-alto) (It.) Alto Flute.

flauto[flauti] piccolo (Fl. Picc.) (It.) Piccolo.

flebile (It.) Feeble, plaintive, mournful.

fliessend (fließend) (G.) Flowing.

Flöten (G.) Flutes.

flüssig (G.) Flowing, smooth.

flute (Fl.) (E.) *Flauto (grande)* (It.), *(grosse) Flöte (große Flöte)* (G.), *flûte* (F.).

flûte[s] (Fl.) (F.) Flute.

flûte[s] en sol (F.) Alto Flute.

fluttertongue (E.) *Frullanto* (It.), *Flatterzunge* (G.), *trémolo* (F.).

fois (It.) Time(s).

forte (It.) Loud.

fortepiano (It.) Loud, then soft.

fortissimo (It.) Very loud.

forza, con (It.) Powerful, forceful, loud.

forzando (It.) A sharp accent.

fou (F.) Frantic.

fouet (F.) Slapstick.

frappez (F.) To strike.

frei (G.) Free, especially in free tempo.

freihäng, freihängendes (G.) Hanging freely. An indication to the percussionist to let the cymbals vibrate freely.

French horn see **horn**.

frisch (G.) Brisk, gay, fresh, new.

Frosch, am (G.) With the frog of the bow.

frullanto (It.) Fluttertongue.

frusta di carta (It.) Slapstick.

fuoco, con (It.) With fire, passionately, excited.

fuori, di (It.) From outside (from backstage).

furioso (It.) Wild, passionate.

fusto, al (It.) On the shell (of a drum).

gaillard (F.) Happy, gay, sprightly.

ganz (G.) Quite, wholly, very.

ganze (G.) Whole note (*ganze Note*) or whole rest (*ganze Pause*).

ganzton (G.) Whole tone.

gedämpft (ged.) (G.) Muted, muffled.

gedeckt (G.) Stopped (in horns).

geheimnisvoll (G.) Mysteriously.

Geige[n] (G.) Violin.

gentilmente (It.) Gently, with refinement.

Gesang (G.) Song.

geschlagen (G.) Pulsating; beaten.

gestopft (gest.) (G.) Stopped (in horns).

gestrichen (G.) Bowed.

geteilt (get.) (G.) Divided; indicates that the instrumental group should be divided into two parts to play the passage in question.

getragen (G.) Sustained.

gewöhnlich (G.) As usual.

giocoso (It.) Jocose, humorous.

Gitarre (Git.) (G.) Guitar.

giusto, guistamente (It.) Just, right, appropriate.

gli altri (It.) The rest of the section.

glissando (gliss.) (It.) Rapid scales produced by running the fingers rapidly over all the strings.

Glöcken (G.) Bells (Chimes).

Glockenspiel (Glocken.) (E., G.) *Campanelli* (It.), *carillon* (F.).

glorioso (It.) Glorious, splendid.

gracieux, gracieuse (F.) Graceful.

gradamente (It.) Gradually.

gran cassa (Gr. Cassa, Gr. C., G. C.) (It.) Bass drum.

grand détaché (F.) Alternate up bows and down bows, but with long strokes.

grande (It.) Broadly.

grandioso (It.) Grandiose.

grave, gravemente (It.) Solemn, serious, slow.

grazioso (It.) Graceful and easy.

gridando (It.) A shriek.

grelots (F.) Sleigh bells.

Griffbrett, am (G.) Bow over the fingerboard.

grosse caisse (Gr. c.) (F.) Bass drum.

grosse (große) Flöte[n] (Fl. gr.) (G.) Flute.

grosse (große) Trommel (Gr. Tr.) (G.) Bass drum.

grosser auftakt (G.) Big upbeat.

guitar (E.) *Chitarra* (It.), *Gitarre* (G.), *guitare* (F.).

guitare (F.) Guitar.

gusto, con (It.) With style, with zest.

gut (G.) Good, well.

halb (G.) Half.

halbe (G.) Half note (*halbe Note*) or half rest (*halbe Pause*).

hälfte (G.) Half.

Hälfte, die (G.) Half of the section.

Händen, mit den (G.) With the hands.

Harfe[n] (Hrf.) (G.) Harp.

harmonic (E.) *Armonico* (It.), *Flageolett-Töne* (G.), *harmonique* (F.).

Harmonie (G.) Harmony, chords.

harmonique (F.) Harmonic.

harp (Hp., Hrp.) (E.) *Arpa* (It.), *Harfe* (G.), *harpe* (F.).

harpe[s] (Hp.) (F.) Harp.

harpsichord (E.) *Cembalo* (It., G.), *clavecin* (F.).

Hauptstimme (G.) Primary melodic line.

Haupzeitmass (G.) Original tempo.

Hautbois (*Hb.*) (F.) Oboe.

heilig (G.) Sacred, holy.

Herdengeläut (G.) Cowbells.

héroïque (F.) Noble, grand.

hervortretend (G.) Prominent.

Hoboe[n] (G.) Oboe.

hoch (G.) High, nobly.

Holz (G.) Woodwinds.

Holzblasinstrument (G.) Woodwind instrument.

Holzblock (G.) Wood block.

Holzrand, auf den (G.) On the rim.

Holzschlegel (G.) Wooden drumstick.

horn (*Hr., Hn.*) (E.) *Corno[corni]* (It.), *Horn[Hörner]* (G.), *cor[s], cor[s] à pistons* (F.).

humeur, avec (F.) With humor.

Humor, mit (G.) With humor.

i (It.) The.

il (It.) The.

im (G.) In the.

im gleichen Rhythmus (G.) In the same rhythm.

immer (G.) Always, constantly.

impeto, con (It.) With violence, rushing in.

in Oktaven (G.) In octaves.

incantando (It.) Enchanting, delighting.

insensibilemente (It.) Slightly, imperceptibly.

instrument à vent (F.) Wind instrument.

instrument à vent en bois (F.) Woodwind.

intenso, intensito, intensamente, con intensità (It.) Intensely.

irato (It.) Furious, enraged.

istesso tempo, l' (It.) At the same tempo.

jante, a la (F.) At the edge (of a cymbal or drumhead).

jeté (F.) Throwing the bow against the string so that it will rebound several times on the down bow.

jeu (F.) Playful.

joyeux (F.) Happy, lighthearted.

jusqu'à (F.) Up to, until.

Kadenz (G.) Cadence, cadenza.

kadenzieren (G.) To cadence.

kaum (G.) Scarcely, hardly.

kein, keine, keiner (G.) No, none.

kettledrums (*K.D.*) (E.) *Timpani* (It.), *Pauken* (G.), *timbales* (F.).

klagend (G.) Lamenting.

Klangfarbenmelodie (G.) A "melody" of tone colors, shifting colors as a primary melodic effect.

klar (G.) Clear, distinct.

Klarinette[n] (*Kl.*) (G.) Clarinet.

Klavier (G.) Piano.

kleine (G.) Little.

kleine Flöte[n] (*Kl. Fl.*) (G.) Piccolo.

kleine Trommel (*Kl. Tr.*), *Leinentrommel* (G.) Snare drum.

klingen (G.) To sound.

klingen lassen (G.) Let vibrate.

komisch bedeutsam (G.) Very humorously.

Kontrabass[Kontrabässe] (*Kontrabaß*) (*Kb.*) (G.) Double bass.

Kontrabassklarinette[n] (*Kontrabaßklarinette*) (G.) Contrabass clarinet.

Kontrafagott[e] (*Kfg.*) (G.) Contrabassoon.

Kornett[e] (G.) Cornet.

Kreuz (G.) Sharp.

Kuhglocke (G.) Cowbell.

Kuppe(l), auf die (G.) On the dome (of a cymbal).

kurz, kurze, kurzer (G.) Short, brief.

l' (F.) The.

l.h. (E.) Abbreviation for "left hand."

la (F., It.) The.

lacrimoso (It.) Mournful, tearful.

laisser vibrer (F.) Let vibrate.

lamento, con (It.) Mournful, plaintive.

Ländler (G.) A dance similar the a slow waltz.

lang, lange, langer (G.) Long, long-lasting.

langsam (G.) Slow.

langsamer (G.) Slower.

languendo, langeur (It., F.) Languor.

largamente (It.) Broadly.

largando (It.) Becoming broader, slowing down.

large (F.) Broad, full, fairly slow.

larghetto (It.) A slow tempo, not quite as slow as largo.

largo (It.) Slow, solemn, sustained, a tempo slower than lento but not as slow as grave.

lasci (It.) To abandon.

lasciare vibrare (It.) Let vibrate.

lassen (G.) To let, to allow.

lässig (G.) Slow, lackadaisical.

laut (G.) Loud.

le (F., It.) The.

lebhaft (G.) Lively.

lebhafter (G.) Livelier.

legatissimo (It.) A more forceful indication of legato.

legato (It.) Smooth, even, without any break between notes.

léger (F.) Light, quick.

légèrement, leggieramente (F., It.) Lightly.

leggerezza, con (It.) Lightly, nimbly.

leggiero (legg.) (It.) Light and graceful.

leggio (It.) Desk or stand.

legno, col (It.) Playing with the wood of the bow by bouncing it against the strings.

leicht (G.) Light.

leidenschaftlich (G.) Passionately.

Leinentrommel (G.) Snare drum.

lent (F.) Slow.

lentamente (It.) Slowly.

lento (It.) A slow tempo.

les (F.) The.

let vibrate (E.) *Lasciare vibrare* (It.), *klingen lassen* (G.), *laisser vibrer* (F.).

libero (It.) Freely.

libre (F.) Free, unrestrained.

licenza (It.) Freedom.

lieblich (G.) Lovely, sweet, melodious.

lion's roar (E.) *Ruggito del leone* (It.), *Löwengebrüll* (G.), *rugissement de lion* (F.).

lirico, liricamente (It.) Lyrical, poetic.

lo (It.) The.

loco (It.) Indicates a return to the written pitch following a passage played an octave higher or lower than written.

lontano (It.) Distant, echolike.

louré (F.) A legato bowing but with emphasis on each note.

Luftpause (G.) Pause for breath; a slight pause for phrasing.

lunga, lungo (It.) Long, sustained.

lusingando (It.) Caressing.

lustig (G.) Merry, cheerful.

lyrique (F.) Sweetly singing, melodious.

lyrisch (G.) Sweetly singing, melodious.

ma (It.) But.

maestoso (It.) With dignity, nobly.

maggiore (It.) Major.

mais (F.) But.

majestätisch (G.) Stately, majestic.

majestueux (F.) Stately, majestic.

majeur (F.) Major.

major (M.) (E.) *Maggiore* (It.), *Dur* (G.), *majeur* (F.).

mandolin (Mand.) (E.) *Mandolino* (It.), *Mandoline* (G.), *mandoline* (F.).

mano, con la (It.) With the hand.

marcatissimo (marcatiss.) (It.) With very marked emphasis.

marcato, marcata (marc.) (It.) Accented, stressed, marked.

marche (F.) March.

marcia (It.) March.

marciale (It.) Marchlike, martial.

margine, al (It.) At the edge (of a cymbal or drumhead).

Marsch (G.) March.

marschmässig, nicht eilen (G.) Moderate-paced march, not rushed.

martelé (F.) Heavy, detached up-and-down bowings, played by releasing each bow stroke suddenly and using the point of the bow.

marziale (It.) Martial, military.

mässig (mäßig) (G.) Moderately.

measure (E.) *Battuta* (It.), *Takt* (G.), *mesure* (F.).

melancholisch (G.) Sad.

mélancolique (F.) Sad, mournful, plaintive.

melodia (It.) Melody.

melodico (It.) Melodic, tuneful.

Melodie (G.) Melody.

mélodique (F.) Melodious, tuneful.

même (F.) Same.

meno (It.) Less.

mezzo, mezza (It.) Medium, half.

mesure (F.) Measure.

metà, alla (It.) In the middle (of a cymbal or drumhead).

milieu, au (F.) In the middle.

mindestens (G.) At least.

mineur (F.) Minor.

minor (m.) (E.) *Minore* (It.), *Moll* (G.), *mineur* (F.).

minore (It.) Minor.

misterioso (It.) Mysterious, secretive.

misura (It.) Measured.

mit (G.) With.

Mitte, in der (G.) In the center (of a drumhead or cymbal).

mobile (It.) Changeable, capricious.

moderato (mod.) (It.) A moderate tempo, neither fast nor slow.

modo (It.) Manner, style.

moins (F.) Less.

Moll (G.) Minor.

molle, mollemente (It.) Soft, languid.

molto (It.) Very, much.

mordente (It.) Biting, pungent.

morendo (It.) Dying away.

mormorato, mormorando, come un mormorio (It.) Murmured.

mosso (It.) Moved, agitated.

moto (It.) Motion.

moto, con (It.) Somewhat lively, not too slowly.

mouvement (mouv., mouvt.) (F.) Tempo.

moyen (F.) Medium.

Mund zu (G.) Mouth closed.

muta, mutano (It.) Change the tuning of the instrument as specified.

mute (E.) *Sourdina* (It.), *Dämpfer* (G.), *sourdine* (F.).

mystérieux (F.) Mysterious.

nach (G.) After, behind, in the manner of, according to.

nach und nach (G.) Little by little, gradually.

Nagel, mit den (G.) With the fingernail.

naturel (F.) In the normal manner of playing.

ne—pas (F.) Do not.

Nebenstimme (G.) Secondary part.

nehmen (G.) Take.

nel, nell', nella, nello (It.) In the, inside, within, at, on, to.

neuen (G.) New.

nicht (G.) Not.

niente (It.) Nothing.

nimmt (G.) To take; to seize.

noch (G.) Still, yet.

noch einmal (G.) Once more, again.

non (It.) Not.

normale (It.) Indication to return to normal tuning, pitch, or octave.

note blanche, note plain (F.) Half note.

note noir (F.) Quarter note.

nuovo (It.) New.

o (It.) Or.

obere, oberer (G.) Upper, leading.

oboe (ob.) (E.) *Oboe [oboi]* (It.), *Hoboe[n]* (G.), *Hautbois* (F.).

od (It.) Or.

oder (G.) Or.

oder langsamer (G.) Or slower.

offen (G.) Open.

ohne (G.) Without.

ondeggiante (It.) Undulating movement of the bow, which produces a tremolo effect.

onges, sons d' (F.) With the fingernail.

opus (op.) (L.) Work.

ordinaire, jeu (F.) In the normal manner of playing.

ordinario (ord., ordin.) (It.) In the usual way (generally cancelling an instruction to play using some special technique).

organ (Org.) (E.) *Organo* (It.), *Orgel* (G.), *orgue* (F.).

organo (It.) Organ.

Orgel (G.) Organ.

orgue (F.) Organ.

ossia (It.) Or, an alternative (usually easier) version of a passage.

ostinato (It.) A steady bass accompaniment, repeated over and over.

ôtez vite les sourdines (F.) Remove the mutes quickly.

ottava (It.) Octave, usually meaning an octave higer or lower in pitch.

ottetto (It.) Octet.

ottoni (It.) Brass instruments.

ou (F.) Or.

ouvert (F.) Open.

panno (It.) A piece of cloth used to muffle a drum.

parte (It.) Part.

passionato (It.) Passionately.

pastorale (It.) In pastoral style.

patetico (It.) With great emotion.

pathetisch (G.) With great emotion.

pathétique (F.) With great emotion.

Pauken (Pk.) (G.) Kettledrums (K.D.).

paukenschlegel (G.) Timpani stick.

pausa (It.) Rest.

pausa di croma (It.) Eighth rest.

Pause (G.) Rest.

pavillons en l'air (F.) An indication to the player of a wind instrument to raise the bell of the instrument upward.

pedal, pedale (ped., P.) (It.) In piano music, indicates that the damper pedal should be depressed; an asterisk indicates the point of release. Brackets below the music are also sometimes used for this purpose.

pedal tone (E.) *Suono-pedale* (It.), *Pedalton* (G.), *son pédale, fondamentales* (F.).

pedale celeste (It.) Damper pedal.

pedale del forte (It.) Sustaining pedal.

peneramente, tenero (It.) Tenderly, gently.

per (It.) During.

percussion (Perc.) (E.) *Percussione* (It.), *Schlagzeug* (G.), *batterie* (F.).

percussione (It.) Percussion.

perdendo, perdendosi (It.) Dying away.

perpetuo (It.) Constant, perpetual.

pesant (F.) Heavy, slow, deliberate.

pesante (It.) Weighty, ponderous, dull.

petite flûte[s] (F.) Piccolo.

peu (F.) Little, a little.

peu à peu (F.) Little by little, gradually.

phantastisch (G.) Fanciful.

piacevole, piacevolmente (It.) Agreeable, pleasant.

pianissimo (It.) Very soft.

piano (It.) Soft.

piano (E., F.) *Pianoforte* (It.), *Klavier* (G.).

pianoforte (P. -f., Pft.) (It.) Piano.

piatti (P., Ptti., Piat.) (It.) Cymbals.

piatti antichi (It.) Antique Cymbals.

piatto cinese (It.) Crash or Chinese cymbals.

piatto sostenuto dalla sua correggia (It.) Suspended cymbal.

piccolo (Picc.) (E.) *Flauto piccolo* (It.), *kleine Flöte, Pikkoloflöte* (G.), *petite flûte* (F.).

Pikkoloflöte[n] (G.) Piccolo.

Piston (G.) Cornet.

più (It.) More.

più tosto (It.) More quickly.

pizzicato (*pizz.*) (It.) The string plucked with the finger.

placido (It.) Calm, tranquil.

plötzlich (G.) Suddenly, immediately.

plus (F.) More.

plus encore (F.) Still more.

pochissimo (*pochiss.*) (It.) Very little, a very little.

poco (It.) Little, a bit.

poco a poco (It.) Little by little, gradually.

poco meno (It.) A little less.

pointe, à la (F.) With the point of the bow.

ponticello (*pont.*) (It.) The bridge (of a string instrument).

ponticello, sul (It.) Over the bridge, producing a nasal, brittle tone.

pollice, col (It.) With the thumb.

portamento (It.) Continuous smooth and rapid sliding between two pitches.

Posaune[n] (*Ps., Pos.*) (G.) Trombone.

poussé (F.) Up bow.

precedente (It.) Preceeding.

preciso (It.) Exact, very accurate.

premier mouvement (*1er mouvt.*) (F.) At the original tempo.

prende (It.) Take (another instrument, another beater, etc.).

prenez, prendre (F.) Take up.

préparez (F.) Prepare.

près de (F.) Near, nearby.

presque (F.) Almost, nearly.

presser (F.) To press.

prestissimo (It.) As fast as possible.

presto (It.) Fast, faster than allegro.

prima, primo (It.) First, principal, original.

Pritsche (G.) Slapstick.

protubérance, sur la (F.) On the dome (of a cymbal).

Pult (G.) Desk or stand.

punta, a (It.) With the point of the bow.

pupitre (F.) Desk or stand.

pupitre, contre le (F.) On the rim.

quasi (It.) Almost, as if.

quatuor (F.) Quartet.

quintette (F.) Quintet.

r. h. (E.) Abbreviation for "right hand."

rallentando (*rall., rallent.*) (It.) Becoming slower.

Rand(e), am (G.) At the edge of a cymbal or on the rim of a drum.

Randschlag (G.) Rim shot.

rapidamente, rapido (It.) Quickly.

rapide (F.) Fast.

rapidissimo (*rapidiss.*) (It.) Very quickly.

rasch (G.) Quickly.

rascher (G.) Very quickly.

rauschend (G.) Rustling, roaring.

recitando (It.) Singing.

recitativo (*recit.*) (It.) Recitative.

rein (G.) Perfect interval.

reprise (F.) Repeat.

respiro (It.) Pause for breath.

retenu, retenant, retenez (F.) Held back.

rêve (F.) Dream.

Rezitativ (G.) Recitative.

richtig (G.) Correct.

ricochet (F.) See **jeté**.

ridendo (It.) Laughing.

rien (F.) Nothing.

rigore di tempo (It.) Strictness of tempo.

rinforzando (*rf., rfz., rinf.*) (It.) Becoming stronger, a sudden accent on a single note or chord.

ripieni, senza (It.) The first player of each section only.

riposo, con (It.) Restful, peaceful.

risoluto (It.) Boldly, decisively, vigorously.

ritardando (*rit., ritard.*) (It.) Becoming slower.

ritenuto (*riten.*) (It.) Immediately slower, held back.

ritmico (It.) Rhythmic.

ritornando (It.) Return.

ritornello (ritor.) (It.) Refrain.

ronde (F.) Whole note.

rubato (It.) Taking a portion of the time value from one note and giving it to another note (usually) within the same measure, without altering the duration of the measure as a whole.

ruhig (G.) Quiet, soft.

rustico (It.) Rustic, plain, simple.

Saite (G.) String.

Saiten, auf den (G.) On the strings.

saltando (It.) A short rapid stroke that makes the bow bounce lightly off the string.

sanft (G.) Soft.

sans (F.) Without.

Satz (G.) Movement.

sautillé (F.) A short rapid stroke that makes the bow bounce lightly off the string.

Saxophon[e] (G.) Saxophone.

saxophone[s] (F.) Saxophone.

saxophono [saxophoni] (It.) Saxophone.

schalltrichter (G.) Horn.

Schellen (G.) Sleigh bells.

Schellentrommel (G.) Tambourine.

scherzando (scherz.) (It.) Playful.

scherzo (It.) Referring to the tempo and mood of a scherzo movement.

Schlegel (G.) Stick, mallet, beater.

schlagen (G.) To strike in a usual manner.

Schlagzeug (Schlag.) (G.) Percussion.

schleppen, schleppend (G.) Dragging.

schluss (G.) End, cadence, conclusion.

schmetternd (G.) Brassy.

schmissig (G.) With verve or fire.

schütteln (G.) Shake.

schnell (G.) Fast.

schneller (G.) Faster.

schon (G.) Already.

Schwammschlegeln (G.) Sponge-headed drumstick.

scordata (It.) Loosened (as in drumheads), out of tune, out of pitch.

scordatura (It.) Tuning the strings to different pitchs than normal.

scorrevole (It.) Flowing, gliding.

secco (It.) Dry, plain, simple, unadorned.

Sechzehntelnote, Sechzentepause (G.) Sixteenth note, sixteenth rest.

secunda (It.) Second.

segno (It.) Sign, meaning the sign: ✵

segue (It.) Continue without pausing.

sehr (G.) Very.

semibreve (It.) Whole note.

semicroma (It.) Sixteenth note.

semplice (It.) Simple, unaffected.

semplicita (It.) Simplicity.

sempre (semp.) (It.) Always, continually, throughout.

sentiment (F.) Feeling, mood.

sentimento, con (It.) With feeling.

senza (It.) Without.

separato (It.) Detached.

septuor (F.) Septet.

seul, seule (F.) Alone.

seulement (F.) Only.

sforzando (sf., sfz) (It.) Forced, with a strong accent.

sharp (E.) *Diesis* (It.), *Kreuz* (G.)♯ *dièse* (F.).

si piace (It.) Especially pleasing.

siciliano (It.) A Sicilian dance in   meter and fairly slow tempo.

signe (F.) Sign, usually ✵

simile (sim.) (It.) Similarly, in a like manner.

sin (L.) Without.

sin' (It.) Up to, until.

singstimme (G.) Singing voice.

sino al (It.) Up to the...

siren (E.) *Sirena* (It.), *Sirene* (G.), *sirène* (F.).

sirena (G.) Siren.

sirène (F.) Siren.

Sirene (G.) Siren.

slapstick (E.) *Frusta di carta* (It.), *Pritsche* (G.), *fouet* (F.).

sleigh bells (E.) *Sonagli* (It.), *Schellen* (G.), *grelots* (F.).

smorzando (*smorz.*) (It.) Dying away.

smorzato (It.) Intense vibrato.

snare drum (S. D.) (E.) *Tamburo militare* (It.), *kleine Trommel, Leinentrommel* (G.), *caisse claire, casse roulante, tambour militaire* (F.).

sofort (G.) Immediately.

soilés, sons (F.) Covered.

solo (It.) Single, alone, a part performed by one performer.

sombre (F.) Melancholy, gloomy.

sonagli (*Son.*) (It.) Sleigh bells.

sonore (F.) Resonant.

sonoro (It.) Resonant, full-toned.

sopra (It.) Over, above.

sopranino clarinet (E.) *Clarinetto [clarinetti] piccolo* (It.).

sordino, sordina (It.) Mute(s).

sospirando (It.) Sighing, plaintive.

sostenuto (It.) Sustained.

sotto (It.) Under, below.

sotto voce (It.) Softly, in a low voice.

soupir (It.) Quarter rest; sigh, breath, gasp.

sourdine (F.) Mute or damper.

soutenu (F.) Sustained.

speranza, senza (It.) Without hope, lacking confidence.

spiccato (It.) A light staccato played between the frog and the midpoint of the bow, at slow to moderate speed.

spiel, spielen (G.) To play.

spieler (G.) Player, performer.

spiritu, con (L.) With spirit.

Spitze, an der (G.) At the tip of the bow.

spugna (It.) Sponge.

staccato (It.) Detached, with each note separated from the next and quickly released.

Steg, am (G.) On (near) the bridge.

stentando, stentare, stentato (It.) Delaying, hard, difficult.

stesso (It.) The same.

still (G.) Quiet, soft.

Stimme (G.) Voice.

stimmen (G.) To tune.

strascinare, strasciando, strascicamente (It.) To drag.

streichinstrumente (G.) Bowed string instruments.

strepitoso (It.) Noisy, loud.

stretto (It.) Accelerated, faster. In a nonfugal composition, indicates a concluding section at an increased speed.

stringendo (*string.*) (It.) Pressing on, hurrying, speeding up.

strumento a fiato (It.) Wind instrument.

subito (*sub.*) (It.) Suddenly, immediately, at once.

sul, sulla, sulle (It.) On the.

superius (L.) In older music, the uppermost part.

sur (F.) On, over.

suspended cymbals (E.) *Piatto sostenuto dalla sua correggia* (It.), *Becken am Rieman hängend* (G.), *cymbales suspendues par une courroie* (F.).

sussurando (It.) Whispering.

t.c. (It.) Short for *tre corde*.

table, près de la (F.) Near the sounding board.

tace (It.) Be silent.

tacet (It.) The instrument or vocal part so marked is silent.

Takt (G.) Measure.

tallone, al (It.) At the frog of the bow.

talon, du (F.) At the frog of the bow.

tam-tam (Tam.-T) (E.) *Tam-tam* (It.), *Tam-Tam* (G.), *tam-tam* (F.).

tambour à corde (F.) Lion's roar.

tambour de basque (*T. de B., Tamb. de Basque*) (F.) Tambourine.

tambour militaire (*Tamb. milit.*) (F.) Snare drum.

tambourine (Tamb.) (E.) *Tamburo, tamburello basco* (It.), *Schellentrommel, Tamburin* (G.), *tambour de basque* (F.).

Tamburin (G.) Tambourine.

tamburo basco (Tamb.) (It.) Tambourine.

tamburo militaire (Tamb. milit.) (It.) Snare drum.

tanto (It.) Much, so much, as much.

tardo (It.) Slow, serious; late, delayed.

tasto (It.) Fingerboard.

tasto solo (It.) In a continuo part, this indicates that only the string instrument plays. The chord-playing instrument is silent.

tema (It.) Theme, subject.

Tempelblocks (G.) Temple blocks.

temple blocks (E., It., F.) *Tempelblocks* (G.).

tempo (It.) Time, rate of speed.

tempo di (It.) In the tempo of.

tempo primo (tempo 1) (It.) At the original tempo.

tempo, a (It.) Return to the original speed.

tenuto (ten.) (It.) Held, sustained.

terza (It.) Third.

tief (G.) Deep, low.

tierce (F.) Third.

timbales (Timb.) (F.) Kettledrums.

timbre (F.) Tone color.

timbro (It.) Tone color; the jingle of a tambourine.

timido (It.) Shy, bashful, hesitant.

timpani (Timp., Tp.) (It.) Kettledrums.

tiré (F.) Downbow.

Todeslied, Todesgesang (G.) A dirge, a lament.

ton (F.) Tone, sound, pitch.

Ton (G.) Tone, sound, pitch.

touche (F.) Fingerboard, fret, key.

toujours (F.) Always, constantly.

tous, tout, toute (F.) All, every, whole.

tr. (It.) Short for trillo.

tre (It.) Three.

tre corde (t.c.) (It.) Release the soft (una corda) pedal.

tremolo (trem.) (It.) A slight steady wavering of pitch.

trémolo (trém.) (F.) Fluttertongue; tremolo.

trepidamente (It.) Anxious, fearful, trembling.

très (F.) Very, much.

Triangel (G.) Triangle.

triangle (Trgl. Tri.)/(Triang.) (E., F.) *Triangolo* (It.), *Triangel* (G.).

triangolo (Trgl.) (It.) Triangle.

trill (tr.) (E.) The rapid alternation of a given note with the diatonic second above it.

trille (F.) Trill.

Triller (G.) Trill.

trillo (It.) Trill.

triple-croche (F.) Thirty-second note.

triste (F., It.) Sad, mournful.

tromba[trombe] (Tr.) (It.) Trumpet.

tromba[trombe] piccola (Tr. picc.) (It.) Trumpet in D.

trombone (Tr., Tbe., Trb.) (E., F.) *Trombone [tromboni]* (It.), *Posaune[n]* (G.).

Trommel (G.) Drum.

trommschlag (tromm.) (G.) Drumbeat.

Trompete[n] (Tr., Trp.) (G.) Trumpet.

trompette[s] (Tr.) (F.) Trumpet.

trop (F.) Too, too much.

trumpet (Tpt., Trpt., Trp.) (E.) *Tromba [trombe]* (It.), *Trompete[n]* (G.), *trompette[s]* (F.).

tuba[tube] (It.) Tuba.

tutta la forza (It.) Very emphatically.

tutta, tutte, tutti (It.) All, total; full orchestra or chorus.

tutte le corde (It.) See *tre corde*.

über (G.) Over, above.

übergreifen (G.) To overlap.

übertonend (G.) Drowning out.

umstimmen (G.) Re-tune.

un, una, uno (It.) A, one.

un, une (F.) A, one.

una corda (u. c.) (It.) With the "soft" pedal of the piano depressed.

und (G.) And.
unghia, colla (It.) With the fingernail.
unmerklich (G.) Imperceptible.
unstimmen (G.) To change the tuning.
up bow (E.) *Arcata in su* (It.), *Aufstrich* (G.), *poussé* (F.).
vago (It.) Vague, uncertain.
valse (F.) Waltz.
variazione (It.) Variation.
velocissimo, veloce, velocemente (It.) Very swiftly.
verklingen lassen (G.) To let die away.
Verschiebung, mit (G.) With the damper pedal.
via (It.) Away, remove.
vibrare (It.) To sound.
vibrato (vibr.) (It.) Pulsation of musical sound, reverberating, resounding, ringing.
vibrierend (G.) Vibrant, vibrating.
viel (G.) Much, a lot of.
vierfach (G.) Quadruple.
vierhändig (G.) Four-handed piano music.
Viertelnote, Viertelpause (G.) Quarter note, quarter rest.
vif (F.) Lively.
viola (Va., Vl., pl. Vas.) (E.) *Viola [viole]* (It.), *Bratsche[n]* (G.), *alto[s]* (F.).
viole (Vle.) (It.) Plural form of viola.
violin (V., Vl., Vln., Vi.) (E.) *Violino [violini]* (It.), *Violine[n]* (G.), *violon[s]* (F.).
Violine[n] (V., Vl., Vln.) (G.) Violin.
violino[violini] (V., Vl., Vln.) (It.) Violin.
violon[s] (V., Vl., Vln.) (F.) Violin.
violoncelle[s] (F.) Violoncello, 'cello.
violoncello (Vcl., Vc., Vcllo.) (E., It.), *Violoncell[e]* (G.), *violoncelle[s]* (F.).
virtuoso (It.) Brilliant, technically very difficult.
vite (F.) Fast, rapid.
vivace (It.) A lively tempo, somewhat faster than allegro.

vivamente, vivo (It.) Lively.
volles orch. (G.) Entire orchestra.
volta (It.) Time.
volti subito (V. S.) (It.) Turn (the page) quickly.
von (G.) From.
vor (G.) Before, in front of, previous to.
vorhang auf (G.) Curtain up.
vorhang zu (G.) Curtain down.
vorher (G.) Beforehand, previously.
voriges, vorig, vorige, voriger (G.) Preceding.
vuota (It.) Open; empty; grand pause.
weg (G.) Away, off.
weich (G.) Mellow, smooth, soft.
wenig (G.) Little.
wie aus der fern (G.) As if from afar.
wie zu anfang dieser szene (G.) As at the beginning of this scene.
wieder (G.) Again.
wind instrument (E.) *Strumento a fiato* (It.), *Blasinstrument* (G.), *instrument à vent* (F.).
wood blocks (E.) *Blocks cinesi, testa di morto* (It.), *Tempelblock* (G.), *blocs chinois* (F.).
xilofono (It.) Xylophone.
Xylophon (G.) Xylophone.
xylophone (E., F.) *Xilofono* (It.), *Xylophon* (G.).
zart (It.) Tenderly, delicately.
Zeit (G.) Time, duration, tempo.
zögernd (G.) Slower.
zu (G.) To, too.
zum (G.) To the, in addition.
zurückhaltend (G.) Slackening in speed.
zurücktreten (G.) To withdraw, to become softer.
zweihändig (G.) With two hands.

D Appendix: *Additional Listening*

As suggested in the preface, you can improve your skills as an arranger by careful listening and study of the work of other composers. Listen to a recording of the works on the following list, both with and without a score. Each work has been annotated to call your attention to certain features, but these brief notes are in no way exhaustive and should be viewed only as a starting point for your study.

Bartók, Béla. Concerto for Orchestra (1943). Berliner Philharmoniker, Mehta. (CD 4, Cuts 29–30)

Only movements I and II are included here, but the remaining movements bear careful study. The third movement, in particular, should be examined for the coloristic use of harp, woodwind arpeggios, and muted brass effects.

I (*Introduzione*) [CD 4, Cut 29]

(Andante)

m. 1 [0:00] Monophonic texture in 'cellos and basses, answered by muted upper strings in bowed tremolo in m. 6. Flutes enter in m. 10 with a cadential motive. Similar material in m. 12–21. Monophonic line in m. 22 adds violas to the 'cellos and basses.

m. 30 [1:19] Flute solo states PM against string tremolo texture.

m. 35 [1:32] Material like the opening becomes more active in lower strings, with timpani roll beneath. Three trumpets state PM in harmony against this background in m. 39. Trombone is added near the end of the passage.

m. 51 [2:20] PM in violins in octaves, doubled with flutes and oboes, against moving figures in low strings. Note role of horns in the background supporting the bass figures.

m. 63 [2:51] Moving background figure assumes center stage, with increasing woodwind doubling. RS in background in sustained horns, trumpets, and timpani.

(Allegro)

m. 76 [3:05] PM in violins unison against HRS in lower strings and the winds closing with bold motive in horns doubled by violins, followed by scales in woodwinds.

m. 95 [3:19] PM in upper strings, with HS in lower strings, and answering SM in woodwinds.

m. 134 [3:50] PM in trombone, HRS in strings and SM in woodwinds.

m. 154 [4:06] PM in oboe, HRS in strings and horn. Note answering figure in harp.

m. 174 [4:25] PM in clarinets in octaves, background continues as above.

m. 192 [4:42] PM in flutes and oboe, with rhythmically active variant in muted upper strings; SM in clarinet, bass clarinet, and harp. In m. 210 low strings, upper woodwinds, and trombones answer each other on PM.

m. 231 [5:22] PM from m. 51 shared between violins and trumpets. Running figures in woodwinds and strings.

m. 248 [5:33] Canon in strings and woodwinds. Builds to tutti.

m. 272 [5:51] PM in clarinet. SM and background in strings.

m. 288 [6:08] PM in English horn.

m. 313 [6:32] Return of allegro theme, expanded, followed by an extended fugatto in brass, punctuated
by strings and woodwinds. Builds to tremendous climax.

m. 396 [7:24] Similar to m. 174.

m. 438 [8:01] Note unusual harp effect: wooden or metal stick scraping strings.

m. 456 [8:17] Similar to m. 192.

m. 488 [8:45] Return of allegro theme, but heavier doubling in the strings (violins, violas, and 'cellos)

m. 514 [9:00] PM in full brass.

II (*Giuoco Della Coppie*) [CD 4, Cut 30]

This movement is a study of melodic doubling at various intervals with like instruments. The following list refers primarily to those elements, although there are a number of other interesting details of orchestration throughout the movement.

m. 9 [0:11] Minor sixths in bassoons.

m. 25 [0:34] Minor thirds in oboes.

m. 45 [1:00] Minor sevenths in clarinets.

m. 60 [1:22] Perfect fifths in flutes.

m. 90 [2:05] Major seconds in muted trumpets.

m. 123 [2:52] Homorhythmic texture in brass, first emphasizing the bright brass, then in m. 147 the mellow brass.

m. 165 [3:53] Minor sixths in bassoons, with SM in third bassoon.

m. 181 [4:16] Major thirds in oboes, with mirror-image material in minor thirds in clarinets.

m. 198 [4:40] Minor sevenths in flutes, with parallel material in minor sevenths in clarinets.
m. 212 [5:00] Parallel open-position first-inversion major triads in flutes and one oboe. Clarinets are added to this texture later on, partly to cover lower ranges.
m. 228 [5:23] Major seconds in muted trumpets.

Berlioz, Hector. *Symphony Fantastique*, **op. 14. Berliner Philharmoniker, Barenboim. (CD 1, Cuts 31–32–33)**

To attempt to list all the striking orchestral effects in this work would go beyond the space limitations of the book. The following list for movements III ("In the country"), IV ("Procession to the Stake"), and V ("A witches' sabbath") contains only the most unusual effects. The entire work should be carefully studied.

III ("In the country") [CD 1, Cut 31]

m. 1 [0:00] Solo English horn answered by off-stage oboe at the octave. Violas enter later with muted bowed tremolo chords.
m. 20 [2:03] PM in violin I and flute; light pizzicato accompaniment in strings.
m. 33 [3:17] PM and PSM in violins and flutes, SM in clarinet (later with horn). Light pizzicato accompaniment in strings later.
m. 49 [4:42] PM and PSM in upper woodwinds.
m. 87 [7:38] PM in bassoons, 'cellos, and basses, answered by upper woodwinds. Violin and viola bowed tremolos are marked "very sharp."
m. 100 [8:29] PM in octaves in full strings plus bassoons.
m. 113 [9:22] PM and PSM in flutes and oboes (joined later by clarinets) in unison.
m. 117 [9:42] PM in clarinet and flute, SM pizzicato violin II and violas.
m. 146 [11:55] PM and PSM in strings. An expanded monophonic texture for the most part.
m. 175 [14:32] Solo English horn returns, answered by four timpani tuned to different pitches. These timpani "chords" are quite striking.

IV ("Procession to the Stake") [CD 1, Cut 32]

m. 1 [0:00] Four-part pizzicato chords in double basses, with two timpani tuned in thirds. PM in horns.
m. 25 [0:41] PM in lower strings, SM in four bassoons in upper register.
m. 49 [1:20] PM in pizzicato strings (upper and lower parts are mirror image of each other), SM in four bassoons staccato.
m. 62 [1:40] Full wind band, including woodwinds, horns, trumpets, cornets, trombones, and tubas, with timpani. Strings and other percussion join later.

V ("A witches' sabbath") [CD 1, Cut 33]

m. 1 [0:00] Pianissimo bowed tremolo chords in muted upper strings, punctuated by timpani and lower strings.
m. 7 [0:27] Flute, oboe, piccolo in octaves. Note glissandos.

m. 40 [1:34] PM in E-flat clarinet accompanied by oboes and clarinet. PM doubled in octaves with piccolo later. Notice bizarre arpeggios in four bassoons as passage continues.

m. 86 [2:24] Monophonic passage in bassoons, 'cellos, and basses. This explores the lower ranges of these instruments.

m. 102 [2:50] Two large bells tuned to C and G behind stage. These continue throughout the following sections.

m. 127 [3:19] Bassoons and tubas state *dies irae* theme.

m. 147 [3:41] PM and PSM in horns and trombones.

m. 157 [3:51] Upper woodwinds and upper strings pizzicato PM and PSM. Following passages alternate among the effects described above in m. 127, 147, and 157.

m. 241+ [5:13] The witches' round dance. Many colorful effects.

m. 363 [7:15] Bass drum roll begins almost inaudibly and builds to fortissimo.

m. 414 [8:06] *Dies irae* in winds with witches' round dance in strings, with percussion.

m. 444 [8:36] *Col legno* in violins and violas.

Bizet, George.
L'Arlésienne
Suite no. 1.
Toronto
Symphony,
Davis. (CD 1,
Cuts 34–35–36–
37)

I (Prelude) [CD 1, Cut 34]

m. 1 [0:00] An extended monophonic passage with winds doubling strings.

m. 17 [0:33] Woodwind quintet consisting of flute, English horn, clarinet, and two bassoons. Flutes double English horn and clarinet has PM.

m. 33 [1:07] Tutti orchestra, pianissimo with crescendo to forte. Note snare drum in this passage.

m. 49 [1:40] A trio consisting of bassoon, horn, and 'cello. A good example of standard dovetailing in bassoon and horn, where the lines are broken between like instruments to provide breathing places.

m. 65 [2:32] Tutti orchestra, fortissimo.

m. 81 [3:03] Horns and cornet unison passage.

m. 83 [3:08] Flute, clarinet, and bassoon in octaves.

m. 90 [3:28] An extended alto saxophone solo (PM), with muted string accompaniment and SM in clarinet. HS in winds later in the passage.

m. 107 [4:33] Harp, woodwinds, and horn.

m. 113 [5:01] PM in octaves for viola and violin I, HRS in remaining strings, and HS in winds.

m. 119 [5:20] PM in octaves for violin I, violin II, violas, 'cellos. HRS in winds. SM in trombone and basses later in the passage.

m. 138 [6:21] Bowed tremolo passage in strings. Crescendo is supported by HS entrances in the winds.

m. 143 [6:48] Chord in upper woodwinds against pizzicato in strings.

II (Minuetto) [CD 1, Cut 35]

m. 1 [0:00] String orchestra with some light wind HRS. Oboe doubles violins to support fortissimo at the close of the passage.
m. 9 [0:19] Winds vs. strings in an antiphonal passage.
m. 25 [0:57] Open fifths extensively doubled in winds and strings.
m. 29 [1:02] PM in clarinet and alto saxophones in octaves, SM in I violin, with HRS in remaining strings.
m. 45 [1:23] PM in violin and 'cello in octaves, SM in flute, clarinet, and harp, with HRS in woodwinds and strings.
m. 61 [1:42] PM with PSM in flutes (later doubled by clarinets and bassoons), SM in alto saxophone, and pizzicato HRS in strings.
m. 77 [2:02] Like m. 45, with more extensive doubling of PM in upper strings.
m. 92 [2:20] PM in oboe, light HRS in winds and strings.
m. 101 [2:30] PM in violin I, with diminuendo emphasized by gradually reducing the number of stands playing.
m. 108 [2:39] Like m. 1 (minuetto da capo)

III (Adagietto) [CD 1, Cut 36]

The entire movement is muted string orchestra with PM in violin I.

IV (Carillon) [CD 1, Cut 37]

m. 1 [0:00] Carillon motive in horn, harp, strings (pizzicato and arco).
m. 5 [0:06] PM in violin I (violin II added later), HRS in lower strings, winds, with carillon motive continuing as SS. Builds to tutti.
m. 21 [0:47] PM and PSM in violins and flutes, accompaniment continuing in similar manner.
m. 49 [1:10] Antiphonal passage: carillon motive in alto saxophone, horn, cornet, harp, and strings, answered by woodwinds.
m. 61 [1:30] PM and PSM in flutes with light string accompaniment. Second flute becomes SM later in the passage.
m. 72 [1:57] Oboes join flutes on PM and SM (sometimes PSM).
m. 85 [2:28] PM and SM in flutes, oboes, and violin I (div.). New SM in alto saxophone and 'cello.
m. 98 [2:59] Hints of carillon motive appear in horn. PM and SM in flutes and violin I.
m. 106 [3:20] PM in oboe, SS (carillon motive) in horn and harp, light HRS in strings.
m. 114 [3:30] PM and PSM in violin I-II, carillon motive continues, winds in HRS build to full during passage (similar to m. 21+).

Copland, Aaron. *El Salon Mexico* **(1936). New Philharmonia, Copland. (CD 4, Cut 31)**

This work is particularly striking for its imaginative use of percussion. The following list concentrates on the percussion, but there are many other striking effects.

m. 1 [0:00] Repeated chords in bright brass with suspended cymbal struck with snare stick, alternating with string and woodwind doubled melodic motive. (Cymbal missing on m. 1–2 in this recording!)
m. 10 [0:10] Woodblock emphasizing repeated notes.
m. 18 [0:26] Snare drum roll and bass drum punctuation. (Note the stopped horn notes in m. 19.)
m. 20 [0:31] Brush on suspended cymbal doubling bassoon, trombone chords.
m. 34 [1:25] Timpani solo, doubled by bass pizzicato and low piano.
m. 98 [3:20] Timpani with hard sticks.
m. 124 [3:57] Woodblock.
m. 133 [4:11] Timpani.
m. 145 [4:29] Snare drum, gourd (güiro). Bass drum and timpani in m. 147.
m. 156 [4:43] Cymbal with snare stick and xylophone.
m. 163 [4:52] Timpani. Snare drum added in m. 167, and bass drum in m. 172.
m. 217 [6:53] Gourd (güiro).
m. 228 [7:16] Timpani.
m. 263 [8:14] Temple blocks. (Güiro in m. 268, and temple blocks again in m. 289.)
m. 308 [9:09] Tambourin de Provence (Long drum).
m. 324 [9:33] Timpani.
m. 353 [10:11] Snare drum, gourd (güiro). Bass drum and Timpani in m. 355.
m. 364 [10:25] Cymbal with snare stick and bass drum.
m. 373 [10:37] Snare drum. (Timpani added in m. 380.)
m. 391 [11:02] Crash cymbals and bass drum alternating with xylophone.
m. 402 [11:21] Timpani, snare drum, and bass drum alone close the work.

Debussy, Claude. Prelude to "The Afternoon of a Faun" (1892–1894). St. Louis Symphony, Slatkin. (CD 2, Cut 29)

A masterpiece of subtle orchestration. The following list presents only some of the more-striking effects the first time they appear in the work.

m. 1 [0:00] Flute solo in lower register.
m. 4 [0:26] Woodwind and horn chord with harp glissando.
m. 11 [1:03] Bowed tremolo *sur la touche* in divided, muted strings. A very subtle rustle.
m. 14 [1:25] The oboe takes over from the flute. The gradual transformation of color as flute dies away and oboe becomes stronger is quite striking.
m. 31 [3:22] Strings for the first time remove mutes.
m. 37 [3:50] Oboe solo.
m. 40 [4:00] Violins in octaves. A brilliant sound.
m. 55 [5:06] PM in flute, oboe, English horn, and clarinets in octaves. Bassoons and horns added in m. 60–61.

m. 63 [5:48] PM in violins, violas and 'cellos, with background in woodwinds and harps. One of the more beautiful textures in the orchestral literature.

m. 74 [6:39] Horns in three parts. Solo violin in m. 75, with clarinet SM in m. 75, changing to oboe in m. 77.

m. 83 [7:28] Three muted horns in oscillating background.

m. 94 [8:22] Fingered and bowed tremolo in strings, with antique cymbals above the texture. Two solo violins in octaves in m. 95.

m. 100 [9:06] Flute and solo 'cello in octaves. An unusual doubling.

m. 107 [10:07] Homorhythmic texture in two horns and first violins.

m. 108 [10:17] Antique cymbals, harp harmonics.

Grainger, Percy. Lincolnshire Posy. Cleveland Symphonic Winds, Fennell. (CD 2, Cuts 30–31–32)

Grainger's innovative scoring and idiosyncratic musical approach are in evidence throughout this work. Only the first three movements are included here, but the remaining movements contain many similar effects and bear careful study.

1. "Lisbon" [CD 2, Cut 30]

m. 1 [0:00] PM in muted trumpet I; PSM in muted trumpet II, stopped horn, and bassoon. Saxophones join in briefly in m. 14. An excellent example of expanded monophonic texture.

m. 18 [0:18] PM in flute I and clarinet I; PSM in flute II, oboes, English horn, clarinet II, alto clarinet, and alto saxophone I; SM in bassoons, E-flat clarinet, clarinet III, bass clarinet, soprano saxophone, alto saxophone II, tenor saxophone, baritone saxophone, euphonium, and string bass, joined by timpani from time to time.

m. 34 [0:32] PM in clarinet I, SM (nearly PSM in some cases) in clarinet II-III, alto clarinet, bass clarinet, and bassoon.

m. 37 [0:35] A new PM is added to the texture established in m. 34, scored for soprano saxophone, alto saxophones, tenor saxophone, trumpet I, horns, and baritone. This composite texture continues to m. 50, where new PM leaves the texture. There is an echo of this material in the horns in m. 53, which Grainger marks "as if from afar."

m. 60 [0:59] New homorhythmic texture is layered over the previous material, scored for oboes, English horn, bassoons, saxophones, baritones, tuba, and string bass. This composite texture gradually fades out at the end of the movement.

2. "Horkstow Grange" [CD 2, Cut 31]

This movement is in homorhythmic texture, except for the short trumpet solo in m. 19, which is played against a static background. There are many beautiful details of scoring and some wonderful clashes in m. 34 that Grainger reported as giving him "a thrill." The work should be studied for how skillfully Grainger builds toward and moves away from climax. Don't overlook the role of the percussion in achieving these effects.

3. "Rufford Park Poachers" [CD 2, Cut 32]

m. 1 [0:00] Two-voice counterpoint doubled at the quadruple octave. PM1 in piccolo and clarinet I; PM2 in E-flat clarinet and bass clarinet. A definitive example of the effect of gapped octave doubling of melodic lines.

m. 18 [0:28] A repetitive, planed texture is established in the clarinets against a pedal in other woodwinds. This provides the background for an extensive flügelhorn solo with short SM ideas in English horn and muted trumpet.

m. 44 [1:12] A horn and euphonium chord is added to the previous texture, which builds to the first climax.

m. 46 [1:16] Short melodic motives in trombone, clarinet, and stopped horn, trumpet and euphonium as texture continues to build, as timpani, suspended cymbal, and finally, bass drum are added.

m. 51 [1:30] PM in flutes, oboes, English horn, bassoons, clarinets, bass saxophone, euphonium, tuba, and string bass; HRS in saxophones, trumpets, and horns. Some trumpet parts are marked "triple-tongue as fast as possible; no set number of notes to the beat."

m. 64 [1:56] Short motives in trombones, trumpets, and clarinets, horns and baritone, against a repeated chord texture in remaining instruments. This builds to the largest climax of the movement, which is underlined with suspended cymbal rolls and heavy strokes in timpani and bass drum.

m. 68 [2:10] PM in saxophones, horns, and baritone; HRS in other woodwinds and the tubas. Muted trumpets and English horn enter on a short motive in m. 70. Other brass and woodwinds are gradually added to the texture to achieve a full tutti at piano dynamic level. This resolves itself and dissipates after m. 83.

m. 85 [2:59] A two-voice texture, similar to the opening against a sustained pedal. The interval of doubling is a gapped fifth, resulting in an even more hollow effect. PM1 in piccolo and E-flat clarinet; PM2 in oboe and bassoon. Short motive in muted trumpet in m. 94.

Holst, Gustav.
Second Suite in F for Military Band op. 28, no. 2. Cleveland Symphonic Winds, Fennell. (CD 5, Cuts 37–38–39–40)

1. "March" [CD 5, Cut 37]

m. 1 [0:00] Euphonium and tuba in unison, followed by flutes, oboes, and clarinets in unison (octave in piccolo)

m. 3 [0:02] PM in cornet I, accompaniment in the full remaining brass, with snare drum on RS. A traditional "brass band" sound.

m. 11 [0:10] Full woodwinds are added to the brass band texture above. PM in flutes, oboes, and clarinet I, remaining woodwinds double brass accompaniment parts. Bass drum and cymbal are added. A good example of scoring a complete texture in each section (brass and woodwinds) as separate units.

m. 19 [0:18] Woodwinds with horns. PM in flutes, clarinet I. PSM in oboes and clarinet II, HRS in lower clarinets, bassoon, alto saxophone and horns, RS in triangle.

m. 27 [0:25] Like m. 3.

m. 35 [0:33] Like m. 11.

m. 46 [0:44] PM in euphonium, HRS in horns, trombones and tuba. Snare drum added at some phrase endings.

m. 78 [1:15] Return to full texture, similar to m. 11 in scoring, but not in musical material.

m. 111 [1:47] PM in low clarinets and alto saxophones, HRS in lower saxophones, horns, trombone, euphonium, and tuba.

m. 128 [2:03] Cornets are added for two measures, followed by return to the texture of m. 111.

m. 136 [2:10] PM in flutes, oboe, clarinet, bassoon, alto saxophone, tenor saxophone, and euphonium. HRS in remaining instruments. The effect is melody in woodwinds against accompaniment in brass, a change from the unit scoring of the previous sections.

m. 152 [2:26] Cornet I is added to the melody; cymbals and bass drum are added. Da capo al fine [2:33-end]

2. "Song Without Words" [CD 5, Cut 38]

m. 1 [0:00] PM in clarinet (or oboe and clarinet), HRS in other woodwinds and horn. (This recording opts for both oboe and clarinet on the melody.) Flute is added to the melody late in the section.

m. 19 [1:14] PM in flute, oboe, clarinet and cornet I; SM in clarinets, saxophones, and sometimes bass clarinet, bassoon, and euphonium. HS in horns, trombones, and tuba.

m. 33 [2:11] PM in cornet, SM in clarinet and later, alto saxophone, euphonium, and finally, tuba.

3. "Song of the Blacksmith" [CD 5, Cut 39]

m. 1 [0:00] Full brass band with snare drum in homorhythmic texture. Texture thins out some at the end of the passage.

m. 7 [0:11] PM in oboe, clarinets, alto saxophone, tenor saxophone, and horns; HRS in lower saxophones, trombones, euphonium, and tuba.

m. 11 [0:21] PM in clarinets and cornet II; HRS in oboe, remaining clarinets, bassoon, alto saxophone, tenor saxophone, horn, trombones, euphonium. Potential problem of overbalance between melody and accompaniment here, requiring careful management by the conductor. PM is strengthen by addition of oboe, remaining clarinets, alto saxophone, tenor saxophone, and horns in m. 13. Tuba is added to HRS.

m. 15 [0:31] PM in cornet I; HRS in cornet II, trombones, euphonium, and tuba.

m. 19 [0:40] PM in oboe, clarinet I, and cornet I; SM in trombones I-II, and euphonium; HRS in most remaining instruments. Note the use of anvil and cymbals in this passage.

m. 23 [0:52] PM in flutes, oboe, clarinets, alto saxophone, tenor saxophone, cornet II, and horns; HRS in remaining instruments; RS in snare drum and anvil.

m. 28 [1:02] PM in flutes, oboe, E-flat clarinet, cornet I-II, and euphonium; HRS in remaining instruments. Cymbals, anvil, and snare drum on RS.

4. Fantasia on the 'Dargason' [CD 5, Cut 40]

m. 1 [0:00] PM in alto saxophone (possibly doubled by tenor saxophone).

m. 9 [0:06] PM in clarinet, SS in alto saxophone.

m. 17 [0:13] PM in clarinets; HRS in bass clarinet, bassoon, saxophones, horns, euphonium, and tuba. (Possible overbalance in HRS.)

m. 25 [0:19] PM in clarinets II-III, bass clarinet bassoon, alto saxophone, tenor saxophone; SM in clarinet I; HRS in baritone saxophone, bass saxophone, horns, and tuba.

m. 33 [0:26] PM in clarinets I-II-III, alto saxophone, tenor saxophone; SM in oboe, E-flat clarinet, bass clarinet, bassoon, cornet II, horn I-II, and tuba; SS in trombones and triangle. Texture gradually fills during the passage.

m. 41 [0:33] PM in flutes, oboe, clarinets, cornets I-II; SM in bass clarinet, bassoon, alto saxophone, tenor saxophone, horn I-II, and euphonium; SS and some RS in baritone saxophone, bass saxophone, trombones, tubas, and tambourine.

m. 49 [0:39] PM in flutes, oboe, E-flat clarinet, clarinet I; HRS in clarinets II-III, bass clarinet, bassoon, saxophones, cornets, trombones, euphonium, and tuba; RS in triangle.

m. 57 [0:48] PM in clarinets II-III; SM in euphonium (later clarinet I is added); HS in bass clarinet, bassoon, saxophones, horns, and tuba.

m. 73 [0:59] PM in flutes, E-flat clarinet, clarinets II-III (flutes and E-flat clarinet drop out during the passage); SM in euphonium, clarinet I, and cornet (clarinet I and cornet drop out during passage); HS in bass clarinet, bassoon, saxophones, horns, and tuba.

m. 89 [1:12] PM in bass clarinet, bassoon, alto saxophone, tenor saxophone; HRS in baritone saxophone, bass saxophone, horn I-II, euphonium, and tuba.

m. 97 [1:19] PM in cornet I; HRS in cornet II and trombones, joined later by tuba. Pure bright brass color at the beginning of this passage.

m. 105 [1:25] PM in flutes, oboe, clarinets I-II-III, cornets I-II; SS in other winds; RS in tambourine.

m. 113 [1:32] PM in bass clarinet, bassoon, tenor saxophone, baritone saxophone, bass saxophone, horns, trombones, euphonium, and tuba; mostly SS in remaining winds. Triangle is added to percussion. SM enters in m. 117 in flutes, oboe, clarinets I-II-III, alto saxophone, and cornets I-II.

m. 121 [1:38] PM in clarinets I-II-III, alto saxophone, tenor saxophone; SM in bass clarinet, bassoon, and euphonium; SS in lower saxophones, trombone III, tuba, and bass drum.

m. 129 [1:45] PM in flutes, oboe, upper clarinets, and cornet I; SM in remaining instruments.

m. 137 [1:51] PM in cornets I-II; heavy chords in remaining instruments, supported by cymbal crashes and bass drum strokes.

m. 145 [1:58] PM in flutes, oboe, clarinets; SM in cornets I-II, horn III-IV, euphonium; HS in other instruments. Texture lightens near the end of the passage.

m. 177 [2:26] PM in clarinets II-III, alto saxophone, tenor saxophone; HRS in baritone saxophone, bass saxophone, cornet I-II, horn I-II, trombones, and tuba. RS in triangle.

m. 185 [2:33] PM in euphonium; HRS in clarinets saxophones, trombone, tuba. Bass drum roll supports the texture.

m. 193 [2:39] PM in tuba; HRS in trombones and euphonium.

m. 202 [2:46] PM in piccolo alternating with tuba; HRS in muted cornets. Ends with a crashing tutti chord.

Mahler, Gustave. Symphony No. 4 in G Major (1900). Vienna Philharmonic, Maazel. (CD 3, Cut 32)

Mahler's orchestration is very complex, changing with nearly every measure. Melodic lines are broken up among various instruments in a way that influenced many 20th-century composers, particularly Schoenberg and Webern. The following list contains only the most striking effects in the first movment, which in included on CD 3, but the entire work should be studied with score in hand. Take note, in particular, of the violin solo throughout the second movement, which is played on an instrument tuned a whole step high, and the soprano solo in the final movement.

I "Moderato"

m. 1 [0:00] Opening with flutes and sleighbells, joined by the clarinets in m. 2. Violin I states the principal theme, beginning in m. 3. The accompaniment changes to pizzicato strings in m. 4.

m. 7 [0:19] Accompaniment in clarinets and bassoons, PM in low strings. PM moves to horn in m. 10, and to the violins I-II in m. 11, accompanied by lower strings. The PM is passed to the woodwinds in m. 13, where the accompaniment also moves to the woodwinds. In m. 15 the PM is again in the violins, but moves to oboe and clarinet in the next measure. Such exchanges of melodic material continue throughout the movement.

m. 18 [0:50] PM in violin I with 'cellos in imitation after two beats.

m. 32 [1:31] PM in octaves in clarinet, SM in strings.

m. 38 [1:45] PM in upper register of 'cellos, above the violins and violas, which state a SM.

m. 41 [1:58] PM in oboe, but there is a transformation in color in m. 44, where the violin I joins in unison, and the oboe fades out, only to join in again in the next measure.

m. 47 [2:18] PM again in high 'cellos. Another transformation of color occurs in m. 51, where the flute, oboe, and English horn joins the PM and the 'cellos fade out. Violin I and 'cellos continue the PM in m. 52, and in m. 54 all the upper strings suddenly enter doubling the PM while the 'cellos join the bass line.

m. 71 [3:53] Double basses alone in m. 71 and reduced to a single instrument in m. 72, where the opening texture returns in the woodwinds and sleighbells.

m. 77 [4:11] PM returns to violin I, with imitation after one measure in the oboe.

m. 102 [5:43] Opening texture returns with flutes replaced by clarinets. PM in solo violin in m. 102 is quite striking. The texture becomes like chamber music.

m. 110 [6:06] PM in horn I is quite striking because of the melodic turns.

m. 145 [7:39] Solo in clarinet in m. 145 and in oboe in m. 146 are marked "bell in air," an indication of the rather raw high-register sound Mahler wants here.

m. 150 [7:52] Muted trumpet trio here and in m. 153–5 along with stopped horn note in m. 154 creates a sharp nasal effect.

m. 157 [8:09] Prominent bass line in bassoon doubled in octaves with contrabassoon. Excellent opportunity to hear this combination.

m. 167 [8:34] Four flutes with triangle for emphasis. Col legno in violins in m. 172 and again in m. 179. Sul ponticello in 'cello in m. 180.

m. 203 [9:59] Trumpet solo.

m. 209 [10:14] Full orchestra with prominent timpani, bells, triangle, tamtam. Woodwinds with bells in air. High trumpet solo in m. 221.

m. 224 [10:48] Low trumpet solo on repeated note figure. In m. 232 a muted trumpet replaces the open trumpet sound. A good opportunity to hear this contrast in color.

m. 272 [12:57] PM in high 'cellos, doubled with horns. A glorious sound.

m. 277 [13:22] PM in high strings doubled with high woodwinds. In m. 278 the trumpet joins softly and crescendos in m. 279 while strings descrescendo bringing trumpet color to the fore for one note. Another example of the transformation of color for which Mahler is known.

m. 326 [16:08] Violin I gradually rises to extreme upper register. Some of the highest orchestral writing for violins occurs in this passage.

Vaughan Williams, Ralph. Folk Song Suite. Cleveland Symphonic Winds, Fennell. (CD 2, Cuts 33–34)

2. Intermezzo ("My Bonny Boy") [CD 2, Cut 33]

m. 1 [0:00] Opening chord in woodwinds, horns, and timpani.

m. 3 [0:05] PM in oboe and cornet I; HRS in lower woodwinds and brass. Timpani continues. SM in cornet II enters in m. 7. Many of Vaughan Williams's supporting parts have a contrapuntal character and could sometimes be labeled as SM.

m. 16 [0:40] PM in flutes, clarinet I, cornet I; PSM in oboe, clarinet II, cornet II; HRS in lower woodwinds and brass. RS in snare drum.

m. 18 [0:44] PM in oboe, cornet I; PSM in solo clarinet, cornet II; HRS in lower saxophones, trombone, and tuba.

m. 20 [0:51] PM in flutes, E-flat clarinet (solo clarinet added in m. 22). This part becomes a SM in m. 23, when the PM enters in clarinets, bassoon, and euphonium; HRS in saxophones, horns, and tubas. Cornets added briefly to PM and SM in m. 37.

m. 40 [1:45] PM (actually a continuation of previous SM) in solo clarinet.

m. 43 [1:54] PM in piccolo, oboe, and E-flat clarinet; HRS in clarinet I-II-III, and horns; RS in triangle.

m. 60 [2:14] PM in oboe, alto clarinet, alto saxophone, cornet I, and euphonium; SM in flute, E-flat clarinet, clarinets I-II-III; HRS in lower clarinets, lower saxophones, horns, trombones, and tubas. RS in cymbal. (The background texture is set up in m. 58 before PM enters.)

m. 78 [2:39] PM in tenor saxophone, baritone saxophone, bass saxophone, euphonium, and tuba; HS in trombones.

m. 82 [2:50] PM in clarinet I and cornet I; PSM in clarinet II-III and cornet II-III; HS in lower clarinets, alto saxophone, horns, and trombone I. RS in timpani. Horns join in PSM in m. 83.

m. 85 [2:58] Like m. 78. (End of previous texture overlaps this entrance.)

m. 89 [3:10] Like m. 82.

m. 91 [3:17] PM in flutes, clarinet I, cornet I, and trombone I; PSM in oboe, E-flat clarinet, clarinets II-III, alto clarinet, alto saxophone, cornet II, trumpet, horns, and trombone II; SM in lower saxophones, bass trombone, euphonium, and tuba; RS in snare drum, timpani, and cymbal. SM becomes PM in m. 93, while PM becomes SM.

m. 96 [3:33] Tutti chord with crescendo and decrescendo.

3. March ("Folk Songs from Somerset") [CD 2, Cut 34]

m. 1 [0:00] Monophonic texture in full woodwinds. Horns, tubas, and snare drum join in punctuating chords in m. 3–4.

m. 5 [0:03] PM in cornet I; HRS in clarinet III, baritone saxophone, bass saxophone, horns, euphonium, and string bass.

m. 9 [0:07] PM in flutes, oboe II, clarinet I; PSM in oboes, E-flat clarinets, clarinet II-III, bass clarinet, bassoon, and horns I-II; HRS in saxophones, cornet I, horns III-IV, euphonium, and tuba; RS in triangle.

m. 13 [0:11] PM in flute II, E-flat clarinet I, clarinet III, cornet I-II; HRS (or PSM) in flute I, oboes, clarinet I-II, trumpet. RS in snare drum and triangle. Some redistribution of parts in m. 15.

m. 17 [0:19] PM in cornet I; HRS in clarinets, bassoons, saxophones, horns, euphonium, and tuba; RS in snare drum, bass drum, and cymbal.

m. 21 [0:18] Tutti texture with PM and HRS (or PSM) on material presented in m. 13.

m. 29 [0:25] PM in alto clarinet, alto saxophone, trombones, euphonium; HRS in remaining instruments.

m. 44 [0:41] Like m. 5–28.

m. 69 [1:03] PM in alto clarinet, bass clarinet, bassoons, alto saxophone, tenor saxophone, cornets I-II, and euphonium; SS in upper woodwinds.

m. 73 [1:07] PM in flutes, oboes, and high clarinets; HRS in lower saxophones and brass; RS in snare drum. (HRS is set up in m. 71.) Prominent SM in trumpet is added in m. 80.

m. 88 [1:21] PM in lower clarinets, bassoons, saxophones, trumpet II, trombones, euphonium, tuba; SM and PSM in oboes, clarinets, cornets, trumpet I, and horns; RS in bass drum and cymbals. PM and SM roles are reversed in m. 104, where the parts are redistributed somewhat.

[Section from m. 71–111 is repeated at 1:45.]

[Section from m. 1–68 is repeated at 2:24.]

Other Works for Study:	Bartók, Béla. Music for String Instruments, Percussion, and Celesta.
	Britten, Benjamin. Serenade for Tenor, Horn, and Strings.
	Copland, Aaron. Symphony no. 3.
	Debussy, Claude. *Images pour Orchestra* (1906-1909).
	Debussy, Claude. *La Mer* (1903-1905).
	Debussy, Claude. Nocturnes for Orchestra (1893-1899).
	Dvořák, Antonin. Symphony no. 5 in F Major, op. 76.
	Hindemith, Paul. *Mathis der Maler* (1934).
	Kodály, Zoltán. *Háry János* Suite (1926).
	Mozart, Wolfgang Amadeus. Divertimenti K. 439b.
	Mozart, Wolfgang Amadeus. Symphony no. 40 in G minor, K.550.

Prokofiev, Sergei. Symphony no. 5, op. 100.

Ravel, Maurice. Daphnis and Chloe, Suite No. 2.

Saint-Saëns, Camille. Carnival of the Animals.

Shostakovich, Dimitri. Symphony no. 5 in D Minor, op. 47.

Strauss, Richard. Don Quixote, op. 35.

Strauss, Richard. *Ein Heldenleben*, op. 40.

Stravinsky, Igor. Fire Bird.

Stravinsky, Igor. *Le Sacre du Printemps* (1913).

Stravinsky, Igor. Symphony of Psalms (1930).

Varése, Edgar. Ionisation (1929-1931).

Wagner, Richard. Prelude to *Tristan und Isolde*.

E Appendix: *Composers and Works*

Index